# NUMERICAL METHODS

# NUMERICAL METHODS

*By*

ANDREW D. BOOTH, D.Sc.

*Reader in Computational Methods,*
*University of London*

NEW YORK
ACADEMIC PRESS INC., PUBLISHERS
LONDON
BUTTERWORTHS SCIENTIFIC PUBLICATIONS
1955

BUTTERWORTHS PUBLICATIONS LTD.
88, KINGSWAY, LONDON, W.C.2

*U.S.A. Edition published by*
ACADEMIC PRESS INC., PUBLISHERS
152 EAST 23RD STREET
NEW YORK 10, NEW YORK

*Set in Monotype Baskerville type*
*Printed in Great Britain by Spottiswoode, Ballantyne & Co. Ltd., London & Colchester*

# PREFACE

THE present book has grown out of the series of lectures given by the author to final honours B.Sc. mathematics students at Birkbeck College, London. The purpose of the course has been, not so much to instruct in the detailed tedium of actual calculation, but rather to give an understanding of the basic principles upon which such analyses rest.

Some existing books on numerical analysis lay much stress upon the detailed form in which a given procedure is to be laid out; it has been my experience that such concentration upon actual numbers obscures the underlying mathematical basis upon which the work rests, and so such tabulations are almost entirely absent from this book. Where they are given, as in chapter 7, they illustrate the sort of behaviour which will be encountered in a calculation rather than any detailed form of layout.

Were these didactic points the sole reason there would be little justification for a new book on computation; a far more important consideration lies in the growth, during the past decade, of the science and art of programming for an automatic digital calculator. The classical methods of hand calculation are, to a greater or less extent, unsuitable for the modern machines, and only by having a thorough knowledge of the underlying mathematical principles, is the programmer likely to make effective use of the new tools.

At Birkbeck College Computational Laboratory the teaching of numerical methods has been accompanied by the actual use of an automatic calculator, and demonstrations of such things as differencing and the solution of differential equations have been carried out by the machine and not by the student. Perhaps not unnaturally, this has proved more popular than the old method.

A book of this kind must always owe much to the work of previous authors; it is pleasant to acknowledge the help which the author derived from Freeman's 'Actuarial Mathematics' and, from the classical 'Calculus of Observations' of Whittaker and Robinson, both of which were practically the only available works during the 1930's. In more recent times the paper on 'Difference and Associated Operators' by W. G. Bickley may be mentioned as having particular influence.

Finally it gives me particular pleasure to acknowledge the help of my wife both in making the book more readable than might otherwise have been the case, and also, in collaboration with J. P. Cleave, B.Sc., for checking the examples given in chapter 7.

A. D. B.

Fenny Compton
*November* 1954

# CONTENTS

# THE NATURE AND PURPOSE OF NUMERICAL ANALYSIS

## 1.1 HISTORY

ALTHOUGH numerical analysis is considered by some to be a subject of recent origin and development this is not, in fact, so. Dealing, as it does, with the derivation of results in the form of *numbers*, the numerical analyst is really the lineal descendant of the first caveman who enumerated the number of his wives by putting them into one : one correspondence with the fingers of his hand.

Even in its more modern aspects the subject is antique; thus a primary activity of the scientists of Babylon was the construction of mathematical tables. An example is extant, dating from about 2,000 B.C., which contains on a tablet the squares of the numbers 1–60. Another tablet records the eclipses going back to 747 B.C., so that astronomical calculation formed a part of the activity of these early numerical analysts.

The ancient Egyptians, too, were energetic numerical analysts. They constructed tables whereby complex fractions could be decomposed into the sum of simpler forms with unit denominators, and invented the method of *false position* (see Chapter 9, section 9.3) for the solution of non-linear algebraic equations.

Passing to the Greek mathematicians we find Archimedes, in about 220 B.C., approximating the value of $\pi$ and describing it as less than $3\frac{1}{7}$ but greater than $3\frac{10}{71}$. Heron the elder, in about 100 B.C., made use of the iterative process: $\sqrt{a} \sim \frac{1}{2}\left(x_n + \dfrac{a}{x_n}\right)$ which is usually ascribed to Newton, and the Pythagorean school considered the summation of the series $(1 + 2 + 3 \ldots)$. Diophantus, about A.D. 250, apart from his better known work on indeterminate equations, was responsible for a process for the arithmetical solution of quadratic equations.

The Hindus were the creators of our modern arithmetic notation —usually called Arabic—and devised the method of checking the correctness of an arithmetic calculation known as 'casting out nines'.

Mohammed ibn Musa Al-Khowarizmi was the first Arab arithmetician and was responsible, around A.D. 820, for the systematization of computational processes. He gave the value $\pi = 62832/20000$ and was active in the preparation of astronomical tables. Abul Wefa

(A.D. 960) devised a method for the computation of tables of sines and gave the value of sin $(\frac{1}{2}°)$ correct to nine decimal places; he also used the *tangent* and calculated a table of this function.

Jumping to the seventeenth century, it is interesting to note that Napier's first table of logarithms was produced before the use of exponents was current, and that his 'logarithm' differs from any in current use since:

$$\text{Naperian } \log x = 10^7 \log_e (10^7/x).$$

In 1614 Napier published his *Mirifici logarithmorum canonis descriptio* and, posthumously, his *Mirifici logarithmorum canonis constructio* in 1619. Briggs, only slightly later in 1624, produced his *Arithmetica logarithmica*, which contains the logarithms, to 14 places of the numbers 1–20,000 and 90,000–100,000. Vlacq produced, in 1628, a table which is still fundamental of the 14-place logarithms of the numbers 1–100,000. The first authoritative publication of the logarithms of trigonometric functions was made at about the same time (1620), by Gunter, who invented the words 'cosine' and 'cotangent', and was responsible for the so-called 'Gunter's chain'.

In the nineteenth century there occurred one of the triumphs of numerical analysis, the simultaneous prediction by Adams and le Verrier in 1845, of the existence and position of the planet Neptune. This century saw also the rise and development of automatic calculating machinery, from the crude desk multiplier of Thomas de Colmar to the almost unmodified Brunsviga of the present day, the Hollerith punched card census calculator, and the difference and analytical engines of Charles Babbage.

Not until the end of the 1930's did the fully automatic calculators begin to come into use, and since the late 1940's there has been a revolution and renaissance in numerical analysis. New methods have been developed and problems which could not previously have been contemplated, even for a life's work, are now solved in hours. It is perhaps dangerous to quote examples, but outstanding achievements are the calculation of $\pi$ and $e$ to more than 2000 decimals, which took, on the *E.N.I.A.C.*,[1] only about 12 hr. The demonstration of the primeness of the Mersenne number $2^{1279} - 1$ on *S.E.A.C.* in 13 min. 25 sec., may also be cited as a noteworthy achievement.

## 1.2 THE TOOLS OF ANALYSIS (HAND)

From the classical standpoint of the individual numerical analyst the tools of computation are:

(1) Tables of formulae        (3) A desk calculator
(2) Tables of function values        (4) Pencil, paper *and rubber*

Few investigations are of such a fundamental nature that they make no use of existing mathematical knowledge; probably the most common table of formulae in use is a list of integrals. Four standard works may be mentioned:

(1) PEIRCE, B.O., 'A short table of integrals,' Ginn, Boston (1929)
(2) DWIGHT, H. B., 'Tables of integrals and other mathematical data,' Macmillan, New York (1934)
(3) DE HAAN, D. B., 'Nouvelles tables d'intégrales définies, Stechert, New York (1939)
(4) ' Interpolation and allied tables,' H.M. Stationery Office (1942)

The first two volumes are chiefly concerned with indefinite integrals, and the third exclusively with definite integrals. The last booklet contains most of the useful formulae for interpolation.

Tables of function values are almost too numerous to mention. For 4- or 5-figure accuracy there are the classical:

JAHNKE-EMDE, 'Tafeln höher funktionen,' Teubner (4th edn.), Leipzig (1948)

EMDE, 'Tafeln elementarer funktionen,' Teubner, Leipzig (1940) which, besides giving numerical values, contain useful graphs and formulae. Other moderate accuracy collections are:

'Mathematical Tables from the Handbook of Chemistry and Physics,' Chemical Rubber Pub. Co. Cleveland (1946)

DALE, J. B., 'Five-figure Tables of Mathematical Functions,' Arnold, London (1937)

DWIGHT, H. B., 'Mathematical Tables,' McGraw Hill, New York (1941)

More accurate tables (6 or more decimal digits) are:

'Chamber's Seven-figure Mathematical Tables,' Chambers, London (1937)

'Chamber's Six-figure Mathematical Tables' (2 vols.) (ed. Comrie) London (1948–9)

'Barlow's Tables of Squares, Cubes and Reciprocals' (ed. Comrie) Spon (1941)

For more specialist tables reference can be made to the monumental:

FLETCHER, A., MILLER, J. C. P., and ROSENHEAD, L., 'Index of Mathematical Tables,' Scientific Computing Service (1946)

Unfortunately this work is now out of print and, to some extent, out of date. It may be supplemented by reference to 'Mathematical Tables and other Aids to Computation' (*M.T.A.C.*) which maintains a cumulative description of new tables.

Numerous desk calculators are now available but none can be said to possess such excellence as to satisfy all felt wants and to out-shine the others. Our experience recommends the Brunsviga and Facit machines in the hand-operated range, and the Marchant, Facit and Mercedes-Euclid amongst those electrically operated. We shall not attempt any description of the means of using these machines, since a short time with an experienced operator *and* the machine will do more than many pages of words in this direction.

Regarding pencil and paper, we may remark that foolscap paper ruled with feint $\frac{1}{4}$ in. squares seems convenient for most general purposes. Pencils should be soft, B is suitable, and the rubber should not be one degraded by age and use !

## 1.3 THE TOOLS OF ANALYSIS (AUTOMATIC)

IT is hoped that amongst the readers of this book there will be many who have access to one of the automatic digital calculators which become daily more easily available. To these fortunates we would address the following words, do not throw aside the classical tools described in section 1.2. Few problems are of such a nature as to be immediately suitable for an automatic machine and the well-tried aids will almost always be necessary during the period of problem preparation.

Fortunately most of the available automatic machines have 'codes' which are very similar, so that an operator used to one machine can readily apply himself to another. Nevertheless the efficient use of a particular machine will only result from a detailed knowledge of its mathematical structure, and this should always be acquired at the earliest possible moment.

## 1.4 PRECISION, ACCURACY AND ERRORS

In planning a calculation the three factors detailed in the heading must always be considered. First, in any calculation using data obtained by physical measurement, the inherent precision of the data itself must be examined. If no figures for experimental errors are presented and these are not easily obtainable, a knowledge of the experimental technique may give a clue. Measurements of length are rarely accurate to better than 1/10 per cent, measurements of weight often attain 1/10,000 per cent. Electrical measurements are frequently of precision as low as 5 per cent. These circumstances should be taken into account at the planning stage, and a rough working rule is to calculate to two places more than those given by the data.

The accuracy of the calculation (excluding errors of the careless type) will depend on the numerical process involved. Additions and subtractions neither increase nor decrease the precision of the data; multiplications and divisions, however, lead to round off procedures and thus to an overall decrease in accuracy. Hand calculations are seldom of such length as to cause trouble from the growth of round off errors, but with automatic calculators the situation is different. Thus a typical matrix inversion may lead to over 10,000 multiplications, and this, in turn, to a rounding error which has a probable value of the order of 100 units in the last place.

Errors are of two main types, mathematical and human. The former may result from the use of approximations, which are inevitable consequences of the use of discrete processes to represent continuous ones. The latter class of error should be avoidable, at least in the long run, by the provision of adequate checks.

In manual calculation it has long been a platitude that a person should never check his own work and that, if possible, the same method should not be used. This has tended to become forgotten in connection with the use of automatic digital calculators, and it is frequently suggested that because the machine has produced the same answer twice in succession it must be correct. Unfortunately most machines suffer at times from 'pattern sensitivity', that is they will work with complete accuracy on all numbers except *one*. Under these circumstances the same *wrong* answer can be produced as often as required, and the only valid check is a completely different computing routine.

In practice it is often possible to check the results of a long series of calculations by some completely external means, such as differencing (see Chapter 3, section 3.2), or, alternatively, from a knowledge of the observations with which the calculations are intended to agree. When this is not so (with an automatic digital calculator) a good plan is to repeat the calculation after an interval of several days, since few, if any, of these machines survive such a period without adjustment, and adjustment almost always varies any pattern sensitivity which may be present.

Formulae may be used in different ways and with differing resultant accuracy. Thus, we may calculate

$$\sin \theta \simeq \theta - \theta^3/6 + \theta^5/120 \qquad \ldots (1.4.1)$$

in two ways. In the first the terms are formed separately and then added. In this event the round off *may* be equal to $1 \cdot 5$ in the last place. On the other hand, by forming:

$$[(\tfrac{1}{120}\theta^2 - \tfrac{1}{6})\theta^2 + 1]\theta \qquad \ldots (1.4.2)$$

5

the greatest error will be 0·5 in the last place. This example is also instructive in that it illustrates an efficient means of calculating a polynomial. Thus a direct calculation of equation 1.4.1 involves two divisions, four multiplications and two additions or subtractions, whereas in equation 1.4.2 the multiplications are reduced to three.

Considerations such as those mentioned above should always precede any numerical calculation and might be multiplied indefinitely. Some pointers will be given at appropriate places in the text, but pencil and paper analysis can only be learned by long practice and, in our experience, no two expert analysts agree upon the best detailed layout for any particular case. For this reason the details will be left to the reader and such numerical examples as appear are illustrations of such things as convergence, rather than of computational layout.

### REFERENCE

[1] BOOTH, A. D., and BOOTH, K. H. V., 'Automatic Digital Calculators,' p. 14, Butterworth, London (1953)

# TABULATIONS AND DIFFERENCES

## 2.1 THE NATURE OF TABULATED FUNCTIONS

THE differential calculus had its origin in a consideration of the mode of variation of a function $y = f(x)$ with the argument $x$. In the process of defining the differential coefficient, $\dfrac{dy}{dx}$, it is necessary to consider the limit of a finite difference ratio:

$$f(x + \delta x) - f(x)/(x + \delta x) - x$$

as $\delta x \to 0$. When a function is represented by a set of numerical values contained in a table, it is natural to consider the analogues of the differentials $dy$ and $dx$ which can be deduced immediately from the tabular values. Suppose that a function $u_x$ is defined by a table:

| $x$ | $u_x$ |
|---|---|
| 0 | $u_0$ |
| 1 | $u_1$ |
| 2 | $u_2$ |
| $\vdots$ | |
| $n$ | $u_n$ |

Then, corresponding to $dx$, we have $(1 - 0)$, $(2 - 1)$, $(n - \{n - 1\})$ all of which are equal to unity. And corresponding to $dy$ we have the differences $(u_1 - u_0)$, $(u_2 - u_1)$, . . . $(u_n - u_{n-1})$.

Since the interval of tabulation (*i.e.* 1 in this case) is by no means always unity, it is customary to represent this by the symbol $\Delta(x)$, and in a like manner: $u_{m+1} - u_m$ is represented by $\Delta(u_m)$.

Now just as it possible to proceed to differential coefficients higher than the first, so can the differences of a tabulated function be extended thus:

| $x$ | $f(x)$ | $\Delta f$ | $\Delta^2 f$ | $\Delta^3 f$ |
|---|---|---|---|---|
| 0 | $u_0$ | $\Delta u_0 = u_1 - u_0$ | $\Delta^2 u_0 = \Delta u_1 - \Delta u_0 = u_2 - 2u_1 + u_0$ | $\Delta^3 u_0 = \Delta^2 u_1 - \Delta^2 u_0 = u_3 - 3u_2 + 3u_1 - u_0$ |
| 1 | $u_1$ | $\Delta u_1 = u_2 - u_1$ | $\Delta^2 u_1 = \Delta u_2 - \Delta u_1 = u_3 - 2u_2 - u_1$ | $\Delta^3 u_1 = \Delta^2 u_2 - \Delta^2 u_1 = u_4 - 3u_3 + 3u_2 - u_1$ |
| 2 | $u_2$ | $\Delta u_2 = u_3 - u_2$ | *etc.* | *etc.* |
| 3 | $u_3$ | $\Delta u_3 = u_4 - u_3$ | | |
| 4 | $u_4$ | $\Delta u_4 = u_5 - u_4$ | | |
| 5 | $u_5$ | $\Delta u_5 = u_6 - u_5$ | | |

The differences on the first line, namely, $\Delta u_0$, $\Delta^2 u_0$, $\Delta^3 u_0$ *etc.* are referred to as leading differences.

## 2.2 SOME ACTUAL TABLES

Before proceeding to a consideration of the uses to which differences may be put, it is instructive to consider some existing mathematical tables and their relation to differences.

As a first example consider the following section of a typical schoolboy's 4-place logarithm table:

| $x$ | 0 | 1 | 2 | 3 | 4 | 5 | 6 | 7 | 8 | 9 | Proportional Parts 1 2 3 4 5 6 7 8 9 |
|---|---|---|---|---|---|---|---|---|---|---|---|
| 10 | 0000 | 0043 | 0086 | 0128 | 0170 | 0212 | 0253 | 0294 | 0334 | 0374 | 4  8 12 17 21 25 29 33 37 |
| 11 | 0414 | 0453 | 0492 | 0531 | 0569 | 0607 | 0645 | 0682 | 0719 | 0755 | 4  8 11 15 19 23 26 30 34 |
| 12 | 0792 | 0828 | 0864 | 0899 | 0934 | etc. | | | | | etc. |

This is a typical example of what may be called a 'two dimensional' table in that, to each lattice point of a two dimensional co-ordinate system is assigned a functional value. Such tables are usually only available for the most elementary functions and at a very low level of precision. First consider the differences of the function at the finest interval available in the table, namely ·001.

| $x$ | $f(x)$ | $\Delta$ | $\Delta^2$ |
|---|---|---|---|
| 100 | 0000 | 0043 | 0 |
| 101 | 0043 | 0043 | $-1$ |
| 102 | 0086 | 0042 | 0 |
| 103 | 0128 | 0042 | |
| 104 | 0170 | | |

It is intuitively clear that, since the second difference is sensibly constant, a linear relationship exists between the function and its argument in the intervals between tabulated values. It follows that, at any rate approximately, if the value of $f(x)$ at a non-tabulated value is required no great error will result from assuming:

$$f(x_0 + \delta) = f(x_0) + \delta.[f(x_1) - f(x_0)]$$

or

$$f(x_0 + \delta) = f(x_0) + \delta.\Delta[f(x_0)]$$

where $\delta$ is a *proportion* of the interval $(x_1 - x_0)$, and in any case the error will not exceed unity [*i.e.* the value of $\Delta^2\{f(x_0)\}$]. On the other hand, consider the table of 'proportional parts'. These purport to contain the values of $\delta\Delta[(f(x_0)]$ *etc.* for $\delta = ·0001, ·0002 \ldots ·0009$. But since:

$$\Delta f(100) = 0043$$
$$\Delta f(109) = 0040$$

it is evident that the proportional parts can only be approximate and

8

interpolation. Instead second central differences (see section 3.4 *infra*) have been given and these make possible a reasonable interpolation process (that of Everett, section 3.4, equation 3.4.8) for the evaluation of intermediate values.

## REFERENCE

[1] Table of Sines and Cosines to 15 decimal places at hundredths of a degree. *U.S. Nat. Bur. Stand.* Applied Mathematics Series. No. 5, Washington, 1949.

# INTERPOLATION

## 3.1 NOTATION

THE reader will be familiar with the notion of a difference as defined in section 2.1; this is not, however, the only type of difference which is convenient in numerical work. The notation:

$$\Delta u_n = u_{n+1} - u_n \qquad \ldots (3.1.1)$$

is usually referred to as the 'forward' difference at $u_n$ for a reason which will be apparent from the following scheme:

| $x$ | $f(x)$ | $\Delta f(x)$ | $\Delta^2 f(x)$ | $\Delta^3 f(x)$ |
|-----|--------|---------------|-----------------|-----------------|
| 0 | $u_0$ | | | |
| | | $\Delta u_0$ | | |
| 1 | $u_1$ | | $\Delta^2 u_0$ | |
| | | $\Delta u_1$ | | $\Delta^3 u_0$ |
| 2 | $u_2$ | | $\Delta^2 u_1$ | |
| | | $\Delta u_2$ | | $\Delta^3 u_1$ |
| 3 | $u_3$ | | $\Delta^2 u_2$ | |
| | | $\Delta u_3$ | | |
| 4 | $u_4$ | | | |

which represents, a convenient method of tabulation.

On the other hand, it is equally possible to form the differences $(u_0 - u_{-1})$, $(u_{-1} - u_{-2})$, $(u_{-2} - u_{-3})$ etc., and it is convenient to have a 'notation' for these, although it must be borne in mind that they do not really differ from appropriate entries in the forward difference table. The customary notation for the 'backward' difference is

$$\nabla u_n = u_n - u_{n-1} \qquad \ldots (3.1.2)$$

and its position in tabulation is shown below:

| $x$ | $f(x)$ | $\nabla f(x)$ | $\nabla^2 f(x)$ | $\nabla^3 f(x)$ |
|-----|--------|---------------|-----------------|-----------------|
| $-4$ | $u_{-4}$ | | | |
| | | $\nabla u_{-3}$ | | |
| $-3$ | $u_{-3}$ | | $\nabla^2 u_{-2}$ | |
| | | $\nabla u_{-2}$ | | $\nabla^3 u_{-1}$ |
| $-2$ | $u_{-2}$ | | $\nabla^2 u_{-1}$ | |
| | | $\nabla u_{-1}$ | | $\nabla^3 u_0$ |
| $-1$ | $u_{-1}$ | | $\nabla^2 u_0$ | |
| | | $\nabla u_0$ | | |
| 0 | $u_0$ | | | |

At this point it should be noticed that the forward difference is particularly appropriate at the start of a table, and the backward difference at the end where, in the absence of analytical knowledge about the nature of the tabulated function, forward differences are not defined.

For intermediate points a third type of difference is appropriate, this is the so-called 'central difference' defined by :

$$\delta u_n = u_{n+\frac{1}{2}} - u_{n-\frac{1}{2}} \qquad \ldots (3.1.3)$$

The table then becomes:

| $x$ | $f(x)$ | $\delta f(x)$ | $\delta^2 f(x)$ | $\delta^3 f(x)$ | $\delta^4 f(x)$ |
|---|---|---|---|---|---|
| $-2$ | $u_{-2}$ | | | | |
| | | $\delta u_{-\frac{3}{2}}$ | | | |
| $-1$ | $u_{-1}$ | | $\delta^2 u_{-1}$ | | |
| | | $\delta u_{-\frac{1}{2}}$ | | $\delta^3 u_{-\frac{1}{2}}$ | |
| $0$ | $u_0$ | | $\delta^2 u_0$ | | $\delta^4 u_0$ |
| | | $\delta u_{\frac{1}{2}}$ | | $\delta^3 u_{\frac{1}{2}}$ | |
| $1$ | $u_1$ | | $\delta^2 u_1$ | | |
| | | $\delta u_{\frac{3}{2}}$ | | | |
| $2$ | $u_2$ | | | | |

which suggests the appropriateness of the central difference in the body of a table.

A further operator, which is of great utility, is defined by:

$$E u_n = u_{n+1} \qquad \ldots (3.1.4)$$

or

$$Ef(x) = f(x + \delta x)$$

Successive application of 3.1.4 leads to the symbolic equation:

$$E^m u_n = u_{n+m} \qquad \ldots (3.1.5)$$

Again, 3.1.1 can be re-written:

$$u_{n+1} = u_n + \Delta u_n$$

whence, formally,

$$E u_n = (1 + \Delta) u_n$$

or

$$E \equiv 1 + \Delta \qquad \ldots (3.1.6)$$

This relation is one of great power in deriving relationships between a function and its differences.

In a similar manner, from equation 3.1.2:

$$\nabla u_n = u_n - E^{-1} u_n$$

or

$$\nabla \equiv (E - 1)/E \qquad \ldots (3.1.7)$$

13

And, from equation 3.1.3:

$$\delta u_n = E^{\frac{1}{2}}u_n - E^{-\frac{1}{2}}u_n$$

or

$$\delta \equiv E^{\frac{1}{2}} - E^{-\frac{1}{2}} \qquad \dots(3.1.8)$$

A further operator which is in common use is the 'averaging operator' $\mu$, this is defined by:

$$\mu u_n = \tfrac{1}{2}(u_{n+\frac{1}{2}} + u_{n-\frac{1}{2}}) \qquad \dots(3.1.9)$$

whence:

$$\mu \equiv \tfrac{1}{2}(E^{\frac{1}{2}} + E^{-\frac{1}{2}}) \qquad \dots 3.1.10$$

The use of the operator $E$ is not the only method of forming $f(x + \delta x)$ from $f(x)$. Thus Taylor's theorem gives:

$$f(x + \delta x) = f(x) + \delta x f'(x) + \frac{(\delta x)^2}{2!}f''(x) + \dots$$

or, writing the differential in operator form such that:

$$f'(x) = Df(x)$$
$$f^n(x) = D^n f(x)$$

$$f(x + \delta x) = f(x) + \delta x Df(x) + \frac{(\delta x)^2}{2}D^2 f(x) + \dots$$

whence, symbolically:

$$Ef(x) = \left[1 + \delta x D + \frac{(\delta x D)^2}{2} + \dots\right]f(x)$$

or

$$E \equiv e^{\delta x D} \qquad \dots(3.1.11)$$

The operator $(\delta x)D$ is sometimes represented by

$$U \equiv (\delta x)D \qquad \dots(3.1.12)$$

## 3.2 SOME EXPANSIONS

We shall now use the notation and operators defined in section 3.1 to obtain a number of useful results. In a short account, such as the present, it is not possible to justify the operational procedures rigorously, but the reader can, if he so desires, refer to one of the standard texts, mentioned in the references, for a complete demonstration. In the meanwhile, it is worth mentioning that the operational method enables most of the standard finite-difference formulae to be worked out quickly and, as such, is a great *aide memoire* when no compilation is available.

First let us attempt to evaluate $\Delta^n u_0$ in terms of the functional values, $u_0, u_1 \ldots$ etc. We have:

$$\Delta^n (u_0) \equiv (E - 1)^n u_0$$

$$\equiv \left\{ \begin{array}{l} E^n - \dfrac{n}{1\,!} E^{n-1} + \dfrac{n(n-1)}{2\,!} E^{n-2} \\[2mm] - \dfrac{n(n-1)\,(n-2)}{3\,!} E^{n-3} \ldots (-1)^n \end{array} \right\} u_0$$

$$= u_n - \frac{n}{1\,!} u_{n-1} + \frac{n(n-1)}{2\,!} u_{n-2} \ldots (-1)^n u_0 \quad \ldots (3.2.1)$$

A standard notation for the $r$th binomial coefficient is given by:

$$n_r = \frac{n(n-1)\,(n-2) \ldots (n-r+1)}{r\,!} \qquad \ldots (3.2.2)$$

so that equation 3.2.1 takes the simple form:

$$\Delta^n u_0 = u_n - n_1 u_{n-1} + n_2 u_{n-2} \ldots (-1)^r n_r u_{n-r} \ldots (-1)^n u_0 \\ \ldots (3.2.3)$$

At this point it is worth pausing to discuss the application of differencing techniques to the detection of errors in tabulated functions. It is clear from equation 3.2.3 that if the $m$th tabulated value of a function is in error by a small quantity $\epsilon$, the effect on the differences will increase in a regular fashion and, for the $n$th difference, will have a maximum effect along a central difference line pointing to the incorrect value. This is shown in the section of table below, where the presence of an error in the functional value at $x = 38 \cdot 5°$ is clearly indicated. The magnitude and mode of

| $x^0$ | $\sin x$ | $\Delta$ | $\Delta^2$ | $\Delta^3$ | $\Delta^4$ |
|---|---|---|---|---|---|
| 38·0 | ·6157 | | | | |
| | | 13 | | | |
| ·1 | ·6170 | | 1 | | |
| | | 14 | | − 1 | |
| ·2 | ·6184 | | 0 | | 0 |
| | | 14 | | − 1 | |
| ·3 | ·6198 | | − 1 | | − 2 |
| | | 13 | | − 3 | |
| ·4 | ·6211 | | − 4 | | 17 |
| | | 9 | | 14 | |
| | | ← | | | |
| ·5 | ·6220 | | 10 | | − 30 |
| | | 19 | | − 16 | |
| ·6 | ·6239 | | − 6 | | 23 |
| | | 13 | | 7 | |
| ·7 | ·6252 | | 1 | | − 8 |
| | | 14 | | − 1 | |
| ·8 | ·6266 | | 0 | | |
| | | 14 | | | |
| ·9 | ·6280 | | | | |

propagation of the disturbance produced by a single unit error is shown more clearly below:

| $f$ | $\Delta$ | $\Delta^2$ | $\Delta^3$ | $\Delta^4$ |
|---|---|---|---|---|
| 0 | | | | |
| | 0 | | | |
| 0 | | 0 | | |
| | 0 | | 0 | |
| 0 | | 0 | | 1 |
| | 0 | | 1 | |
| 0 | | 1 | | $-4$ |
| | 1 | | $-3$ | |
| 1 | | $-2$ | | 6 |
| | $-1$ | | 3 | |
| 0 | | 1 | | $-4$ |
| | 0 | | $-1$ | |
| 0 | | 0 | | 1 |
| | 0 | | 0 | |
| 0 | | 0 | | |
| | 0 | | | |
| 0 | | | | |

A second expansion is obtainable as follows. Consider $u_n$, this may be written:

$$u_n = E^n u_0 = (1 + \Delta)^n u_0$$
$$= u_0 + n_1 \Delta u_0 + n_2 \Delta^2 u_0 \ldots + n_r \Delta^r u_0 \ldots + \Delta^n u_0 \quad \ldots (3.2.4)$$

from which it can be seen that if the first $n$ leading differences of a function are given (for a known interval), and if the initial value is known, $n$ tabular values are calculable. An extension of this occurs when the $n$th differences of a function are known to be constant. In this event all differences of order greater than $n$ are zero, and 3.2.4 thus enables a complete tabulation to be made. Actually direct application of 3.2.4 is seldom made since it is easier to proceed directly from the table; this appears below in the tabulation of $x^3$, a function for which third differences are constant.

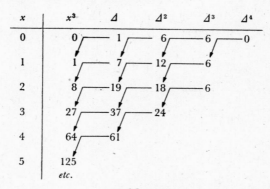

| $x$ | $x^3$ | $\Delta$ | $\Delta^2$ | $\Delta^3$ | $\Delta^4$ |
|---|---|---|---|---|---|
| 0 | 0 | 1 | 6 | 6 | 0 |
| 1 | 1 | 7 | 12 | 6 | |
| 2 | 8 | 19 | 18 | 6 | |
| 3 | 27 | 37 | 24 | | |
| 4 | 64 | 61 | | | |
| 5 | 125 | | | | |

etc.

16

The assumption of constancy of $r$th differences is easily seen to imply that $u$ is a function of degree $r$ in the interval. This is clear from equation 3.2.4 since, when $\Delta^r u_0 = \text{const}$, $\Delta^{r+k} u_0 = 0$ ($k = 1 \ldots$), and thus $n_{r+k}$ will be multiplied by a zero coefficient. Since $n_r$ is of degree $r$ in the interval, the result follows. An alternative demonstration is the following:

$$\Delta x^r = [x + (\delta x)\,]^r - x^r$$
$$= r(\delta x)x^{r-1} + O(x^{r-2}) \qquad \ldots (3.2.5)$$

Thus the operation $\Delta$ on $x^r$ lowers the degree of the function by unity. Repeating $r$ times:

$$\Delta^r x^r = r!\,(\delta x)^r \qquad \ldots (3.2.6)$$

which is the required result.

A frequently used notation in finite difference work is

$$x^{(m)} = x(x - 1)(x - 2) \ldots (x - m + 1) \ldots \quad (3.2.7)$$

we leave it as an exercise to the reader to prove that:

$$\Delta x^{(m)} = m x^{(m-1)} \qquad \ldots (3.2.8)$$

### 3.3 INTERPOLATION FORMULAE

We have seen that the values of a function at the points which are integral multiples of the difference interval are obtainable from equation 3.2.4. The assumption is that the function is representable by a polynomial of degree $r$ in the interval ($r$th differences assumed constant), and, if it can be taken that between tabulation intervals the same polynomial is an adequate representation of the function:

$$u_x = u_0 + x_1 \Delta u_0 + x_2 \Delta^2 u_0 + \ldots + x_r \Delta^r u_0 \ldots (3.3.1)$$

where

$$x_r = \frac{x(x - 1) \ldots (x - r + 1)}{r!} \qquad \ldots (3.3.2)$$

It must be made quite clear, however, that this result, known as the 'Newton-Gregory' interpolation formula, does make the assumption of polynomial representability. To emphasize this point more strongly, assume that $r + 1$ tabular values are given, so that no differences above the $r$th are calculable. It follows from equation 3.2.4 that

$$u_n = \sum_{s=0}^{r} n_s \Delta^s u_0$$

17

Now we may add to $u_n$ any function:

$$\phi = n(n-1)(n-2) \ldots (n-r+1)\psi(n)$$

where $\psi(n)$ is arbitrary, since $\phi$ is zero at all tabulated values and will, in consequence, not be observed. Unfortunately, however, $\phi$ will not, in general, be zero at non-tabulated values, e.g. at $u_x$ $(0 < x < 1)$ and any use of the Newton-Gregory formula in these circumstances will lead to error.

Even when $u_n$ is given at *all* points $(-\infty \leqslant n \leqslant \infty)$ for integral $n$ there is still the possibility of an added function:

$$\phi = \sum_{t=0}^{\infty} a_t \sin \pi t n$$

so that care is required here also.

The reader may consider that these cases are exceptional, but the following example is one which, in modified form, might be encountered in practice, and for which Newton-Gregory interpolation is impossible.

| $x$ | $f(x)$ | $\Delta$ | $\Delta^2$ | $\Delta^3$ | $\Delta^4$ |
|---|---|---|---|---|---|
| 0 | 1 | 3 | 9 | 27 | 81 |
| 1 | 4 | 12 | 36 | 108 | |
| 2 | 16 | 48 | 144 | | |
| 3 | 64 | 192 | | | |
| 4 | 256 | | | | |

We require to find $f(\frac{1}{2})$, and the Newton-Gregory formula gives:

$$f(\tfrac{1}{2}) = 1 + \frac{(\tfrac{1}{2})}{1!} \cdot 3 + \frac{(\tfrac{1}{2})(-\tfrac{1}{2})}{2!} \cdot 9 + \frac{(\tfrac{1}{2})(-\tfrac{1}{2})(-\tfrac{3}{2})}{3!} \cdot 27$$

$$+ \frac{(\tfrac{1}{2})(-\tfrac{1}{2})(-\tfrac{3}{2})(-\tfrac{5}{2})}{4!} \cdot 81 + \ldots$$

$$= 1 + \tfrac{3}{2} - \tfrac{9}{8} + \tfrac{27}{16} - \tfrac{405}{128} \ldots$$

from which it is evident that the series diverges and will never produce the correct value $(4)^{\frac{1}{2}} = 2$.

Quite apart from such exceptional functions, the Newton-Gregory formula is not of great use in real interpolation because it makes use of tabular values which are all in *advance* of the point at which a function value is desired. This is shown in the scheme:

| $n$ | $f$ | $\Delta$ | $\Delta^2$ | $\Delta^3$ | $\Delta^4$ | |
|---|---|---|---|---|---|---|
| $-4$ | $u_{-4}$ | | | | | |
| | | $\Delta u_{-4}$ | | | | |
| $-3$ | $u_{-3}$ | | $\Delta^2 u_{-4}$ | | | |
| | | $\Delta u_{-3}$ | | $\Delta^3 u_{-4}$ | | |
| $-2$ | $u_{-2}$ | | $\Delta^2 u_{-3}$ | | $\Delta^4 u_{-4}$ | |
| | | $\Delta u_{-2}$ | | $\Delta^3 u_{-3}$ | | |
| $-1$ | $u_{-1}$ | | $\Delta_2 u_{-2}$ | | $\Delta^4 u_{-3}$ | |
| $0$ | $u_0$ | $\Delta u_{-1}$ | $\Delta^2 u_{-1}$ | $\Delta^3 u_{-2}$ | $\Delta^4 u_{-2}$ | Gauss 'backward' |
| | | $\Delta u_0$ | | $\Delta^3 u_{-1}$ | | Gauss 'forward' |
| $1$ | $u_1$ | | $\Delta^2 u_0$ | | $\Delta^4 u_{-1}$ | |
| | | $\Delta u_1$ | | $\Delta^3 u_0$ | | |
| $2$ | $u_2$ | | $\Delta^2 u_1$ | | $\Delta^4 u_0$ | |
| | | $\Delta u_2$ | | $\Delta^3 u_1$ | | |
| $3$ | $u_3$ | | $\Delta^2 u_2$ | | | Newton-Gregory |
| | | $\Delta u_3$ | | | | |
| $4$ | $u_4$ | | | | | |

A more reasonable procedure would be to make use of functional values which straddle the point at which interpolation is required. Two such schemes are shown in the diagram, and these lead to the Gaussian interpolation formulae:

$$u_x = u_0 + x\Delta u_0 + x_2\Delta^2 u_{-1} + (x+1)_3\Delta^3 u_{-1} + (x+1)_4\Delta^4 u_{-2} + \ldots$$
$$\ldots\ldots(3.3.3)$$

which is the Gauss 'forward' formula, and:

$$u_x = u_0 + x\Delta u_{-1} + (x+1)_2\Delta^2 u_{-1} + (x+1)_3\Delta^3 u_{-2} + (x+2)_4\Delta^4 u_{-2} + \ldots$$
$$\ldots\ldots(3.3.4)$$

which is the Gauss 'backward' formula. $x_r$ has been defined in equation 3.3.2.

It has been remarked by COMRIE [1] that these formulae, and also that of Stirling are never used in good modern practice, and for this reason we do not give a detailed proof. The reader will satisfy himself as to the correctness of the first few terms in the 'forward' formula by substituting from:

$$\Delta^2 u_0 = \Delta^2 u_{-1} + \Delta^3 u_{-1}$$
$$\Delta^3 u_0 = \Delta^3 u_{-1} + \Delta^4 u_{-1}$$
$$\Delta^4 u_{-1} = \Delta^4 u_{-2} + \Delta^5 u_{-2}$$
$$etc.$$

in the Newton-Gregory result (3.3.1) and re-arranging. The 'backward' formula is likewise obtained by substituting from :

$$\Delta u_0 = \Delta u_{-1} + \Delta^2 u_{-1}$$
$$\Delta^2 u_0 = \Delta^2 u_{-1} + \Delta^3 u_{-1}$$
$$\Delta^3 u_{-1} = \Delta^3 u_{-2} + \Delta^4 u_{-2}$$
$$etc.$$

19

A general derivation has been given by FREEMAN[2].

If we take the mean of the two Gauss formulae (3.3.3 and 3.3.4) we obtain:

$$u_x =$$

$$u_0 + \tfrac{1}{2}x(\Delta u_0 + \Delta u_{-1}) + \frac{x^2}{2!}\Delta^2 u_{-1} + \frac{x(x^2 - 1^2)}{2.3!}(\Delta^3 u_{-1} + \Delta^3 u_{-2})$$

$$+ \frac{x^2(x^2 - 1^2)}{4!}\Delta^4 u_{-2} + \frac{x(x^2 - 1^2)(x^2 - 2^2)}{2.5!}(\Delta^5 u_{-2} + \Delta^5 u_{-3})$$

$$+ \; etc. \quad \dots \quad (3.3.5)$$

which is known as Stirling's formula.

We now proceed to derive the two formulae which are of most common use in actual problems. Since they appear at this point they will be expressed in terms of the forward difference operator $\Delta$. It is, however, more usual to work in central differences and an alternative proof in terms of these operators will be given later, in section 3.4.

First we transform the origin of the Gauss backward formula from $u_0$ to $u_1$ so that $x$ becomes $(x - 1)$ and:

$$u_x = u_1 + (x - 1)\Delta u_0 + \frac{x(x - 1)}{2!}\Delta^2 u_0 + \frac{x(x - 1)(x - 2)}{3!}\Delta^3 u_{-1}$$

$$+ \frac{(x + 1)x(x - 1)(x - 2)}{4!}\Delta^4 u_{-1} + \dots \quad \dots (3.3.6)$$

Taking the mean of equations 3.3.6 and 3.3.3,

$$u_x = \tfrac{1}{2}(u_1 + u_0) + (x - \tfrac{1}{2})\Delta u_0 + \frac{x(x - 1)}{2.2!}(\Delta^2 u_{-1} + \Delta^2 u_0) + \dots$$

$$\dots \quad (3.3.7)$$

which is Bessel's formula.

Finally,[3] we may write the Gauss forward formula (equation 3.3.3):

$$w_{1+x} = w_1 + x\Delta w_1 + x_2\Delta^2 w_0 + (x + 1)_3\Delta^3 w_0 + (x + 1)_4\Delta^4 w_{-1} + \dots$$

and similarly equation 3.3.6:

$$w_x = w_1 + (x - 1)\Delta w_0 + x_2\Delta^2 w_0 + x_3\Delta^3 w_{-1} + (x + 1)_4\Delta^4 w_{-1}$$

Now if we subtract $w_x$ from $w_{1+x}$ we obtain:

$$\Delta w_x = x\Delta w_1 + (x + 1)_3\Delta^3 w_0 + \dots$$

$$- (x - 1)\Delta w_0 - x_3\Delta^3 w_{-1} - \dots$$

(since $w_{1+x} - w_x = \Delta w_x$ by definition)

20

whence, on placing $u_x = \Delta w_x$:

$$u_x = xu_1 + (x+1)_3\Delta^2 u_0 + \cdots$$
$$- (x-1)u_0 - x_3\Delta^2 u_{-1} \cdots$$

or

$$u_x = xu_1 + \frac{x(x^2-1)}{3!}\Delta^2 u_0 + \cdots - (x-1)u_0$$

$$- \frac{(x-1)(\{x-1\}^2-1)}{3!}\Delta^2 u_{-1} \cdots \quad \cdots (3.3.8)$$

which is Everett's formula.

## 3.4 CENTRAL DIFFERENCES

It is clear from the analysis of section 3.3 that a difference interpolation formula, for use in the body of a table, suggests the notion of central differences (which were mentioned briefly in section 3.1). We shall now examine an operational method for obtaining central difference formulae in a natural manner.

First observe, from the central difference notation table of section 3.1, that the only central differences of $u_0$, $u_1$ which are available from the tabular values are the even ones $\delta^2$, $\delta^4$ *etc.* Let us, therefore, attempt to find an expansion for $u_x$ in terms of $\delta^{2n}u_0$ and $\delta^{2n}u_1$.

Operationally we have,

$$u_x = E^x u_0 = e^{xU} . u_0 \qquad \cdots (3.4.1)$$

where $U$ is defined by equation 3.1.12.

Assuming that an expansion is possible in terms of $\delta^{2n}u_0$ and $\delta^{2n}u_1$, this will be of the form:

$$F(\delta).u_0 + G(\delta)u_1 \qquad \cdots (3.4.2)$$

where $F$ and $G$ are *even* functions of $\delta$.
Now

$$u_1 = Eu_0 = e^U u_0 \qquad \cdots (3.4.3)$$

whence, from equations 3.4.1, 3.4.2 and 3.4.3:

$$e^{xU} \equiv F(\delta) + G(\delta)e^U \qquad \cdots (3.4.4)$$

Now from equations 3.1.8 and 3.1.11 we have:

$$\frac{\delta}{2} = \sinh\left(\frac{U}{2}\right) \qquad \cdots (3.4.5)$$

so that $\delta$ is an odd function of $U$. Now, since $F$ and $G$ are even functions of $\delta$, they are also even functions of $U$. Thus, replacing $U$ by its negative in equation 3.4.4, we obtain:

$$e^{-xU} = F(\delta) + G(\delta)e^{-U} \qquad \dots (3.4.6)$$

and, after some manipulation:

$$\left. \begin{array}{l} F(\delta) = \sinh (1 - x)U/\sinh U \\ G(\delta) = \sinh xU/\sinh U \end{array} \right\} \qquad \dots (3.4.7)$$

From these expressions, together with equation 3.4.5 it can be shown that:

$$F(\delta) = (1 - x) + \frac{[(1 - x)^2 - 1^2]}{3!} \delta^2$$

$$+ \frac{[(1 - x)^2 - 1^2][(1 - x)^2 - 2^2]}{5!} \delta^4 + \dots$$

and that

$$G(\delta) = x + \frac{(x^2 - 1^2)}{3!} \delta^2 + \frac{(x^2 - 1^2)(x^2 - 2^2)}{5!} \delta^4 + \dots$$

so that:

$$u_x = (1 - x) \left\{ u_0 + \frac{[(1 - x)^2 - 1^2]}{3!} \delta^2 u_0 \right.$$

$$\left. + \frac{[(1 - x)^2 - 1^2][(1 - x)^2 - 2^2]}{5!} \delta^4 u_0 + \dots \right\}$$

$$+ x \left\{ u_1 + \frac{(x^2 - 1^2)}{3!} \delta^2 u_1 + \frac{(x^2 - 1^2)(x^2 - 2^2)}{5!} \delta^4 u_1 + \dots \right\}$$

$$\dots (3.4.8)$$

which is Everett's formula in central difference form. The reader will see, by renaming the forward difference symbols in equation 3.3.8 that it is identical with equation 3.4.8.

Bessel's formula can also be obtained in central difference form by means of the operational equation:

$$E^x u_0 = F(\delta) (u_1 + u_0) + G(\delta)u_{\frac{1}{2}}$$

the form of which is suggested by equation 3.3.7, and where $F$ is again an *even* function of $\delta$ but $G(\delta)$ is this time *odd*. The final result is:

$$u_x = \tfrac{1}{2}(u_0 + u_1) + (x - \tfrac{1}{2})\delta u_{\frac{1}{2}} + B^{\mathrm{ii}}(x)(\delta^2 u_0 + \delta^2 u_1) + B^{\mathrm{iii}}(x)\delta^3 u_{\frac{1}{2}}$$

$$+ B^{\mathrm{iv}}(x)(\delta^4 u_0 + \delta^4 u_1) + B^{\mathrm{v}}(x)\delta^5 u_{\frac{1}{2}} + \dots \qquad \dots (3.4.9)$$

where the symbols $B^n(x)$ are given by:

$$B^{ii}(x) = x(x-1)/2.2\,!$$
$$B^{iii}(x) = x(x-\tfrac{1}{2})(x-1)/3\,!$$
$$B^{iv}(x) = (x+1)x(x-1)(x-2)/2.4\,!$$
$$B^{v}(x) = (x+1)x(x-\tfrac{1}{2})(x-1)(x-2)/5\,!$$

$$....(3.4.10)$$

$$etc.$$

The notation used here is that suggested by Comrie, *loc. cit.*

### 3.5 MODIFIED DIFFERENCES

In use, Bessel's formula is often modified by means of a numerical accident. Noting that $\delta u_{\frac{1}{2}} = u_1 - u_0$, we see that equation 3.4.9 can be written, to fourth differences:

$$u_x = u_0 + x\delta u_{\frac{1}{2}} + B^{ii}(x)(\delta^2 u_0 + \delta^2 u_1) + B^{iii}\delta^3 u_{\frac{1}{2}} + B^{iv}(x)(\delta^4 u_0 + \delta^4 u_1)$$
$$....(3.5.1)$$

Now reference to equation 3.4.10 shows that:

$$B^{iv}(x) = \frac{(x+1)(x-2)}{12}\,B^{ii}(x) \qquad ....(3.5.2)$$

and a calculation shows that the quadratic coefficient of $B^{ii}(x)$ has only a limited variation in the range $(0 \leqslant x \leqslant 1)$. This is shown in *Figure 3.5.1.*

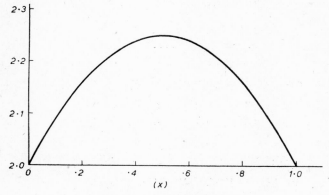

Figure 3.5.1.—12 $B^{iv}(x)/B^{ii}(x)$

23

The limits of variation are between $-2 \cdot 0$ at $x = 0$, $x = 1$ and $-2 \cdot 25$ at $x = \frac{1}{2}$. It follows that

$$B^{\mathrm{iv}}(x) = C B^{\mathrm{ii}}(x)$$

where $C$ varies between $-\cdot 166\dot{6}$ and $-\cdot 1875$.

It has thus become customary to modify the second differences in Bessel's formula by subtracting from them a proportion $C$ of the fourth difference. The value of $C$ is taken to be $\cdot 184$ since this minimizes the residual error. The constant proportion of fourth difference is often called the 'throwback', and the modified second differences are represented by:

$$\delta_m{}^2 u_n = \delta^2 u_n - \cdot 184 \delta^4 u_n \qquad \ldots (3.5.3)$$

## 3.6 DIVIDED DIFFERENCES

When the values of a function are given for values of the argument which are not equally spaced, it is still possible to define a system of differences. Consider the table:

| $x$ | $f(x)$ |
|---|---|
| $x_0$ | $u_0$ |
| $x_1$ | $u_1$ |
| $x_2$ | $u_2$ |
| $x_3$ | $u_3$ |

The first divided differences are then defined to be:

$$\Delta' u_0 = (u_1 - u_0)/(x_1 - x_0)$$
$$\Delta' u_1 = (u_2 - u_1)/(x_2 - x_1)$$
$$.. = \quad \ldots$$
$$\Delta' u_r = (u_{r+1} - u_r)/(x_{r+1} - x_r) \qquad \ldots (3.6.1)$$

Similarly, for second divided differences,

$$\Delta'^2 u_0 = (\Delta' u_1 - \Delta' u_0)/(x_2 - x_0)$$
$$\Delta'^2 u_1 = (\Delta' u_2 - \Delta' u_1)/(x_3 - x_1)$$
$$etc.$$

and, in general:

$$\Delta'^{r+1} u_0 = (\Delta'^r u_1 - \Delta'^r u_0)/(x_{r+1} - x_0)$$
$$\Delta'^{r+1} u_n = (\Delta'^r u_{n+1} - \Delta'^r u_n)/(x_{n+r+1} - x_n) \qquad \ldots (3.6.2)$$

24

There exists the analogue of the Newton-Gregory formula for divided differences:

$$u_x = u_0 + (x - x_0)\Delta'u_0 + (x - x_0)(x - x_1)\Delta'^2u_0$$
$$+ (x - x_0)(x - x_1)(x - x_2)\Delta'^3u_0 + \ldots$$
$$(x - x_0)(x - x_1) \ldots (x - x_{r-1})\Delta'^r u_0 + \ldots (3.6.3)$$

It can be seen from equations 3.6.1 and 3.6.2 that when the intervals $x_{r+1} - x_r$ become equal (to $\delta x$, say) the divided difference formulae reduce to:

$$\Delta'u_n = \Delta u_n/\delta x$$
$$\Delta'^2 u_n = \Delta^2 u_n / 1 . 2 . (\delta x)^2$$
$$\Delta'^3 u_n = \Delta^3 u_n / 1 . 2 . 3 (\delta x)^3$$
$$etc.$$
$$\Delta'^r u_n = \Delta^r u_n / n! (\delta x)^n \qquad \ldots (3.6.4)$$

so that equation 3.6.3. may be written :

$$u_x = u_0 + \frac{x\Delta u_0}{\delta x} + x(x - \delta x)\frac{\Delta^2 u_0}{2!(\delta x)^2} + x(x - \delta x)(x - 2\delta x)\frac{\Delta^3 u_0}{3!(\delta x)^3} + \ldots$$

$$+ x(x - \delta x)(x - 2\delta x) \ldots [x - (r - 1)\delta x]\frac{\Delta^r u_0}{r!(\delta x)^r} + \ldots$$

or

$$u_x = u_0 + \xi_1\Delta u_0 + \xi_2\Delta^2 u_0 + \ldots \xi_r\Delta^r u_0 + \ldots$$

where $\xi_r$ is as defined in equation 3.3.2 with $x = \xi = \left(\dfrac{x}{\delta x}\right)$ and $x_0 = 0$.

This is the ordinary Newton-Gregory formula of equation 3.3.1 for interval $\delta x$.

## 3.7 LAGRANGEAN INTERPOLATION

An alternative formula for interpolation at unequal intervals is due to Lagrange. Suppose that, as before, functional values:

| $x$ | $f(x)$ |
|---|---|
| $x_0$ | $u_0$ |
| $x_1$ | $u_1$ |
| $x_2$ | $u_2$ |
| $\vdots$ | $\vdots$ |
| $x_{n-1}$ | $u_{n-1}$ |

are given, and that they are $n$ in number. An interpolation formula

25        C

consists in finding a polynomial, of degree $(n-1)$, passing through the given values. Assume that:

$$f(x) = (x-x_0)(x-x_1) \ldots (x-x_{n-1}) \sum_{r=0}^{n-1} \frac{A_r}{(x-x_r)} \quad \ldots (3.7.1)$$

Put $x = x_s$ $(s = 0, 1 \ldots n-1)$ then:

$$A_s = \frac{f(x_s)}{(x_s-x_0)(x_s-x_1) \ldots (x_s-x_{s-1})(x_s-x_{s+1}) \ldots (x_s-x_{n-1})}$$
$$= u_s/(x_s-x_0)(x_s-x_1) \ldots (x_s-x_{s-1})(x_s-x_{s+1}) \ldots (x_s-x_{n-1})$$
$$\ldots (3.7.2)$$

Equations 3.7.1 and 3.7.2, together, constitute Lagrange's interpolation formula.

### 3.8 CAUTIONS AND PRECAUTIONS

One example has already been given (section 3.3) of the dangers which arise from the blind use of direct interpolation formulae. The reverse process, called inverse interpolation, and sufficiently defined by the statement: 'given $f(x)$, find $x$', is perhaps even more strewn with pitfalls for the unwary. As an indication of these, suppose that the values:

| $x$ | $f(x)$ |
|---|---|
| 1 | 0 |
| 4 | 1 |
| 16 | 2 |
| 64 | 3 |
| 256 | 4 |

are given, and that it is desired to find $f(x)$ when $x = 32$. (The reader will notice that this is really inverse interpolation from the table given previously in section 3.3.)

The appropriate Lagrange formula is:

$$f(x) = 1 \cdot \frac{(x-1)(x-16)(x-64)(x-256)}{(4-1)(4-16)(4-64)(4-256)}$$
$$+ 2 \cdot \frac{(x-1)(x-4)(x-64)(x-256)}{(16-1)(16-4)(16-64)(16-256)}$$
$$+ 3 \cdot \frac{(x-1)(x-4)(x-16)(x-256)}{(64-1)(64-4)(64-16)(64-256)}$$
$$+ 4 \cdot \frac{(x-1)(x-4)(x-16)(x-64)}{(256-1)(256-4)(256-16)(256-64)}$$

from which it is easily verified that $f(32) = -\cdot 263$, which differs considerably from the true value $+ 2.5$!

The reason for this behaviour is quite evident when the mode of variation of the function, and of its Lagrangean approximation, are considered. The two expressions are shown in *Figure 3.8.1.*

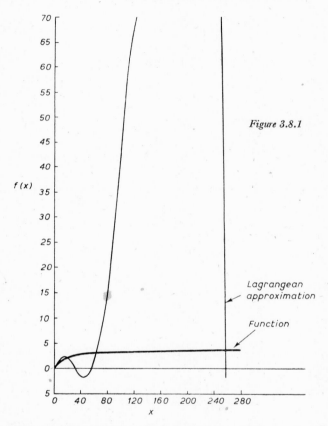

*Figure 3.8.1*

In this particular example it happens that a linear interpolation, in the range concerned, would give a far better result. This emphasizes the fact that, before using an interpolation formula on any tabulated function, it should be carefully ascertained that the function behaves in a manner capable of representation by the formula.

### REFERENCES

[1] COMRIE, L. J., Chamber's Six-Figure Tables, 2 (1949) p. xxviii
[2] FREEMAN, H., *J. Inst. Actuaries*, L, (1924), 31
[3] LIDSTONE, *J. Inst. Actuaries*, LX (1934) 349

**4**

# NUMERICAL DIFFERENTIATION
# AND INTEGRATION

## 4.1 OPERATORS

THE differential of a function has already been introduced as $D$ in section 3.1. In a similar manner we may introduce an operational symbol for integration as:

$$\int \equiv \frac{1}{D} \ (\equiv D^{-1}) \qquad \dots (4.1.1)$$

Now from equation 3.1.11 we have:

$$\delta x D \equiv \log_e E = \log_e (1 + \Delta).$$

whence, expanding:

$$\delta x D \equiv \Delta - \frac{\Delta^2}{2} + \frac{\Delta^3}{3} - \dots$$

or

$$D \equiv \frac{\Delta}{\delta x} \left[ 1 - \frac{\Delta}{2} + \frac{\Delta^2}{3} \dots + (-1)^r \frac{\Delta^r}{r+1} + \dots \right] \dots (4.1.2)$$

which, when applied to $y = f(x)$ at $x = x_0$ gives:

$$\left( \frac{dy}{dx} \right)_{x = x_0} = \frac{1}{\delta x} [\Delta f(x_0) - \tfrac{1}{2} \Delta^2 f(x_0) + \tfrac{1}{3} \Delta^3 f(x_0) - etc. \dots] \dots (4.1.3)$$

In a like manner, raising 4.1.2 to power $n$.

$$D^n \equiv \frac{\Delta^n}{(\delta x)^n} \left( 1 - \frac{\Delta}{2} + \frac{\Delta^2}{3} \dots \right)^n \qquad \dots (4.1.4)$$

from which:

$$D^2 \equiv \frac{\Delta^2}{(\delta x)^2} \left( 1 - \Delta + \frac{11}{12} \Delta^2 - \frac{5}{6} \Delta^3 + \dots \right) \qquad \dots (4.1.5)$$

and

$$D^3 \equiv \frac{\Delta^3}{(\delta x)^3} \left( 1 - \frac{3}{2} \Delta + \frac{7}{4} \Delta^2 \dots \right) \qquad \dots (4.1.6)$$

These formulae provide a convenient means of obtaining the differential coefficients of a function which is given by a table of values, and not in analytical form.

## 4.2 CENTRAL DIFFERENCE FORMULAE FOR DIFFERENTIATION

In many applications it is more convenient to have expressions for the differential coefficients of a function in terms of central differences. The operational method may again be applied in the following manner.

From equation 3.4.5:

$$U(= \delta x D) \equiv 2\sinh^{-1}\frac{\delta}{2}$$

where $\delta$ is the central difference operator.

Unfortunately $U$ is an odd function of $\delta$ so that this equation will produce a series of *odd* powers of $\delta$ for all *odd* derivatives. Since such values of $\delta$ cannot be obtained directly from tabular entries (see the third diagram of section 3.1) a more satisfactory procedure has to be found. This can be done by means of the operator $\mu$, defined by equation 3.1.10.

Clearly

$$\mu\delta \equiv \tfrac{1}{2}(E^1 - E^{-1}) \qquad \dots(4.2.1)$$

so that

$$\mu\delta u_0 = \tfrac{1}{2}(u_1 - u_{-1})$$

which can be found directly from a table.

Also:

$$2\mu + \delta \equiv 2E \qquad \dots(4.2.2)$$

$$2\mu - \delta \equiv 2E^{-1} \qquad \dots(4.2.3)$$

whence

$$4\mu^2 - \delta^2 \equiv 4$$

or

$$\mu^2 \equiv \tfrac{1}{4}\delta^2 + 1 \qquad \dots(4.2\ 5)$$

Now we may write:

$$\left(\frac{U}{\delta}\right)^n \equiv \left(\frac{\sinh^{-1}\tfrac{1}{2}\delta}{\tfrac{1}{2}\delta}\right)^n \qquad \dots(4.2.6)$$

which will give, for *even* values of $n$, an expansion for $D^n$ in terms of *even* powers of $\delta$. Alternatively:

$$\frac{1}{\mu}\left(\frac{U}{\delta}\right)^n = \frac{1}{\mu}\left(\frac{\sinh^{-1}\tfrac{1}{2}\delta}{\tfrac{1}{2}\delta}\right)^n \qquad \dots(4.2.7)$$

which, by virtue of equation 4.2.5, will give expansions of $D^n$ for *odd* values of $n$, in terms of *even* powers of $\delta$ multiplied by $\mu\delta^n$ which, since $n$ is *odd*, can be found from tabular entries.

To obtain the series we make use of two general results due to BICKLEY[1] :

$$\left(\frac{U}{\delta}\right)^n = 1 - \frac{n}{24}\delta^2 + \frac{5n^2 + 22n}{5760}\delta^4 - \frac{35n^3 + 462n^2 + 1528n}{2903040}\delta^6 +$$

$$+ \frac{175n^4 + 4620n^3 + 40724n^2 + 119856n}{1393459200}\delta^8 -$$

$$- \frac{385n^5 + 16940n^4 + 279884n^3 + 2057968n^2 + 5682048n}{367873228800}\delta^{10}$$

$$+ \cdots \qquad \ldots (4.2.8)$$

$$\frac{1}{\mu}\left(\frac{U}{\delta}\right)^n = 1 - \frac{n+3}{24}\delta^2 + \frac{5n^2 + 52n + 135}{5760}\delta^4 -$$

$$- \frac{35n^3 + 777n^2 + 5749n + 14175}{2903040}\delta^6 +$$

$$+ \frac{175n^4 + 6720n^3 + 96794n^2 + 619776n + 1488375}{1393459200}\delta^8 -$$

$$- \frac{385n^5 + 22715n^4 + 536294n^3 + 6333250n^2 + 37408281n + 88409475}{367873228800}\delta^{10}$$

$$+ \cdots \qquad \ldots (4.2.9)$$

These results hold for positive *and* negative values of $n$.

From equation 4.2.8 we have:

$$\left(\frac{U}{\delta}\right)^2 \equiv 1 - \tfrac{1}{12}\delta^2 + \tfrac{1}{90}\delta^4 - etc.$$

which gives:

$$D^2 \equiv \frac{1}{(\delta x)^2}\left(\delta^2 - \tfrac{1}{12}\delta^4 + \tfrac{1}{90}\delta^6 - etc.\right) \qquad \ldots (4.2.10)$$

Also from equation 4.2.9:

$$\frac{1}{\mu}\left(\frac{U}{\delta}\right) \equiv 1 - \tfrac{1}{6}\delta^2 + \tfrac{1}{30}\delta^4 - \tfrac{1}{40}\delta^6 + etc.$$

leading to:

$$D \equiv \frac{1}{(\delta x)}\left[(\mu\delta) - \tfrac{1}{6}\delta^2(\mu\delta) + \tfrac{1}{30}\delta^4(\mu\delta) - \tfrac{1}{40}\delta^6(\mu\delta) + etc.\right]$$

$$\ldots (4.2.11)$$

30

When applied to a functional value ($u_0$, say) 4.2.11 may be written (by virtue of equation 4.2.1)

$$D(u_0) = \frac{1}{2(\delta x)} \left[ (u_1 - u_{-1}) - \tfrac{1}{6}(\delta^2 u_1 - \delta^2 u_{-1}) \right.$$
$$\left. + \tfrac{1}{30}(\delta^4 u_1 - \delta^4 u_{-1}) - etc. \right] \qquad \dots (4.2.12)$$

which is in a suitable form for tabular use.

Higher derivatives can be evaluated in a similar manner by the use of equations 4.2.8 and 4.2.9.

### 4.3 NUMERICAL INTEGRATION

In many problems it becomes necessary to evaluate the integral of a given function between certain limits, and although the derivatives can always be found when the analytic form of the function is given, the same is not necessarily (or even frequently) true of the integral.

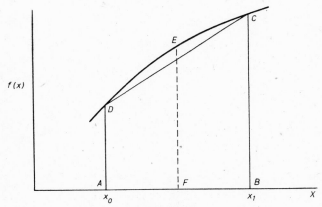

*Figure 4.3.1*

Thus numerical integration, sometimes called 'mechanical quadrature', is a process of importance in its own right, and quite apart from its use with tabulated functions.

The simplest form of numerical integration may be described as trapezoidal approximation. Thus, with reference to *Figure 4.3.1*, it is evident that a rough approximation to the integral:

$$\int_{x_0}^{x_1} f(x)\,\mathrm{d}x$$

31

is given by the area $ABCD$, *i.e.* by:

$$\tfrac{1}{2}(AD + BC)(x_1 - x_0)$$
$$= \tfrac{1}{2}(x_1 - x_0)(f(x_1) + fx_0)$$

Clearly, a better approximation may be obtained by representing the arc $DEC$ by means of a quadratic expression in $x$, and forming the integral for the resulting function.

The quadratic function can easily be obtained from the Newton Gregory formula, and is:

$$f_q(x) = f(0) + x\Delta f(0) + \frac{x(x - 1)}{2}\Delta^2 f(0) \quad \ldots (4.3.1)$$

where $f_q(x)$ is the quadratic approximation to $f(x)$, and we have taken the intervals $AF = FB = 1$. Equation 4.3.1 can be integrated to give:

$$\int_0^2 f_q(x)\mathrm{d}x = 2f(0) + 2\Delta f(0) + \tfrac{1}{3}\Delta^2 f(0) \quad \ldots (4.3.2)$$

or, replacing the differences by their tabular values:

$$\int_0^2 f_q(x)\mathrm{d}x = \tfrac{1}{3}[f(2) + 4f(1) + f(0)] \quad \ldots (4.3.3)$$

which is usually known as 'Simpson's rule'.

The extension to the case in which the interval in $x$ is $(\delta x)$ instead of unity is immediate and leads to the formula:

$$\int_0^{2(\delta x)} f_q(x)\mathrm{d}x = \frac{(\delta x)}{3}[f(2) + 4f(1) + f(0)] \quad \ldots (4.3.4)$$

When a function is to be integrated over an extensive range it is, in general, better to add the contributions arising from the application of Simpson's rule to successive groups of three ordinates, rather than to seek an approximating polynomial which represents the function over the whole range (see, for example section 3.8). Thus:

$$\int_0^{2n(\delta x)} f(x)\mathrm{d}x \simeq \int_0^{2(\delta x)} f_{q_1}(x)\mathrm{d}x + \int_{2(\delta x)}^{4(\delta x)} f_{q_2}(x)\mathrm{d}x + \ldots$$

$$+ \int_{(2n-2)(\delta x)}^{2n(\delta x)} f_{q_n}(x)\mathrm{d}x$$

$$= \frac{(\delta x)}{3}[f(0) + 4f(1) + 2f(2) + 4f(3) + \ldots + f(2n)] \quad \ldots (4.3.5)$$

from equation 4.3.4. This expression is often referred to as the *extension* of Simpson's rule. It should be noted that the approximating function in this case, is not necessarily a smooth curve.

32

A further approximation to the integral of a function, between limits 0 and 3 can be obtained by adding a further term to the Newton-Gregory formula (4.3.1). We then obtain:

$$f_c(x) = f(0) + x\Delta f(0) + \frac{x(x-1)}{2}\Delta^2 f(0) + \tfrac{1}{6}x(x-1)(x-2)\Delta^3 f(0)$$

where $f_c(x)$ is a *cubic* approximation to $f(x)$. Integrating we obtain:

$$\int_0^3 f_c(x)\,\mathrm{d}x = 3f(0) + \tfrac{9}{2}\Delta f(0) + \tfrac{9}{4}\Delta^2 f(0) + \tfrac{3}{8}\Delta^3 f(0) \quad \ldots (4.3.6)$$

or, writing the values of $\Delta$, $\Delta^2$ and $\Delta^3$ in tabular form:

$$\int_0^3 f_c(x)\,\mathrm{d}x = \tfrac{3}{8}[f(0) + 3f(1) + 3f(2) + f(3)] \quad \ldots (4.3.7)$$

which is called the 'three eights' rule.

A still more accurate numerical integration procedure is 'Weddle's rule', which may be derived as follows. Take the first 6 differences and apply the Newton-Gregory expansion:

$$f_s(x) = f(0) + x\Delta f(0) + \frac{x(x-1)}{2!}\Delta^2 f(0) + \frac{x(x-1)(x-2)}{3!}\Delta^3 f(0)$$

$$+ \frac{x(x-1)(x-2)(x-3)}{4!}\Delta^4 f(0) + \frac{x(x-1)\ldots(x-4)}{5!}\Delta^5 f(0)$$

$$+ \frac{x(x-1)\ldots(x-5)}{6!}\Delta^6 f(0)$$

Integrating this expression over the range $0 - 6$ we obtain:

$$\int_0^6 f_s(x)\,\mathrm{d}x = 6f(0) + 18\Delta f(0) + 27\Delta^2 f(0) + 24\Delta^3 f(0)$$

$$+ \tfrac{123}{10}\Delta^4 f(0) + \tfrac{33}{10}\Delta^5 f(0) + \tfrac{41}{140}\Delta^6 f(0) \quad \ldots (4.3.8)$$

Now, with an error of $\Delta^6/140$, we may write the last term in equation 4.3.8 as $\tfrac{42}{140}\Delta^6 f(0) = \tfrac{3}{10}\Delta^6 f(0)$. The expression then becomes, on substituting for the differences in terms of the tabular values:

$$\int_0^6 f_s(x)\,\mathrm{d}x = \tfrac{3}{10}(u_0 + 5u_1 + u_2 + 6u_3 + u_4 + 5u_5 + u_6) \quad \ldots (4.3.9)$$

which is Weddle's formula in the usual notation.

The foregoing results are sometimes known as Newton-Cotes integration formulae of the *closed* type. The expression *closed* is inserted to indicate that the approximating polynomials pass through the end points or limits of integration.

33

For the purpose of solving differential equations it is useful to have available integration formulae of the Newton-Cotes *open* type. That corresponding to Simpson's rule can be obtained by integrating the quadratic approximation 4.3.1, shifted to operate on $x = 1$ as base point. Thus:

$$f_q(x) = f(1) + x\Delta f(1) + \frac{x(x-1)}{2}\Delta^2 f(1)$$

and

$$\int_0^4 f_q(x)\,\mathrm{d}x = \tfrac{4}{3}[2f(1) - f(2) + 2f(3)]$$

or, for interval $(\delta x)$

$$\int_0^{4(\delta x)} f_q(x)\,\mathrm{d}x = \tfrac{4}{3}(\delta x)[2f(1) - f(2) + 2f(3)] \quad \ldots\ldots(4.3.10)$$

## 4.4 THE EULER-MACLAURIN EXPANSION

A general integration formula which is often quoted in numerical analysis is that due to Euler and Maclaurin.

Consider the summation:

$$\sum_{x=a}^{x=a+(n-1)\delta x} f(x) = \left(\sum_{r=0}^{n-1} E^r\right) f(a) \qquad \ldots\ldots(4.4.1)$$

Proceeding in terms of operators we have:

$$\sum_{r=0}^{n-1} E^r \equiv \frac{E^n - 1}{E - 1} \qquad \ldots\ldots(4.4.2)$$

Now, by virtue of equation 3.1.11 $E = e^{(\delta x D)} \equiv e^U$ and we may write:

$$\frac{1}{E-1} \equiv \frac{1}{e^U - 1} \equiv \frac{1}{U}\left[\frac{U}{e^U - 1}\right] \qquad \ldots\ldots(4.4.3)$$

and the well-known [2] expansion

$$\frac{U}{e^U - 1} = 1 - \frac{U}{2} + B_1\frac{U^2}{2!} - B_2\frac{U^4}{4!} + B_3\frac{U^6}{6!} - + (-1)^{r+1}B_r\frac{U^{2r}}{(2r)!} + \ldots$$

where $B_r$ is the $r$th Bernoulli number, enables equation 4.4.3 to be written:

$$\frac{1}{E-1} \equiv \frac{1}{U} - \frac{1}{2} + B_1\frac{U}{2!} - B_2\frac{U^3}{4!} + B_3\frac{U^5}{6!}\ldots \qquad \ldots\ldots(4.4.4)$$

34

The numerical values of the first few Bernoulli numbers are:

$$B_1 = \tfrac{1}{6}, \qquad B_2 = \tfrac{1}{30}, \quad B_3 = \tfrac{1}{42}, \qquad B_4 = \tfrac{1}{30}, \qquad B_5 = \tfrac{5}{66},$$

$$B_6 = \tfrac{691}{2730}, \quad B_7 = \tfrac{7}{6}, \quad B_8 = \tfrac{3617}{510}, \quad B_9 = \tfrac{43867}{798}, \quad B_{10} = \tfrac{174611}{330}$$

Substituting from equations 4.4.4 and 4.4.2 in equation 4.4.1, and observing that $U = (\delta x D)$, $\dfrac{1}{U} = \dfrac{1}{\delta x}\!\int$, we obtain :

$$\sum_{x=a}^{x=a+(n-1)\delta x} f(x) =$$

$$= (E^n - 1)\left[ \frac{1}{\delta x}\!\int f(a)\,\mathrm{d}a - \tfrac{1}{2}f(a) + \frac{B_1}{2!}(\delta x)f'(a) - \frac{B_2}{4!}(\delta x)^3 f^{\mathrm{iii}}(a) + \cdots \right]$$

or

$$\sum_{x=a}^{x=a+(n-1)\delta x} f(x) = \frac{1}{\delta x}\int_a^{a+n\delta x} f(x)\,\mathrm{d}x - \tfrac{1}{2}[f(a + n\delta x) - (f(a)]$$

$$+ \frac{B_1}{2!}(\delta x)[f'(a + n\delta x) - f'(a)] - \frac{B_2}{4!}(\delta x)^3[f^{\mathrm{iii}}(a + n\delta x) - f^{\mathrm{iii}}(a)] + etc.$$

Finally, on rearrangement, we obtain:

$$\int_a^{a+n\delta x} f(x)\,\mathrm{d}x = \frac{(\delta x)}{2}\,[f(a) + 2f(a + \delta x) + 2f(a + 2\delta x) + \cdots$$

$$+ 2f(a + (n - 1)\delta x) + f(a + n\delta x)]$$

$$- \frac{(\delta x)^2}{12}\,[f'(a + n\delta x) - f'(a)] + \frac{(\delta x)^4}{720}\,[f^{\mathrm{iii}}(a + n\delta x) - f^{\mathrm{iii}}(a)]$$

$$- \frac{(\delta x)^6}{30240}\,[f^{\mathrm{v}}(a + n\delta x) - f^{\mathrm{v}}(a)] + etc. \qquad \ldots (4.4.5)$$

which is the normal form of the expansion.

It may be mentioned that the Euler-Maclaurin formula is of little practical use as an integration procedure. It finds an application, however, in the summation of series and, in this connection, will receive attention in Chapter 5.

## 4.5 CENTRAL DIFFERENCE FORMULAE FOR INTEGRATION

The Bickley expansions (equations 4.2.8 and 4.2.9) can be used to obtain several useful formulae for integration which involve central differences. Thus, from equation 4.2.8 with $n = -2$ we obtain:

$$\left(\frac{\delta}{U}\right)^2 = 1 + \tfrac{1}{12}\delta^2 - \tfrac{1}{240}\delta^4 + \tfrac{31}{60480}\delta^6 - \cdots \qquad \ldots (4.5.1)$$

which may be written:

$$\delta^2 \cdot \frac{1}{D^2}(f_0) = (\delta x)^2 (f_0 + \tfrac{1}{12}\delta^2 f_0 - \tfrac{1}{240}\delta^4 f_0 + \tfrac{31}{60480}\delta^6 f_0 \ \cdot \ \cdot \ \cdot)$$

$$\ldots . (4.5.2)$$

Now putting $f_0 = g''_0 = D^2(g_0)$ equation 4.5.2 becomes:

$$\delta^2 g_0 = (\delta x)^2 (g''_0 + \tfrac{1}{12}\delta^2 g''_0 - \tfrac{1}{240}\delta^4 g''_0 + \tfrac{31}{60480}\delta^6 g''_0 - \ \cdot \ \cdot \ \cdot)$$

$$\ldots . (4.5.3)$$

which expresses the second central difference in terms of the central difference of the second derivative at the point in question, and has several applications to the solution of differential equations.

Again, if we put $n = -1$ in equation 4.2.9, there results:

$$\frac{1}{\mu}\left(\frac{\delta}{U}\right) = 1 - \tfrac{1}{12}\delta^2 + \tfrac{11}{720}\delta^4 - \tfrac{191}{60480}\delta^6 + \ \ldots \quad \ldots (4.5.4)$$

or

$$\delta \cdot \frac{1}{D}(f_0) = (\delta x)[\mu f_0 - \tfrac{1}{12}\delta^2(\mu f_0) + \tfrac{11}{720}\delta^4(\mu f_0) - \tfrac{191}{60480}\delta^6(\mu f_0) + \ldots]$$

$$\ldots . (4.5.5)$$

Now, replace $f_0$ by $g'_{\frac{1}{2}} = D(g_{\frac{1}{2}})$, and observe that:

$$\delta g_{\frac{1}{2}} = \delta E^{\frac{1}{2}} g_0 = (E^{\frac{1}{2}} - E^{-\frac{1}{2}})E^{\frac{1}{2}} g_0 = (E - 1)g_0 = g_1 - g_0 \ \left.\begin{array}{c} \\ \\ \end{array}\right\}$$
$$\mu g_{\frac{1}{2}} \equiv \mu E^{\frac{1}{2}} g_0 \equiv \tfrac{1}{2}(E^{\frac{1}{2}} + E^{-\frac{1}{2}})E^{\frac{1}{2}} g_0 \equiv \tfrac{1}{2}(E + 1)g_0 \equiv \tfrac{1}{2}(g_1 + g_0)\left.\begin{array}{c} \end{array}\right\} \cdots$$

$$\ldots . (4.5.6)$$

whence, equation 4.5.5 becomes:

$$g_1 - g_0 = \tfrac{1}{2}(\delta x)[g'_1 + g'_0 - \tfrac{1}{12}(\delta^2 g'_1 + \delta^2 g'_0)$$
$$+ \tfrac{11}{720}(\delta^4 g'_1 + \delta^4 g'_0) - \tfrac{191}{60480}(\delta^6 g'_1 + \delta^6 g'_0) \ \cdot \ \cdot \ \cdot] \quad \ldots (4.5.7)$$

This is clearly an integration formula expressing

$$g_1 - g_0 \left( = \int_0^1 g'(x)\,\mathrm{d}x \right)$$

in terms of the relevant functional values of $g'(x)$.

Finally we shall consider the expansion of the operator $(\mu\delta)$. We have:

$$(\mu\delta)f_0 = \tfrac{1}{2}(E^{\frac{1}{2}} + E^{-\frac{1}{2}})(E^{\frac{1}{2}} - E^{-\frac{1}{2}})f_0 = \tfrac{1}{2}(E^1 - E^{-1})f_0 = \tfrac{1}{2}(f_1 - f_{-1})$$

$$\ldots . (4.5.8)$$

Again, equation 4.5.4 may be written:

$$\mu\left(\frac{\delta}{U}\right) = \mu^2(1 - \tfrac{1}{12}\delta^2 + \tfrac{11}{720}\delta^4 - \tfrac{191}{60480}\delta^6 + \ \cdot \ \cdot \ \cdot)$$

or, observing that $\mu^2 = 1 + \tfrac{1}{4}\delta^2$ (equation 4.2.5)

$$\frac{\mu\delta}{U} = 1 + \tfrac{1}{6}\delta^2 - \tfrac{1}{180}\delta^4 + \tfrac{1}{1512}\delta^6 - \ldots \ldots \ldots (4.5.9)$$

It follows that:

$$\tfrac{1}{2}\frac{(f_1 - f_{-1})}{U} = f_0 + \tfrac{1}{6}\delta^2 f_0 - \tfrac{1}{180}\delta^4 f_0 + \tfrac{1}{1512}\delta^6 f_0 - \ldots$$

or, writing: $f_x = g'_x = Dg_x$

$$\mu\delta g_0 = \tfrac{1}{2}(g_1 - g_{-1}) = (\delta x)\left(g'_0 + \tfrac{1}{6}\delta^2 g'_0 - \tfrac{1}{180}\delta^4 g'_0 + \tfrac{1}{1512}\delta^6 g'_0 - \ldots\right)$$
$$\ldots (4.5.10)$$

which is the required result.

## 4.6 THE CHEBYSHEV INTEGRATION FORMULAE

Integration formulae of the Simpson-Weddel type are advantageous when used in conjunction with a table of functional values, since they make use of equal intervals. On the other hand, each of the function values has, in general, to be multiplied by a different coefficient. When function values have to be calculated for the purpose of the integration, it is often more convenient to use an integration formula in which all such values are treated in the same manner.

We thus examine the possibility of finding an integration formula:

$$\int_a^b g(x)\,\mathrm{d}x = k[g(x_1) + g(x_2) + g(x_3) \ldots + g(x_n)] + R_n \quad \ldots (4.6.1)$$

in which $k$ and $x_1, x_2, \ldots x_n$ are independent of the particular function $g(x)$ being integrated.

Actually, a slightly more general result, given by MILNE-THOMSON [3] will be examined:

$$\int_{-1}^{+1} F(x)g(x)\,\mathrm{d}x = k[g(x_1) + g(x_2) + \ldots + g(x_n)] + R_n \quad \ldots (4.6.2)$$

where $k, x_1, x_2, \ldots x_n$ depend on $F(x)$ but *not* on $g(x)$.

First, assume that $g(x)$ can be expanded in a Maclaurin series:

$$g(x) = g(0) + xg'(0) + \frac{x^2}{2!}g''(0) + \ldots + \frac{x^n}{n!}g^n(0) + \frac{x^{n+1}}{(n+1)!}g^{n+1}(\xi)$$
$$\ldots (4.6.3)$$

in which the remainder term has $0 \leqslant \xi \leqslant x$.

We then have:

$$\int_{-1}^{+1} F(x)g(x)\,dx = \int_{-1}^{+1} F(x)\left[ g(0) + xg'(0) + \frac{x^2}{2\,!}g''(0) + \cdots \right.$$

$$\left. + \frac{x^n}{n\,!}g^n(0) + \frac{x^{n+1}}{(n+1)\,!}g^{n+1}(\xi) \right]dx$$

$$= \sum_{m=0}^{n} \frac{g^m(0)}{m\,!}\int_{-1}^{+1} F(x)\cdot x^m\,dx + \frac{g^{n+1}(\xi)}{(n+1)\,!}\int_{-1}^{+1} x^{n+1}F(x)\,dx \quad \ldots(4.6.4)$$

Again, using equation 4.6.3 with $x = x_1, x_2 \ldots x_n$:

$$k\left[g(x_1) + g(x_2) + \cdots + g(x_n)\right] = kng(0) + kg'(0)\sum_{r=1}^{n}x_r$$

$$+ \frac{kg''(0)}{2\,!}\sum_{r=1}^{n}x_r^2 + \cdots + \frac{kg^n(0)}{n\,!}\sum_{r=1}^{n}x_r^n + \frac{k}{(n+1)!}\sum_{r=1}^{n}x_r^{n+1}g^{n+1}(\xi_r)$$

$$\ldots(4.6.5)$$

Whence, if equations 4.6.4 and 4.6.5 are to be identical to the error specified by $R_n$ in equation 4.6.2, we have, on equating coefficients of $g(0)$, $g'(0) \ldots g^n(0)$:

$$\left.\begin{array}{c} kn = \displaystyle\int_{-1}^{+1} F(x)\,dx \\[2mm] k\displaystyle\sum_{r=1}^{n}x_r = \int_{-1}^{+1} xF(x)\,dx \\[2mm] k\displaystyle\sum_{r=1}^{n}x_r^2 = \int_{-1}^{+1} x^2F(x)\,dx \\[2mm] \cdots \\[2mm] k\displaystyle\sum_{r=1}^{n}x_r^m = \int_{-1}^{+1} x^mF(x)\,dx \end{array}\right\} \quad \ldots(4.6.6)$$

Together with:

$$R_n = \frac{g^{n+1}(\xi)}{(n+1)\,!}\int_{-1}^{+1} x^{n+1}F(x)\,dx - \frac{k}{(n+1)\,!}\sum_{r=1}^{n}x_r^{n+1}g^{n+1}(\xi_r)$$

$$\ldots(4.6.7)$$

where $\quad 0 \leqslant \xi \leqslant x$ and $0 \leqslant \xi_r \leqslant x_r$ $(r = 1 \ldots n)$.

To determine the values of $x_1, x_2 \ldots x_n$ from equation 4.6.6 we may adopt the following procedure.

First let:

$$\sum_{r=1}^{n}x_r^m = s_m \qquad\qquad \ldots(4.6.8)$$

so that $$s_m = \frac{1}{k}\int_{-1}^{+1} x^m F(x)\,\mathrm{d}x = \frac{n\int_{-1}^{+1} x^m F(x)\,\mathrm{d}x}{\int_{-1}^{+1} F(x)\,\mathrm{d}x} \quad \dots(4.6.9)$$

The quantities $s_m$ are thus the sums of the $m$th powers of the $n$ quantities $x_1, x_2, \dots x_n$ which suggests the roots of an equation of degree $n$. Assume then that $x_1, x_2 \dots x_n$ are the roots of:

$$f_n(x) \equiv x^n + a_1 x^{n-1} + a_2 x^{n-2} + \dots + a_n = 0 \quad \dots(4.6.10)$$

so that: $$x^n + a_1 x^{n-1} + a_2 x^{n-2} \dots + a_n$$
$$\equiv (x - x_1)(x - x_2) \dots (x - x_n) \quad \dots(4.6.11)$$

Now put $x = 1/y$ so that, dividing both sides by $y^n$ equation 4.6.11 becomes:

$$1 + a_1 y + a_2 y^2 \dots + a_n y^n \equiv (1 - x_1 y)(1 - x_2 y) \dots (1 - x_n y)$$

Taking logs of both sides:

$$\log_e(1 + a_1 y + a_2 y^2 \dots a_n y^n) = \sum_{r=1}^{n} \log_e(1 - x_r y)$$

$$= -\sum_{r=1}^{n}\left(x_r y + x_r^2 \frac{y^2}{2} + x_r^3 \frac{y^3}{3} \dots + x_r^m \frac{y^m}{m} + \dots\right)$$

$$= -s_1 y - \frac{s_2}{2} y^2 - \frac{s_3}{3} y^3 \dots - s_m y^m - \dots$$
$$\dots(4.6.12)$$

on expansion and by virtue of equation 4.6.8.

Next take exponentials of both sides:

$$1 + a_1 y + a_2 y^2 + \dots + a_n y^n$$
$$= \exp\left[-s_1 y - (s_2/2)y^2 - (s_3/3)y^3 \dots - (s_m/m)y^m - \dots\right]$$
$$\dots(4.6.13)$$

So that, upon expanding the exponential, and equating coefficients, we can determine the coefficients $a_m$ in terms of the power sums $s_m$. The first few are:

$$a_1 = -s_1$$
$$a_2 = -\tfrac{1}{2}s_2 + \tfrac{1}{2}s_1^2$$
$$a_3 = -\tfrac{1}{3}s_3 + \tfrac{1}{2}s_1 s_2 - \tfrac{1}{6}s_1^3$$
$$a_4 = -\tfrac{1}{4}s_4 + \tfrac{1}{3}s_1 s_3 - \tfrac{1}{4}s_1^2 s_2 + \tfrac{1}{8}s_2^2 + \tfrac{1}{24}s_1^4$$
$$a_5 = -\tfrac{1}{5}s_5 + \tfrac{1}{4}s_1 s_4 + \tfrac{1}{6}s_2 s_3 - \tfrac{1}{6}s_1^2 s_3 - \tfrac{1}{8}s_1 s_2^2 + \tfrac{1}{12}s_1^3 s_2 - \tfrac{1}{120}s_1^5$$
$$a_6 = -\tfrac{1}{6}s_6 + \tfrac{1}{5}s_1 s_5 + \tfrac{1}{8}s_2 s_4 + \tfrac{1}{18}s_3^2 - \tfrac{1}{8}s_1^2 s_4 - \tfrac{1}{6}s_1 s_2 s_3$$
$$\qquad - \tfrac{1}{48}s_2^3 + \tfrac{1}{18}s_1^2 s_3 + \tfrac{1}{16}s_1^2 s_2^2 - \tfrac{1}{48}s_1^4 s_2 + \tfrac{1}{720}s_1^6$$

Thus, knowing the form of $F(x)$ and using equation 4.6.9 to determine the values of $s_m$, we can write down the equation 4.6.10 and, by solving it, obtain the values of $x_1 \ldots x_n$.

The most usual technique is to take $F(x) = 1$, we thus obtain the following equations $f_n(x) = 0$, and the relevant roots for insertion in 4.6.2.

| $n$ | $k(=2/n)$ | $f_n(x)$ | Roots |
|---|---|---|---|
| 2 | 1 | $x^2 - \frac{1}{3}$ | $\pm \cdot 5773\ 503$ |
| 3 | $\frac{2}{3}$ | $x(x^2 - \frac{1}{2})$ | $0, \pm \cdot 7071\ 068$ |
| 4 | $\frac{1}{2}$ | $x_4 - \frac{2}{3}x^2 + \frac{1}{45}$ | $\pm \cdot 1875\ 925 \pm \cdot 7946\ 545$ |
| 5 | $\frac{2}{5}$ | $x(x^4 - \frac{5}{9}x^2 + \frac{7}{72})$ | $0, \pm \cdot 3745\ 414 \pm \cdot 8324\ 975$ |
| 6 | $\frac{1}{3}$ | $x^6 - x^4 + \frac{1}{5}x^2 - \frac{1}{105}$ | $\pm \cdot 2666\ 353 \pm \cdot 4225\ 186, \pm \cdot 8662\ 476$ |

It should be noticed that the remainder, after an $n$ point integration using the Chebyshev method, is zero if $g(x)$ is a polynomial of degree not greater than $n$.

The Chebyshev method is particularly suited to use on an automatic digital computer since, in such machines, the fewer different kinds of arithmetic operations which have to be performed to arrive at a given result the better.

[An alternative method of approach, which gives the polynomials $f_n(x)$ directly, is as follows:

Let

$$f_n(z) \equiv (z - x_1)(z - x_2) \ldots (z - x_n) = 0$$

then:

$$f_n(z) = z^n \left(1 - \frac{x_1}{z}\right)\left(1 - \frac{x_2}{z}\right) \ldots \left(1 - \frac{x_n}{z}\right)$$

$$= z^n \exp \sum_{r=1}^{n} \log \left(1 - \frac{x_r}{z}\right)$$

$$= z^n \exp \sum_{r=1}^{n} \left(- \sum_{t=1}^{\infty} \frac{x_r^t}{tz^t}\right)$$

Since $n$ is finite, we may interchange the summation symbols so that:

$$f_n(z) = z^n \exp - \sum_{t=1}^{\infty} \left(\frac{\Sigma x_r^t}{tz^t}\right)$$

but, by equation 4.6.9,

$$\sum_{r=1}^{n} x_r^t = n \int_{-1}^{+1} x^t F(x) \mathrm{d}x \Big/ \int_{-1}^{+1} F(x) \mathrm{d}x$$

whence,

$$f_n(z) = z^n \exp - \overset{\infty}{\underset{t=1}{\Sigma}} n \int_{-1}^{+1} x^t F(x)\mathrm{d}x \Big/ tz^t \int_{-1}^{+1} F(x)\mathrm{d}x$$

$$= z^n \exp n \int_{-1}^{+1} F(x) \left[ - \overset{\infty}{\underset{t=1}{\Sigma}} \frac{x^t}{tz^t} \right] \mathrm{d}x \Big/ \int_{-1}^{+1} F(x)\mathrm{d}x$$

$$= z^n \exp n \int_{-1}^{+1} F(x)\log\left(1 - \frac{x}{z}\right)\mathrm{d}x \Big/ \int_{-1}^{+1} F(x)\mathrm{d}x$$

where $f(z)$ is taken to include only positive powers of $z$ (including zero) in the expansion. When $F(x) = 1$ this becomes very simply:

$$f_n(z) = z^n \exp - n\left(\frac{1}{2.3z^2} + \frac{1}{4.5z^4} + \frac{1}{6.7z^6} + \cdots\right)$$

from which the preceding values of $f_n(x)$ can be quickly derived by expansion.]

It may be noted, in conclusion, that the Chebyshev integration formula becomes unsatisfactory for $n = 8$ and for $n > 9$ since, at this point, the values of $x_r$ are no longer restricted to the range $(-1, +1)$ and, in fact, may not even be real.

## 4.7 THE GAUSSIAN INTEGRATION FORMULA

The Chebyshev method of approximate integration is one of a family of such results which may be written:

$$\int_a^b F(x).g(x)\mathrm{d}x = w_1.g(x_1) + w_2.g(x_2) \ldots + w_n g(x_n) + R_n$$
$$\ldots.(4.7.1)$$

where the weight functions* $(w_r)$ and the associated points $(x_r)$ are independent of the particular function $g(x)$ which is the subject of the integration. [They depend, however, on $F(x)$.]

In section 4.6 we investigated the way in which the values $(x_r)$ had to be chosen in order to make the weight functions equal. We shall now consider the problem in slightly more general terms. First take $F(x) = 1$ and assume that $g(x)$ can be expanded in a convergent power series in $x$ so that:

$$g(x) = a_0 + a_1x + \ldots + a_nx^n + \ldots \quad \ldots.(4.2.2)$$

* Sometimes known as Christoffel numbers.

Next, take *any* set of $n$ points $x_1$ . . . $x_n$ and set up the Lagrangean approximation to $g(x)$ (see section 3.7). This may be written:

$$L(x) = \Pi_n(x) \sum_{r=1}^{n} \frac{g(x_r)}{\Pi_n'(x_r) \cdot (x - x_r)} \qquad \ldots (4.7.3)$$

where

$$\Pi_n(x) = (x - x_1)(x - x_2) \ldots (x - x_n) \qquad \ldots (4.7.4)$$

and $\Pi_n'(x)$ is used to represent $d\Pi_n/dx$.

Now $L(x)$ coincides in value with the function $g(x)$ at each of the points $(x_r)$ $(r = 1 \ldots n)$ so that we may write:

$$g(x) - L(x) = \Pi_n(x)(b_0 + b_1 x + \ldots b_s x^s + \ldots)$$

where the series on the right is again assumed to be convergent. We thus obtain:

$$\int_a^b g(x)\,dx = \int_a^b L(x)\,dx + \int_a^b \left( \Pi_n(x) . \sum_{s=0}^{\infty} b_s x^s \right) dx$$

$$= \sum_{r=1}^{n} w_r g(x_r) + R_n \qquad \ldots (4.7.5)$$

where

$$w_r = \int_a^b \frac{\Pi_n(x)\,dx}{(x - x_r)\Pi_n'(x_r)} \qquad \ldots (4.7.6)$$

and

$$R_n = \int_a^b \left( \Pi_n(x) \sum_{s=0}^{\infty} b_s x^s \right) dx \qquad \ldots (4.7.7)$$

Thus, if $g(x)$ is a polynomial, of maximum degree $n$, we see that $R_n = 0$, and that the $n$ values $(x_r)$ can be chosen arbitrarily so long as we choose $w_r$ as defined by equation 4.7.6.

Since this situation is equivalent to saying that there are arbitrary contants available, it is reasonable to enquire if these can be determined so as to make equation 4.7.5, with $R_n = 0$, true when $g(x)$ is *any* polynomial of degree $(2n - 1)$.

Thus we require

$$R_n = \int_a^b \left[ \Pi_n(x) \sum_{s=0}^{n-1} b_s x^s \right] dx = 0$$

42

for arbitrary $b_s$ $(s \leqslant n - 1)$, and this can only be true if:

$$\int_a^b \Pi_n(x) . x^s \mathrm{d}x = 0 \ (s = 0, 1, \ldots n - 1) \quad \ldots (4.7.8)$$

Now it is well known that the Legendre polynomials, which are conveniently defined for this purpose by means of Rodrigues formula[4]

$$P_0(x) = 1, P_n(x) = \frac{1}{2^n n!} \frac{\mathrm{d}^n}{\mathrm{d}x^n} (x^2 - 1)^n \quad \ldots (4.7.9)$$

are such that[5]:

$$\int_{-1}^{+1} P_n(x) . x^s \mathrm{d}x = 0$$

for all integer values of $s$ less than $n$; furthermore they have $n$ distinct real roots in the interval $(-1, +1)$.

The integral (4.7.8) can be transformed by means of the substitution:

$$x = \frac{b - a}{2} y + \frac{b + a}{2}$$

to take the limits $(-1, +1)$, and it is thus seen that if, after the transformation, we take the values of $(y_r)$ to be the roots of $P_n(y) = 0$ the resulting $n$ point quadrature formula will be exact for all polynomials $g(x)$ whose degree is less than $(2n)$.

An identical argument can be carried out for the more general integral (4.7.1). If this is assumed to be transformed to limits $(-1, +1)$ we have:

$$\int_{-1}^{+1} F(x)g(x)\mathrm{d}x = w_1 . g(x_1) + w_2 . g(x_2) + \ldots + w_n g(x_n) + R_n$$
$$\ldots (4.7.10)$$

where:

$$w_r = \frac{F(x_r)}{\Pi'(x_r)} \int_{-1}^{+1} \frac{\Pi_n(x)}{(x - x_r)} \mathrm{d}x \quad \ldots (4.7.11)$$

and

$$R_n = \int_{-1}^{+1} \left( \Pi_n(x) \sum_{s=0}^{\infty} b_s x^s \right) \mathrm{d}x \quad \ldots (4.7.12)$$

$(x_r)$ $(r = 1 \ldots n)$ being the roots of $P_n(x) = 0$.

The values of the roots $(x_r)$, and of the corresponding weight factors $w_r$, for the important case $F(x) = 1$ are given in *Table*

*4.7.1.* They are taken from the basic table of LOWAN, DAVIDS and LEVENSON [6] who give values to 15 decimal places for values of $n$ up to 16.

Table 4.7.1. *Gaussian integration points and coefficients*

$n = 1$

$x_1 = 0$            $w_1 = 2$

$n = 2$

$x_1 = -x_2 = \cdot 57735\ 02692$      $w_1 = w_2 = 1$

$n = 3$

$x_1 = -x_3 = \cdot 77459\ 66692$      $w_1 = w_3 = \frac{5}{9}$

$x_2 = 0$            $w_2 = \frac{8}{9}$

$n = 4$

$x_1 = -x_4 = \cdot 86113\ 63116$      $w_1 = w_4 = \cdot 34785\ 48451$

$x_1 = -x_3 = \cdot 33998\ 10436$      $w_2 = w_3 = \cdot 65214\ 51549$

$n = 5$

$x_1 = -x_5 = \cdot 90617\ 98459$      $w_1 = w_5 = \cdot 23692\ 68851$

$x_2 = -x_4 = \cdot 53846\ 93101$      $w_2 = w_4 = \cdot 47862\ 86705$

$x_3 = 0$            $w_3 = \cdot 56888\ 88889$

$n = 6$

$x_1 = -x_6 = \cdot 93246\ 95142$      $w_1 = w_6 = \cdot 17132\ 44924$

$x_2 = -x_5 = \cdot 66120\ 93865$      $w_2 = w_5 = \cdot 36076\ 15730$

$x_3 = -x_4 = \cdot 23861\ 91861$      $w_3 = w_4 = \cdot 46791\ 39346$

$n = 7$

$x_1 = -x_7 = \cdot 94910\ 79123$      $w_1 = w_7 = \cdot 12948\ 49662$

$x_2 = -x_6 = \cdot 74153\ 11856$      $w_2 = w_6 = \cdot 27970\ 53915$

$x_3 = -x_5 = \cdot 40584\ 51514$      $w_3 = w_5 = \cdot 38183\ 00505$

$x_4 = 0$            $w_4 = \cdot 41795\ 91837$

$n = 8$

$x_1 = -x_8 = \cdot 96028\ 98565$      $w_1 = w_8 = \cdot 10122\ 85363$

$x_2 = -x_7 = \cdot 79666\ 64774$      $w_2 = w_7 = \cdot 22238\ 10345$

$x_3 = -x_6 = \cdot 52553\ 24099$      $w_3 = w_6 = \cdot 31370\ 66459$

$x_4 = -x_5 = \cdot 18343\ 46425$      $w_4 = w_5 = \cdot 36268\ 37834$

$n = 9$

$x_1 = -x_9 = \cdot 96816\ 02395$      $w_1 = w_9 = \cdot 08127\ 43884$

$x_2 = -x_8 = \cdot 83603\ 11073$      $w_2 = w_8 = \cdot 18064\ 81607$

$x_3 = -x_7 = \cdot 61337\ 14327$      $w_3 = w_7 = \cdot 26061\ 06964$

$x_4 = -x_6 = \cdot 32425\ 34234$      $w_4 = w_6 = \cdot 31234\ 70770$

$x_5 = 0$            $w_5 = \cdot 33023\ 93550$

$n = 10$

$x_1 = -x_{10} = \cdot 97390\ 65285$      $w_1 = w_{10} = \cdot 06667\ 13443$

$x_2 = -x_9 = \cdot 86506\ 33667$      $w_2 = w_9 = \cdot 14985\ 13492$

$x_3 = -x_8 = \cdot 67940\ 95683$      $w_3 = w_8 = \cdot 21908\ 63625$

$x_4 = -x_7 = \cdot 43339\ 53941$      $w_4 = w_7 = \cdot 26926\ 67193$

$x_5 = -x_6 = \cdot 14887\ 43399$      $w_5 = w_6 = \cdot 29552\ 42247$

It may be noted that, $\sum_{r=1}^{n} w_r = 2$—a result which is obtained by taking $F(x) = g(x) = 1$ in equation 4.7.10.

The Gaussian integration method just described may be extended to other ranges than $(-1, +1)$. Probably the most important from the practical point of view are those ranges in which either, or both of $(a, b)$ are infinite. Finiteness of the resulting integral implies that, if $g(x)$ is a polynomial, $F(x)$ is not, and it is natural to relate the extended method to particular forms of $F(x)$. Thus consider the integral:

$$\int_0^\infty e^{-x}g(x)\mathrm{d}x \qquad \ldots(4.7.13)$$

where $g(x)$ is again expressed by equation 4.7.2. We once more seek an integration formula of the type shown in equation 4.7.1 and set up a Lagrangean approximation, but this time to $g(x)$ *only*. If:

$$g(x) - L(x) = \underset{n}{\Pi}(x)(b_0 + b_1x + \ldots + b_sx^s + \ldots)$$

we obtain, from equation 4.7.13

$$\int_0^\infty e^{-x}g(x)\mathrm{d}x = \int_0^\infty e^{-x}L(x)\mathrm{d}x + \int_0^\infty \left[\underset{n}{\Pi}(x)\sum_{s=0}^\infty b_sx^s\right]e^{-x}\mathrm{d}x$$

$$= \sum_{r=1}^n w_rg(x_r) + R_n \qquad \ldots(4.7.14)$$

where

$$w_r = \frac{1}{\underset{n}{\Pi}'(x_r)}\int_0^\infty \frac{e^{-x}\underset{n}{\Pi}(x)}{(x - x_r)}\,\mathrm{d}x \qquad \ldots(4.7.15)$$

and

$$R_n = \int_0^\infty \left[\underset{n}{\Pi}(x)\sum_{s=0}^\infty b_sx^s\right]e^{-x}\mathrm{d}x \qquad \ldots(4.7.16)$$

If we wish equation 4.7.14 to be exact for all polynomials $g(x)$ of degree less than $(2n - 1)$ we thus require:

$$\int_0^\infty \underset{n}{\Pi}(x).x^s.e^{-x}\mathrm{d}x = 0 \qquad (s = 0, 1 \ldots n - 1)$$

Now in this case the Laguerre polynomials defined by:

$$L_n(x) = e^x \frac{\mathrm{d}^n}{\mathrm{d}x^n}(x^ne^{-x}) \qquad \ldots(4.7.17)$$

are appropriate since it can be shown [7] that:

$$\int_0^\infty e^{-x}x^sL_n(x)\mathrm{d}x = 0$$

whenever $s < n$, and we thus take the sampling points $(x_r)$ to be the roots of $L_n(x) = 0$. Some weights and coefficients are given[9] in *Table 4.7.2*.

45

*Table 4.7.2. Laguerre polynomial roots and weight coefficients*

$$n = 1$$

| | |
|---|---|
| $x_1 = 1$ | $w_1 = 1$ |

$$n = 2$$

| | |
|---|---|
| $x_1 = 0 \cdot 58578\ 64$ | $w_1 = \cdot 85355\ 34$ |
| $x_2 = 3 \cdot 41421\ 36$ | $w_2 = \cdot 14644\ 66$ |

$$n = 3$$

| | |
|---|---|
| $x_1 = 0 \cdot 41577\ 46$ | $w_1 = \cdot 71109\ 30$ |
| $x_2 = 2 \cdot 29428\ 03$ | $w_2 = \cdot 27851\ 77$ |
| $x_3 = 6 \cdot 28994\ 51$ | $w_3 = \cdot 01038\ 93$ |

$$n = 4$$

| | |
|---|---|
| $x_1 = 0 \cdot 32254\ 77$ | $w_1 = \cdot 60315\ 41$ |
| $x_2 = 1 \cdot 74576\ 11$ | $w_2 = \cdot 35741\ 87$ |
| $x_3 = 4 \cdot 53662\ 03$ | $w_3 = \cdot 03888\ 79$ |
| $x_4 = 9 \cdot 39507\ 09$ | $w_4 = \cdot 00053\ 93$ |

$$n = 5$$

| | |
|---|---|
| $x_1 = 0 \cdot 26356\ 03$ | $w_1 = \cdot 52175\ 56$ |
| $x_2 = 1 \cdot 41340\ 30$ | $w_2 = \cdot 39866\ 68$ |
| $x_3 = 3 \cdot 59642\ 58$ | $w_3 = \cdot 07594\ 24$ |
| $x_4 = 7 \cdot 08581\ 02$ | $w_4 = \cdot 00361\ 18$ |
| $x_5 = 12 \cdot 64080\ 07$ | $w_5 = \cdot 00002\ 34$ |

Again, if the integral required is of the form:

$$\int_{-\infty}^{+\infty} e^{-x^2} g(x) \mathrm{d}x$$

it is appropriate to consider the Hermite polynomials[8] defined by:

$$H_n(x) = (-1)^n e^{x^2} \frac{\mathrm{d}^n}{\mathrm{d}x^n} (e^{-x^2}) \qquad (4.7.18)$$

for which it can be shown that:

$$\int_{-\infty}^{+\infty} e^{-x^2} x^s H_n(x) \mathrm{d}x = 0$$

whenever $s < n$. These lead to the formula

$$\int_{-\infty}^{+\infty} e^{-x^2} g(x) \mathrm{d}x = \sum_{r=1}^{n} w_r g(x_r) + R_n \qquad \ldots (4.7.19)$$

where

$$w_r = \frac{1}{\prod_n{}'(x_r)} \int_{-\infty}^{+\infty} \frac{e^{-x^2} \prod_n(x)}{(x - x_r)} \mathrm{d}x$$

$$R_n = \int_{-\infty}^{+\infty} \left[ \prod_n(x) \sum_{s=0}^{\infty} b_s x^s \right] e^{-x^2} \mathrm{d}x$$

and $(x_r)$ are the roots of $H_n(x) = 0$.

46

In a like manner the Chebyshev polynomials:

$$T_n(x) = \frac{1}{2^{n-1}} \cos{(n \cos^{-1} x)} \qquad \ldots\ldots (4.7.20)$$

have the property [10]:

$$\int_{-1}^{+1} \frac{x^s T_n(x)}{\sqrt{1-x^2}}\, dx = 0$$

for $s < n$ which leads at once to:

$$\int_{-1}^{+1} \frac{g(x)\,dx}{\sqrt{1-x^2}} = \sum_{r=1}^{n} w_r g(x_r) + R_n \qquad \ldots\ldots (4.7.21)$$

where

$$w_r = \frac{1}{\underset{n}{\Pi'}(x_r)} \int_{-1}^{+1} \frac{\underset{n}{\Pi}(x)}{(x-x_r)\sqrt{1-x^2}} \cdot dx$$

$$R_n = \int_{-1}^{+1} \left[ \underset{n}{\Pi}(x) \sum_{s=0}^{\infty} b_s x^s \right] \frac{dx}{\sqrt{1-x^2}}$$

and the $(x_r)$ are the roots of $T_n(x) = 0$

---

Table 4.7.3.  Roots and weight coefficients for $(1-x^2)\, P'n(x)$

|  |  |
|---|---|
| $n = 1$ | |
| $x_1 = -x_2 = 1$ | $w_1 = w_2 = 1$ |
| $n = 2$ | |
| $x_1 = -x_3 = 1$ | $w_1 = w_3 = 1/3$ |
| $x_2 = 0$ | $w_2 = 4/3$ |
| $n = 3$ | |
| $x_1 = -x_4 = 1$ | $w_1 = w_4 = 0 \cdot 16666\ 67$ |
| $x_2 = -x_3 = 0 \cdot 44721\ 36$ | $w_2 = w_3 = 0 \cdot 83333\ 33$ |
| $n = 4$ | |
| $x_1 = -x_5 = 1$ | $w_1 = w_5 = 0 \cdot 10000\ 00$ |
| $x_2 = -x_4 = 0 \cdot 65465\ 37$ | $w_2 = w_4 = 0 \cdot 54444\ 44$ |
| $x_3 = 0$ | $w_3 = 0 \cdot 71111\ 11$ |
| $n = 5$ | |
| $x_1 = -x_6 = 1$ | $w_1 = w_6 = 0 \cdot 66666\ 67$ |
| $x_2 = -x_5 = 0 \cdot 76505\ 53$ | $w_2 = w_5 = 0 \cdot 37847\ 50$ |
| $x_3 = -x_4 = 0 \cdot 08135\ 70$ | $w_3 = w_4 = 0 \cdot 55485\ 84$ |
| $n = 6$ | |
| $x_1 = -x_7 = 1$ | $w_1 = w_7 = 0 \cdot 04761\ 90$ |
| $x_2 = -x_6 = 0 \cdot 83022\ 39$ | $w_2 = w_6 = 0 \cdot 27682\ 60$ |
| $x_3 = -x_5 = 0 \cdot 46884\ 88$ | $w_3 = w_5 = 0 \cdot 43174\ 54$ |
| $x_4 = 0$ | $w_4 = 0 \cdot 48761\ 90$ |

47

To conclude this section it may be mentioned that it is sometimes desirable to have an integration formula of Gaussian type, but involving the function values at the limits of the range of integration $(a, b)$. Such results are usually known as 'Lobatto's or Radau's formulae' and a typical example results from the use of the polynomial:

$$(1 - x^2)P'_n(x) \qquad \ldots(4.7.22)$$

instead of equation 4.7.9. Formulae based on equation 4.7.22 are less accurate than the true Gaussian results, being exact only for polynomials of degree $(2n - 1)$ when $(n + 1)$ points are used. The chief application is to the integration of functions having the value zero at both ends of the range of integration.

Roots and multiples for the polynomials 4.7.22 are given[11] in *Table 4.7.3*.

## 4.8 ERRORS OF FINITE DIFFERENCE APPROXIMATION

Except in the case of the Chebyshev formula, we have not attempted to estimate the errors produced by the approximate integration formulae. A general method of arriving at such error estimates has been given by MILNE[12], and we shall now indicate its application by considering the error produced by Simpson's rule (4.3.4) and by its Newton-Cotes *open* variant (4.3.10). These particular examples have been chosen because the error estimates will be needed later, in Chapter 6.

In the first place, we make the observation that all finite difference formulae are exact when applied to any polynomial whose degree, $n$, does not exceed a certain upper bound, $N$, say, which is a constant for the particular formula involved. It follows that if the error is to be estimated when the finite difference formula is applied to an arbitrary function, a suitable technique will be to expand that function in a Maclaurin series:

$$f(x) = f(0) + \frac{x}{1!}f'(0) + \frac{x^2}{2!}f''(0) + \ldots + \frac{x^n}{n!}f^{(n)}(0) +$$

$$\frac{x^{n+1}}{(n+1)!}f^{n+1}(\xi) \qquad \ldots(4.8.1)$$

where $0 \leqslant \xi \leqslant x$.

Suppose that the *actual* operation to be performed is $O$ and that the finite difference process is represented by $F$; the error, or remainder $R$, is then given by:

$$R = O[f(x)] - F[f(x)] \qquad \ldots(4.8.2)$$

48

Now, if in equation 4.8.1 we make $n = N$, where $N$ is the highest degree polynomial for which $F$ is exact, we may rewrite 4.8.2 as:

$$R_N = O\left[\frac{x^{N+1}}{(N+1)!}f^{(N+1)}(\xi)\right] - F\left[\frac{x^{N+1}}{(N+1)!}f^{(N+1)}(\xi)\right] \dots (4.8.3)$$

(Since $O$ and $F$ are assumed to be *linear* operators, so that

$$O(f_1 + f_2 + \dots f_n) = O(f_1) + O(f_2) + \dots + O(f_n) \text{ etc.})$$

whence, replacing $f^{(N+1)}(\xi)$ by its maximum value in the interval:

$$R_N \leqslant \frac{1}{(N+1)!}f_{\max}^{(N+1)}\left\{O(x^{N+1}) - F(x^{N+1})\right\} \quad \dots (4.8.4)$$

We now apply this result to estimate the error produced by Simpson's rule. We know that the result is exact for quadratic polynomials, let us therefore try $N = 2$ in equation 4.8.4.

$$O = \int_0^{2(\delta x)} x^3 \mathrm{d}x = 4(\delta x)^4$$

$$F = \frac{(\delta x)}{3}\left[f(2) + 4f(1) + f(0)\right] = \frac{(\delta x)}{3}\left[(2\delta x)^3 + 4(\delta x)^3\right] = 4(\delta x)^4$$

whence the rule is also exact for cubic polynomials.

Next put $N = 3$

$$O = \int_0^{2\delta x} x^4 \mathrm{d}x = 32\frac{(\delta x)^5}{5}$$

$$F = \frac{(\delta x)}{3}\left[(2\delta x)^4 + 4(\delta x)^4\right] = 20\frac{(\delta x)^5}{3}$$

Whence, from equation 4.8.4:

$$R_N \leqslant \frac{1}{4!}f_{\max}^{(4)}(\tfrac{32}{5} - \tfrac{20}{3})(\delta x)^5 = -\frac{(\delta x)^5}{90}f_{\max}^{(4)} \quad \dots (4.8.5)$$

which is the required estimate.

Next consider the Newton-Cotes formula (4.3.10).

Here again it is readily shown that for cubic polynomials the formula is exact. For $N = 3$ we obtain:

$$O = \int_0^{4(\delta x)} x^4 \mathrm{d}x = 1024\frac{(\delta x)^5}{5}$$

$$F = \tfrac{4}{3}(\delta x)\left[2(3\delta x)^4 - (2\delta x)^4 + 2(\delta x)^4\right] = \tfrac{592}{3}(\delta x)^5$$

# NUMERICAL DIFFERENTIATION AND INTEGRATION

Whence, from equation 4.8.4.;

$$R_N \leqslant \frac{1}{4!} f^{(4)}_{max} (\tfrac{1024}{5} - \tfrac{592}{3})(\delta x)^5 = \tfrac{28}{90}(\delta x)^5 f^{(4)}_{max} \quad \ldots (4.8.6)$$

so that the potential error is 28 times that of the Simpson's rule formula.

## REFERENCES

[1] BICKLEY, W. G., *J. Math. Phys.*, 27 (1948) 183
[2] JAHNKE-EMDE, 'Tafeln Höherer Funktionen.' (4th edn.) p. 268. Teubner, Leipzig (1948)
[3] MILNE-THOMSON, L. M. 'The Calculus of finite differences,' (1st edn.), p. 177. Macmillan, London (1951)
[4] HOBSON, E. W. 'The Theory of Spherical and Ellipsoidal Harmonics,' p. 18, Cambridge (1931)
[5] — *ibid.*, p. 36
[6] LOWAN, A. N., DAVIDS, N., and LEVENSON, A. *Bull. Amer. math. Soc.*, 48 (1942), 739
[7] COURANT, R. and HILBERT, D., 'Methods of Mathematical Physics,' vol. 1 p. 94, Interscience (1953)
[8] — *ibid.*, vol. 1, p. 91
[9] REIZ, A., *Ark. Mat. Astr. Fys.*, 29 iv (1943)
[10] LANCZOS, C., 'Tables of Chebyshev Polynomials," p. xiii. *U.S. nat. Bur. Stand.* A.M.S. No. 9
[11] KOPAL, Z., *Astrophys. J.*, 104 (1946) 74
[12] MILNE, W. E., 'Numerical Calculus,' p. 108, Princeton (1949)

# THE SUMMATION OF SERIES

## 5.1 SOME GENERAL OBSERVATIONS

ALTHOUGH the subject of this chapter might be thought properly to belong to algebra, it is unfortunately true that many recent books on this subject give little practical guidance on appropriate methods of summing series numerically. It is therefore proposed, in this short chapter, to give one or two applications of finite difference operator calculus to this problem.

In the first place we may observe that many series have terms which proceed in unit steps of some argument, for example:

$$\phi(x) = \sum_{r=0}^{n} \psi(r, x) \qquad \ldots (5.1.1)$$

where $r$ takes the values $0, 1, 2 \ldots n$.

An alternative method of writing equation 5.1.1 makes use of the operator $E$ and is:

$$\phi(x) = \left( \sum_{r=0}^{n} E^r \right) \psi(0, x) \qquad \ldots (5.1.2)$$

In this form the 'sum' may readily be found from the well-known formula for the geometric progression, thus:

$$\phi(x) = \frac{E^{n+1} - 1}{E - 1} \psi(0, x) \qquad \ldots (5.1.3)$$

Suppose now that $\psi(r, x)$ can be represented as the first difference of some new function $\xi(r, x)$ so that

$$\psi(r, x) = \Delta\xi(r, x)$$

equation 5.1.3 now becomes:

$$\phi(x) = \frac{E^{n+1} - 1}{E - 1} \Delta\xi(0, x)$$

or, observing that $E - 1 \equiv \Delta$,

$$\phi(x) = (E^{n+1} - 1)\xi(0, x)$$

whence:

$$\phi(x) = \xi(n + 1, x) - \xi(0, x) \qquad \ldots (5.1.4)$$

which has thus summed the original series—at least formally. It must, unfortunately, be remarked here that only a limited number of functions exist which are recognizable as first differences of other recognizable functions. We shall consider two classes of these in the next section.

## 5.2 DIFFERENCE FUNCTIONS

An elementary example of a function which can be expressed as the difference of values of a known function has already appeared in section 3.2, equations 3.2.7 and 3.2.8. Thus the factorial function $x^{(m)}$ can always be written as a first difference:

$$x^{(m)} = \Delta \frac{x^{(m+1)}}{(m+1)} \qquad \ldots (5.2.1)$$

and, since any polynomial in $x$ can be expressed as a polynomial in factorial functions, it follows that any series whose terms are polynomials in $x$ can also be summed.

For example:

$$\sum_{z=0}^{n} z^3 = \sum_{z=0}^{n} z(z-1)(z-2) + 3z(z-1) + z$$

$$= \sum_{z=0}^{n} z^{(3)} + 3z^{(2)} + z^{(1)}$$

$$= \frac{(n+1)^{(4)}}{4} + (n+1)^{(3)} + \frac{(n+1)^{(2)}}{2}$$

by virtue of equations 5.1.4 and 5.2.1 and the fact that $0^{(r)} = 0$. Or, by expanding and simplifying:

$$\sum_{z=0}^{n} z^3 = \left[ \frac{n(n+1)}{2} \right]^2$$

which is a well-known result.

Again:

$$\Delta(a^x) = (a^{(x+\delta x)} - a^x) = (a^{\delta x} - 1)a^x \qquad \ldots (5.2.2)$$

so that:

$$a^x = \Delta \left( \frac{a^x}{a^{\delta x} - 1} \right) \qquad \ldots (5.2.3)$$

a relation which enables any series which can be put into the form $\Sigma ca^x$ to be summed.

52

## 5.3 THE EULER TRANSFORMATION

Although the actual result of equation 5.1.4 is of limited utility, the analysis which leads to it can be applied to the summation of slowly convergent series with a considerable improvement in rate of convergence.

Thus, consider the series of alternating terms:

$$S_n = u_0 - u_1 + u_2 - u_3 + \ldots + (-1)^{n-1} u_{n-1} \quad \ldots (5.3.1)$$

This may, by the preceding analysis, be written:

$$S_n = \frac{1 + E^n}{1 + E} u_0 \qquad \ldots (5.3.2)$$

Now if $u_n \to 0$ as $n \to \infty$ we may assume that:

$$S = \operatorname*{Lt}_{n \to \infty} S_n = \frac{u_0}{1 + E}$$

and since $E = 1 + \Delta$

$$S = \tfrac{1}{2} \frac{u_0}{1 + \dfrac{\Delta}{2}}$$

whence, expanding:

$$S = \tfrac{1}{2} \left[ u_0 - \tfrac{1}{2}\Delta u_0 + \tfrac{1}{4}\Delta^2 u_0 - \tfrac{1}{8}\Delta^3 u_0 + etc. \ldots \right] \quad \ldots (5.3.3)$$

which is usually known as the Euler transformation.

As an instance of the power of this transformation we may mention the example given by BROMWICH [1] who considers the sum:

$$S_{\frac{1}{2}} = 1 - \frac{1}{\sqrt{2}} + \frac{1}{\sqrt{3}} - \frac{1}{\sqrt{4}} + \frac{1}{\sqrt{5}} \ldots etc.$$

and shows that, by taking the first 6 terms of this series and evaluating the differences from the next 7 terms (*i.e.* up to and including $1/\sqrt{12}$), the sum is obtained as $S_{\frac{1}{2}} = 0 \cdot 6049$ correct to 4 decimal places. To obtain the same accuracy over $10^8$ terms of the original series would he needed! Practical points in the use of the Euler transformation are that the first few terms of the original series should be added separately and the transformation applied to the remainder. By taking two different starting points, in this manner, a check on the results of the calculation and an estimate of the accuracy can be had.

One of a number of extensions of the Euler transformation, suggested by Tomlinson Fort, is particularly applicable to an oscillatory series in which $u_{n+1}/u_n \simeq \beta^{-1}$. ($\beta > 1$)

We put $u_n = (\beta^{-1})^n v_n$ in the original series and thus obtain:

$$S = \underset{n \to \infty}{\mathrm{Lt}}\, S_n = \frac{v_0}{1 + \beta^{-1}E} = \frac{\beta}{1 + \beta}\, \frac{v_0}{\left(1 + \dfrac{\Delta}{1 + \beta}\right)}$$

or

$$S = \frac{\beta}{1 + \beta}\left[v_0 - \frac{1}{1 + \beta}\Delta v_0 + \frac{1}{(1 + \beta)^2}\Delta^2 v_0 - \frac{1}{(1 + \beta)^3}\Delta^3 v_0 \ldots\right]$$

$$\ldots (5.3.4)$$

Since the series in $v$ has terms which are all nearly equal, the difference series (5.3.4) converges rapidly.

## 5.4 APPLICATION OF THE EULER-MACLAURIN FORMULA

It is evident that the Euler-Maclaurin formula, equation 4.4.5, can be rearranged to give:

$$\sum_{r=0}^{n} f(a + r\delta x) = \frac{1}{(\delta x)}\int_{a}^{a+n\delta x} f(x)\mathrm{d}x + \tfrac{1}{2}[f(a) + f(a + n\delta x)]$$

$$+ \frac{(\delta x)}{12}\left[f'(a + n\delta x) - f'(a)\right] - \frac{(\delta x)^3}{720}\left[f^{\mathrm{iii}}(a + n\delta x) - f^{\mathrm{iii}}(a)\right]$$

$$+ \frac{(\delta x)^5}{30240}\left[f^{\mathrm{v}}(a + n\delta x) - f^{\mathrm{v}}(a)\right] - \ldots \qquad \ldots (5.4.1)$$

or if, as is usual $\delta x = 1$, and $a = 0$

$$\sum_{r=0}^{n} f(r) = \int_{0}^{n} f(x)\mathrm{d}x + \tfrac{1}{2}[f(0) + f(n)] + \tfrac{1}{12}[f'(n) - f'(0)]$$

$$- \tfrac{1}{720}[f^{\mathrm{iii}}(n) - f^{\mathrm{iii}}(0)] + \tfrac{1}{30240}[f^{\mathrm{v}}(n) - f^{\mathrm{v}}(0)] - \ldots \quad \ldots (5.4.2)$$

If, in addition, $f^{(s)}(n) \to 0$ as $n \to \infty$ for all $s$, the series converges and:

$$\sum_{r=0}^{\infty} f(r) = \int_{0}^{\infty} f(x)\mathrm{d}x + \tfrac{1}{2}f(0) - \tfrac{1}{12}f'(0) + \tfrac{1}{720}f^{\mathrm{iii}}(0) - \tfrac{1}{30240}f^{\mathrm{v}}(0)$$

$$+ etc. \qquad \ldots (5.4.3)$$

These formulae are suitable for application to series of slowly convergent positive terms, but are also useful analytically for the algebraic summation of series. Thus, if $f^{(s)}(x)$ is zero for all $s$ greater

54

than some lower limit, equation 5.4.3 will give the sum of the infinite series $\overset{\infty}{\underset{r=0}{\Sigma}} f(r)$ in finite terms.

Any polynomial series can be summed by means of equation 5.4.2. To take the previously discussed example

$$\overset{n}{\underset{r=0}{\Sigma}} r^3 = \int_0^n r^3 dr + \tfrac{1}{2}n^3 + \tfrac{1}{12}.3n^2 - \tfrac{1}{720} \quad (6-6)$$

$$= \frac{n^4}{4} + \frac{n^3}{2} + \frac{n^2}{4} = \left[\frac{n(n+1)}{2}\right]^2$$

in agreement with the result given in section 5.2.

REFERENCE

[1] BROMWICH, T. J. I'A, 'An Introduction to the Theory of Infinite Series,' p. 57, Macmillan, London (1908)

# 6

# THE SOLUTION OF ORDINARY DIFFERENTIAL EQUATIONS

## 6.1 INTRODUCTION

THE numerical solution of a differential equation, ordinary or partial, is a problem which has engaged the attention of mathematicians for many years. Numerous methods have been proposed, and some have actually received practical trial; on the whole, however, there appears to be no authoritative statement as to a *best* method, or even a set of such recommended methods.

Upon examining the literature we find, for example, that WHITTAKER and ROBINSON[1] give only one method of solution (that of Bashforth and Adams) and state that this is the best. On the other hand, HARTREE[2] makes no mention of this method at all, and a like remark is true of MILNE[3], although, in a more recent publication[4], he points out that most methods are in the nature of modifications of the Bashforth-Adams process.

Ordinary differential equations may be divided roughly into two types for the purpose of numerical solution, depending upon the form of the boundary conditions to be satisfied by solution. The first class of boundary condition may be termed 'one-point,' by which it is to be understood that *all* of the conditions have to be satisfied at a particular point $(x,y)$, say. The second class of boundary condition is a 'two-point' one in which, for example, the function value may be given at one end of the range of integration, and the derivative may be given at another. Of course, with equations of order higher than the second 'multi-point' boundary conditions are possible; we shall not, however, be concerned with these in the present work. It may be mentioned that the one-point condition is sometimes said to lead to a 'marching' problem, and the two-point condition to a 'jury' problem, for reasons which will become clear later.

In this chapter we shall be concerned chiefly with one-point problems and shall mention the more complicated two-point variant only in so far as it can be solved by essentially one-point methods. A more satisfactory approach will be given later, in Chapter 8, section 8.6, when relaxation solutions are discussed.

## 6.2 INITIAL VALUES

In many of the finite difference methods of solution it is necessary to have one or more values of the solution, and possibly of its derivatives, near to the starting point. These are usually best obtained by a process rather different from that used in the remainder of the solution and we shall give, briefly, the two methods most frequently used.

The first method is that of Picard, and depends upon the 'guessing' of an initial solution. Consider the first order equation:

$$\frac{dy}{dx} = f(x, y) \qquad \dots (6.2.1)$$

and assume that near to the boundary, $(a, b)$ say, we can guess an approximation:
$$y = g_1(x) \qquad \dots (6.2.2)$$

We then substitute in equation 6.2.1 and integrate to obtain:

$$y = b + \int_a^x f[x, g_1(x)] \qquad [= g_2(x), \text{ say}]$$

the process is now repeated:

$$y = b + \int_a^x f[x, g_2(x)] = g_3(x) \qquad \text{and so on.}$$

This process, if it converges, will give an approximation of any desired degree of accuracy near to the initial point.

The range of application of this method is fairly limited, since the approximating functions $f[x, g_r(x)]$ have to be integrable in closed form. As an example of the use of the method consider the equation: $\frac{dy}{dx} = x^2 + 2xy$ with $x = 0$ when $y = 0$. Take:

$$g_1(x) = \frac{x^3}{3}$$

then

$$g_2(x) = \int_0^x \left( x^2 + \frac{2x^4}{3} \right) dx = \frac{x^3}{3} + \frac{2x^5}{3.5}$$

$$g_3(x) = \int_0^x \left( x^2 + \frac{2x^4}{3} + \frac{4x^6}{3.5} \right) dx = \frac{x^3}{3} + \frac{2x^5}{3.5} + \frac{4x^7}{3.5.7}$$

$$g_4(x) = \int_0^x \left( x^2 + \frac{2x^4}{3} + \frac{4x^6}{3.5} + \frac{8x^8}{3.5.7} \right) dx$$

$$= \frac{x^3}{3} + \frac{2x^5}{3.5} + \frac{4x^7}{3.5.7} + \frac{8x^9}{3.5.7.9} \qquad \text{etc.}$$

E

The reader will easily convince himself that the expression agrees with the analytic solution:

$$y = -\tfrac{1}{2}x + \tfrac{1}{2}e^{x^2} \int_0^x e^{-x^2}\,dx$$

when the latter is expanded in a series. It is also worth noticing that the Picard solution, in the example, is much easier to compute than that derived from the analytic solution.

The second method of obtaining an approximate initial solution is by means of a Taylor series expansion. Thus for $y = b$ at $x = a$ we have:

$$y = b + \frac{(x-a)}{1!}g'(a) + \frac{(x-a)^2}{2!}g''(a) + \ldots + \frac{(x-a)^n}{n!}g^n(a) + \ldots$$

$$\ldots(6.2.3)$$

and, from the differential equation:

$$\frac{dy}{dx} = g'(x) = f(x,y) \qquad \ldots(6.2.4)$$

giving:

$$g'(a) = f(a,b) \qquad \ldots(6.2.5)$$

Differentiating 6.2.4 and substituting the boundary condition and 6.2.5:

$$\frac{d^2y}{dx^2} = \frac{\partial f(x,y)}{\partial x} + \frac{\partial f(x,y)}{\partial y}\cdot\frac{dy}{dx}$$

*i.e.*

$$g''(a) = \left[\frac{\partial f(x,y)}{\partial x}\right]_{\substack{x=a\\y=b}} + \left[\frac{\partial f(x,y)}{\partial y}\right]_{\substack{x=a\\y=b}} \cdot f(a,b).$$

and similarly for derivatives of higher order.

The process may be illustrated by our previous example. Since $x = 0$, $y = 0$, the appropriate expansion (really a Maclaurin series) is:

$$y = xg'(0) + \frac{x^2}{2!}g''(0) + \frac{x^3}{3!}g^{(3)}(0) + \ldots$$

The differential equation, together with $x = 0$, $y = 0$ gives:

$$g'(0) = [x^2 + 2xy]_{0,\,0} = 0$$
$$g''(0) = [2x + 2y + 2xy']_{0,\,0} = 0$$
$$g^{(3)}(0) = [2 + 2y' + 2y' + 2xy'']_{0,\,0} = 2$$
$$g^{(4)}(0) = [4y'' + 2y'' + 2xy^{(3)}]_{0,\,0} = 0$$
$$g^{(5)}(0) = [6y^{(3)} + 2y^{(3)} + 2xy^{(4)}]_{0,\,0} = 16$$
$$g^{(6)}(0) = [8y^{(4)} + 2y^{(4)} + 2xy^{(5)}]_{0,\,0} = 0$$
$$g^{(7)}(0) = [10y^{(5)} + 2y^{(5)} + 2xy^{(6)}]_{0,\,0} = 12.16 \qquad etc.$$

which will be seen to agree with the series previously deduced.

It will be noticed that the Taylor series method, in this example, involves slightly more work than the Picard technique; on the other hand, differentiations involved can *always* be performed, for the commonly encountered functions at least, whereas the integrations of the latter method can only be carried out for relatively simple functions.

On the other hand, it is possible to carry out the Picard integrations numerically, in the required range, and this is often a simple and rapid procedure. Certain integration formulae are required for this operation, and these are obtainable by the same technique as was used in section 4.3. A useful set of results is the following:

$$\int_0^{(\delta x)} f(x)\,dx = \frac{(\delta x)}{720}[251f(0) + 646f(1) - 264f(2) + 106f(3) - 19f(4)]$$
$$+ \frac{27(\delta x)^6}{1440}f^{(6)}_{max}$$

$$\int_0^{2(\delta x)} f(x)\,dx = \frac{(\delta x)}{90}[29f(0) + 124f(1) + 24f(2) + 4f(3) - f(4)]$$
$$+ \frac{16(\delta x)^6}{1440}f^{(6)}_{max}$$

$$\int_0^{3(\delta x)} f(x)\,dx = \frac{(\delta x)}{80}[27f(0) + 102f(1) + 72f(2) + 42f(3) - 3f(4)]$$
$$+ \frac{27(\delta x)^6}{1440}f^{(6)}_{max}$$

$$\int_0^{4(\delta x)} f(x)\,dx = \frac{4(\delta x)}{90}[7f(0) + 32f(1) + 12f(2) + 32f(3) + 7f(4)]$$
$$- \frac{8(\delta x)^7}{945}f^{(7)}_{max}$$

$$\ldots\ldots 6.2.6$$

These are readily obtained by integrating the approximating polynomial:

$$f_f(x) = f(0) + x\Delta f(0) + \frac{x(x-1)}{2!}\Delta^2 f(0) + \frac{x(x-1)(x-2)}{3!}\Delta^3 f(0)$$
$$+ \frac{x(x-1)(x-2)(x-3)}{4!}\Delta^4 f(0) \qquad \ldots(6.2.7)$$

between the appropriate limits, and evaluating the error terms in the manner described in section 4.8. They form one of a set of similar results obtainable from approximating polynomials of

59

various degrees, and are given here, in preference to other members of the group, because they are a compromise between accuracy and ease of working. In suitable cases equations 6.2.6, in conjunction with the Picard technique, will give initial values at $(\delta x) = 0 \cdot 2$ to an accuracy of slightly better than one in $10^5$.

An even more satisfactory technique is to make use of values of $f(x)$ on either side of the origin. This is particularly useful when central difference methods are to be used at a later stage to carry on the solution. The relevant formulae can be obtained, either by integrating equation 6.2.7, or from Everett's formula. For the five points $(-2, -1, 0, +1, +2)$ the results are :

$$\int_{-2(\delta x)}^{0} f(x)\mathrm{d}x = \frac{(\delta x)}{90} [29f(-2) + 124f(-1) + 24f(0) + 4f(1) - f(2)]$$
$$- \frac{41(\delta x)^6}{3600} f^{(6)}_{\max}$$

$$\int_{-(\delta x)}^{0} f(x)\mathrm{d}x = \frac{(\delta x)}{720} [-19f(-2) + 346f(-1) + 456f(0) - 74f(1) + 11f(2)]$$
$$- \frac{11(\delta x)^6}{1440} f^{(6)}_{\max}$$

$$\int_{0}^{(\delta x)} f(x)\mathrm{d}x = \frac{(\delta x)}{720} [11f(-2) - 74f(-1) + 456f(0) + 346f(1) - 19f(2)]$$
$$+ \frac{11(\delta x)^6}{1440} f^{(6)}_{\max}$$

$$\int_{0}^{2(\delta x)} f(x)\mathrm{d}x = \frac{(\delta x)}{90} [-f(-2) + 4f(-1) + 24f(0) + 124f(1) + 29f(2)]$$
$$+ \frac{41(\delta x)^6}{3600} f^{(6)}_{\max}$$
$$\dots(6.2.8)$$

Although we have given the Picard method and certain integration formulae for its application, it is not our practice to use this technique unless the direct analytic integration is possible. We have found that the Taylor series approach is more easily applicable and is, furthermore, readily extended to equations of higher degree than the first. To take only one example, consider:

$$y'' = f(x, y, y') \qquad \dots(6.2.9)$$

with initial conditions $x = x_0, y = y_0, y' = y_0'$.

60

Equation 6.2.9 gives:

$$y_0'' = f(x_0, y_0, y_0')$$

by direct substitution of the initial conditions. Differentiating:

$$y^{(3)} = \frac{d}{dx} f(x, y, y') = \frac{\partial f}{\partial x} + \frac{\partial f}{\partial y} \frac{dy}{dx} + \frac{\partial f}{\partial y'} \frac{d^2 y}{dx^2}$$

so that:

$$y_0^{(3)} = \left(\frac{\partial f}{\partial x}\right)_{x=x_0} + \left(\frac{\partial f}{\partial y}\right)_0 y_0' + \left(\frac{\partial f}{\partial y'}\right)_0 y_0''$$

and so on.

## 6.3 EQUATIONS OF THE FIRST ORDER

The 'classical' method of solution of a first order differential equation:

$$\frac{dy}{dx} = f(x, y) \qquad \qquad \dots (6.3.1)$$

subject to one-point boundary conditions, is that of Runge. It is based upon an idea originally due to Euler and has been extended by Kutta, Heun, and Piaggio. The method is normally used to obtain an initial solution with which to start one of the Bashforth and Adams type methods. Since, in our opinion, it has no advantages over the Taylor series method or the numerical version of the Picard process, we shall do no more than state the relevant formulae in the two most useful cases.

The first Runge–Kutta approximation is the equivalent of Simpson's rule applied to the integration of the $f(x, y)$. If, in equation 6.3.1, we know that $y = y_0$ when $x = x_0$ and require $y_1$, the value of $y$ when $x = x_0 + (\delta x)$. Then:

$$y_1 = y_0 + \tfrac{1}{6}(k_1 + 4k_2 + k_3) \qquad \qquad \dots (6.3.2)$$

where

$$k_1 = (\delta x) . f(x_0, y_0)$$
$$k_2 = (\delta x) . f(x_0 + \tfrac{1}{2}(\delta x), y_0 + \tfrac{1}{2}k_1)$$
$$k_3 = (\delta x) . f(x_0 + (\delta x), y_0 + 2k_2 - k_1)$$

the error in $y_1$ being of order $(\delta x)^4$.

If an error of order $(\delta x)^5$ is required, the Kutta fourth order process:

$$y_1 = y_0 + \tfrac{1}{6}(k_1 + 2k_2 + 2k_3 + k_4) \qquad \ldots (6.3.3)$$

where:
$$k_1 = (\delta x)f(x_0, y_0)$$
$$k_2 = (\delta x)f(x_0 + \tfrac{1}{2}(\delta x), y_0 + \tfrac{1}{2}k_1)$$
$$k_3 = (\delta x)f(x_0 + \tfrac{1}{2}(\delta x), y_0 + \tfrac{1}{2}k_2)$$
$$k_4 = (\delta x)f(x_0 + (\delta x), y_0 + k_3) \qquad \text{may be used.}$$

By increasing the number of steps, still higher accuracy may be attained, but the formulae are considerably more complicated and have not been much used. For a more extensive treatment of Runge–Kutta formulae the reader is referred to the standard literature.[5, 6]

A major criticism of the Runge–Kutta method of solution lies in the fact that it contains, in itself, no means of checking either the accuracy of the solution obtained, or the actual arithmetic by means of which such a solution is derived. The objection is removed in the Bashforth–Adams process for continuing the solution, which we shall now describe.

We first notice that the method initially uses the values of the function previously computed to obtain new values and then uses the new values, and the equations, to check and correct the result. The differential equation itself is used as a source of values of the derivative. We shall require an extrapolation formula which uses only differences which can be computed from existing function values, and this implies the use of backward differences (see section 3.1). Now:

$$f(x) = E^x f(0)$$

and
$$\nabla \equiv (E - 1)/E$$

whence
$$f(x) = f(0)/(1 - \nabla)^x$$

$$= \left[ 1 + x\nabla + \frac{x(x+1)}{2!}\nabla^2 + \frac{x(x+1)(x+2)}{3!}\nabla^3 + \ldots \right] f(0)$$
$$\ldots (6.3.4)$$

Now

$$\int_0^1 f(x)\mathrm{d}x = [1 + \tfrac{1}{2}\nabla + \tfrac{5}{12}\nabla^2 + \tfrac{3}{8}\nabla^3 + \tfrac{251}{720}\nabla^4$$
$$+ \tfrac{95}{288}\nabla^5 + \tfrac{19087}{60480}\nabla^6 + \ldots]f(0)$$

or, for interval $(\delta x)$:

$$\int_0^{(\delta x)} f(x)\mathrm{d}x = (\delta x)(1 + \tfrac{1}{2}\nabla + \tfrac{5}{12}\nabla^2 + \tfrac{3}{8}\nabla^3 + \tfrac{251}{720}\nabla^4 + etc.)f(0)$$
$$\ldots (6.3.5)$$

To solve the equation:

$$\frac{dy}{dx} = f(x, y) \text{ or } y_1 = y_0 + \int_0^{\delta x} f(x, y) \, dx$$

we assume that five initial values, $(x_{-4}, y_{-4})$, $(x_{-3}, y_{-3})$, $(x_{-2}, y_{-2})$, $(x_{-1}, y_{-1})$, $(x_0, y_0)$, say, have been calculated by one of the methods previously described. From these values the table

| $x$ | $y$ | $dy/dx = f(x,y)$ | $\nabla f$ | $\nabla^2 f$ | $\nabla^3 f$ | $\nabla^4 f$ | $\nabla^5 f$ |
|---|---|---|---|---|---|---|---|
| $x_{-4}$ | $y_{-4}$ | $f_{-4}$ | | | | | |
| $x_{-3}$ | $y_{-3}$ | $f_{-3}$ | $\nabla f_{-3}$ | | | | |
| $x_{-2}$ | $y_{-2}$ | $f_{-2}$ | $\nabla f_{-2}$ | $\nabla^2 f_{-2}$ | | | |
| $x_{-1}$ | $y_{-1}$ | $f_{-1}$ | $\nabla f_{-1}$ | $\nabla^2 f_{-1}$ | $\nabla^3 f_{-1}$ | | |
| $x_0$ | $y_0$ | $f_0$ | $\nabla f_0$ | $\nabla^2 f_0$ | $\nabla^3 f_0$ | $\nabla^4 f_0$ | |
| $x_1$ | $y_1$ | $f_1$ | $\nabla f_1$ | $\nabla^2 f_1$ | $\nabla^3 f_1$ | $\nabla^4 f_1$ | $\nabla^5 f_1$ |

is constructed, as far as the broken line $-\,-\,-\,-$. Using the values of $\nabla^r f_0$ up to $r = 4$ in the integration formula (6.3.5) the value $y_1$ may be obtained; this enables $f_1$ to be calculated and, once this is known, the differences $\nabla^r f_1$ can be evaluated.

To check the accuracy of the prediction we may form the integral:

$$\int_0^{-(\delta x)} f(x) = -(\delta x)\left(1 - \tfrac{1}{2}\nabla - \tfrac{1}{12}\nabla^2 - \tfrac{1}{24}\nabla^3 \right.$$

$$\left. - \tfrac{19}{720}\nabla^4 - \tfrac{3}{160}\nabla^5 - \tfrac{863}{60480}\nabla^6 - \ldots\right) f(1)$$

or, in terms of $y_1$, $y_0$ and the differences below the broken line which can now be calculated:

$$y_1 = y_0 + (\delta x)(f_1 - \tfrac{1}{2}\nabla f_1 - \tfrac{1}{12}\nabla^2 f_1 - \tfrac{1}{24}\nabla^3 f_1$$

$$- \tfrac{19}{720}\nabla^4 f_1 - \tfrac{3}{160}\nabla^5 f_1 - \tfrac{863}{60480}\nabla^6 f_1 \ldots) \qquad \ldots\ldots(6.3.6)$$

This formula, up to and including $\nabla^4$, is over ten times more accurate than equation 6.3.5, so that, if the two values of $y_1$ do not differ by more than 5 units in the last decimal place required, we may accept the value derived from equation 6.3.6 as correct. If the deviation is greater than this, the *new* value of $y_1$ can be used to recompute $f_1$, $\nabla f_1$, *etc.* and equation 6.3.6 re-applied until agreement between consecutive values is reached.

The process is now repeated, using subscript 1 instead of 0 as previously, and $y_2$ is thus derived.

A modification of the Bashforth–Adams method, due to Milne will now be described. The central idea is again to predict the value of $y_{n+1}$ from those of $y_n$ and earlier ordinates, and then to correct it (if necessary) by means of a comparison formula which will, in general, involve $y_{n+1}$ itself. Milne recommends that the open Newton–Cotes formula, given by equation 4.3.10, be used to 'predict' and Simpson's rule (equation 4.3.4) to correct. These formula become:

'Predictor'

$$y_{n+1} = y_{n-3} + \tfrac{4}{3}(\delta x)(2f_n - f_{n-1} + 2f_{n-2}) + \tfrac{28}{90}(\delta x)^5 f^{(5)}_{\max} \quad \ldots (6.3.7)$$

'Corrector'

$$y_{n+1} = y_{n-1} + \frac{(\delta x)}{3}(f_{n+1} + 4f_n + f_{n-1}) - \tfrac{1}{90}(\delta x)^5 f^{(5)}_{\max} \quad \ldots (6.3.8)$$

in terms of the solution values $y_n$ and the values $f$ in equation 6.3.1. The interval, $(\delta x)$, should be so chosen that the two values of $y_{n+1}$ differ by less than 14 in the last decimal place required. If this is done, a comparison of the error terms in equations 6.3.7 and 6.3.8 shows that the value derived from 6.3.8 can be taken as correct within the number of places required.

We conclude this section by describing a procedure which has been described by MILNE [7] and, in modified form, by HARTREE [8].
The equation is, as usual, 6.3.1, and from it we can obtain:

$$y' = f$$

$$y'' = \frac{d^2 y}{dx^2} = \frac{\partial f}{\partial x} + f \frac{\partial f}{\partial y} \qquad \ldots (6.3.9)$$

Now the Taylor series expansion, based on $y_n$, gives:

$$y_{n+1} = y_n + (\delta x)y'_n + \frac{(\delta x)^2}{2!}y''_n + \frac{(\delta x)^3}{3!}y^{(3)}_n$$

$$+ \frac{(\delta x)^4}{4!}y^{(4)}_n + \qquad \ldots (6.3.10)$$

whence:

$$-\tfrac{1}{2}(\delta x)y'_{n+1} = \quad -\tfrac{1}{2}(\delta x)y'_n - \tfrac{1}{2}(\delta x)^2 y''_n - \tfrac{1}{2} \cdot \frac{(\delta x)^3}{2!}y^{(3)}_n$$

$$-\tfrac{1}{2} \cdot \frac{(\delta x)^4}{3!}y^{(4)}_n + \ldots$$

$$+\tfrac{1}{12}(\delta x)^2 y''_{n+1} = \quad \tfrac{1}{12}(\delta x)^2 y''_n + \tfrac{1}{12}(\delta x)^3 y^{(3)}_n + \tfrac{1}{12} \cdot \frac{(\delta x)^4}{2!}y^{(4)}_n + \ldots$$

or, adding

$$y_{n+1} = y_n + \tfrac{1}{2}(\delta x)(y'_{n+1} + y'_n) - \tfrac{1}{12}(\delta x)^2(y''_{n+1} - y''_n) + R_c$$

$$\ldots (6.3.11)$$

where $R_c$ can be shown to be given by:

$$R_c = (\delta x)^5 y^{(5)}_{\max}/720$$

Again, by forming the sum of:

$$y_{n+1} \quad = \quad y_n + (\delta x)y'_n + \frac{(\delta x)^2}{2!}y''_n + \frac{(\delta x)^3}{3!}y^{(3)}_n + \frac{(\delta x)^4}{4!}y^{(4)}_n + \cdots$$

$$-2y_n \quad = -2y_{n-1} - 2(\delta x)y'_{n-1} - 2\frac{(\delta x)^2}{2!}y''_{n-1} - 2\frac{(\delta x)^3}{3!}y^{(3)}_{n-1}$$

$$-2\frac{(\delta x)^4}{4!}y^{(4)}_{n-1} - \cdots$$

$$-y_{n-2} \quad = -y_{n-1} + (\delta x)y'_{n-1} - \frac{(\delta x)^2}{2!}y''_{n-1} + \frac{(\delta x)^3}{3!}y^{(3)}_{n-1}$$

$$-\frac{(\delta x)^4}{4!}y^{(4)}_{n-1} + \cdots$$

$$-\tfrac{1}{2}(\delta x)^2 y''_n = \quad\quad -\frac{(\delta x)^2}{2}y''_{n-1} - \frac{(\delta x)^3}{2}y^{(3)}_{n-1}$$

$$-\frac{(\delta x)^4}{4}y^{(4)}_{n-1} - \cdots$$

and then substituting for the derivatives $y'_n$, $y^{(3)}_n$, $y^{(4)}_{(n)}$ in terms of the Taylor series based on $y_{n-1}$, it is easily seen that:

$$y_{n+1} = y_{n-2} + 3(y_n - y_{n-1}) + (\delta x)^2(y''_n - y''_{n-1}) + R_p$$

$$\ldots (6.3.12)$$

where

$$R_p = 60(\delta x)^5 y^{(5)}_{\max}/720.$$

Formula 6.3.12 can be used to predict the value of $y_{n+1}$ given those of $y_n$, $y_{n-1}$ and $y_{n-2}$, the differential equation itself being used to determine $y''_n$ and $y''_{n-1}$ (from equation 6.3.9).

From these predicted values a corrected value can be calculated *via* equation 6.3.11. If the difference between the predicted and corrected values is less than 30 in the last decimal place required, the latter is taken to be correct. If the difference exceeds this figure the corrected value is used to recalculate the derivatives $y'_{n+1}$,

$y''_{n+1}$ in equation 6.3.11, and a new and more accurate value of $y_{n+1}$ is thus obtained. This process is continued until two successive values of $y_{n+1}$ do not differ within the limits of accuracy required. It should be noted that, with a properly chosen value of $(\delta x)$, a re-application of equation 6.3.11 should not often be required. If it is, there is a clear indication that a change in $(\delta x)$ is needed. In a similar manner, if repeated use of 6.3.11 is never required, it suggests that too small a value of $(\delta x)$ is being used. A working rule is that one re-application of equation 6.3.11 should be required every five or so steps.

## 6.4 EQUATIONS OF THE SECOND ORDER

The canonical form of the differential equation of the second order is:

$$\frac{d^2y}{dx^2} = f(x, y) \qquad \dots (6.4.1)$$

and any equation of the second order, linear in the derivatives, can be reduced to the form of equation 6.4.1. Thus:

$$\frac{d^2y}{dx^2} + a(x)\frac{dy}{dx} + b(x, y) = 0$$

reduces to 6.4.1 when the transformation:

$$y = Y \exp\left[-\tfrac{1}{2}\int a(x)dx\right] \qquad \dots (6.4.2)$$

is applied. The transformed equation is:

$$Y'' = [\tfrac{1}{2}a'(x) + \tfrac{1}{4}\{a(x)\}^2]\, Y - b(x, Y)\exp \tfrac{1}{2}\int a(x)dx \qquad \dots (6.4.3)$$

but unless $b(x, y)$ is of the form $y \cdot c(x)$, this is not likely to be suitable for numerical calculation because of the exponential factor. Furthermore, the transformation destroys any periodicity which may exist in solutions of the original equation.

By means of the transformation:

$$z = y' \qquad \dots (6.4.4)$$

the general second order equation:

$$y'' = f(x, y, y') \qquad \dots (6.4.5)$$

is reduced to the pair of simultaneous first order equations:

$$\left. \begin{array}{l} z' = f(x, y, z) \\ z = y' \end{array} \right\} \qquad \dots (6.4.5)$$

66

which may be solved by the methods discussed in section 6.5. This reduction has the merit of simplicity, but is not to be recommended for equations in which $y'$ is absent.

The Bashforth–Adams method can be applied directly to equation 6.4.5 when a suitable set of initial values has been obtained; the detailed procedure is as follows:

(1) Assume that $y_n''$, $y_{n-1}''$ . . . *etc.* are known.
(2) Find $y_{n+1}'$ from $y_n''$, $y_{n-1}''$ *etc.* by means of 6.3.5.
(3) Assume that $y_n'$, $y_{n-1}'$ *etc.* are known.
(4) Find $y_{n+1}$ from $y_{n+1}'$, $y_n'$ . . . *etc.* by means of 6.3.6.
(5) Using these values of $y_{n+1}'$, $y_{n+1}$ compute $y_{n+1}''$ from 6.4.5.
(6) Recompute $y_{n+1}' y_{n+1}$ by means of 6.3.6.

At this stage the usual error estimation can be made and, if necessary, one or more extra cycles of the process can be used to obtain the desired accuracy.

The Bashforth–Adams backward difference formulae are not the only ones which can be used in this process. Thus MILNE [9] suggests that the open Newton–Cotes formula (4.3.10), in the form:

$$y_{n+1}' = y_{n-3}' + \tfrac{4}{3}(\delta x)(2y_n'' - y_{n-1}'' + 2y_{n-2}'')$$

should be used in step (2) (*supra*), and that this should be followed by Simpson's rule:

$$y_{n+1} = y_{n-1} + \frac{(\delta x)}{3}(y_{n+1}' + 4y_n' + y_{n-1}')$$

in step (4) and again in step (6), this time as:

$$y_{n+1}' = y_{n-1}' + \frac{(\delta x)}{3}(y_{n+1}'' + 4y_n'' + y_{n-1}'')$$

For second degree equations in which the first derivative is absent (*i.e.* the canonical form 6.4.1), a simplified procedure is available which, in effect, uses a double integration formula to pass directly from $y''$ to $y$.

One such formula has been obtained in equation 4.5.3; it may be rewritten, for the present purpose:

$$y_{n+1} = 2y_n - y_{n-1} + (\delta x)^2 (y_n'' + \tfrac{1}{12}\delta^2 y_n'' - \tfrac{1}{240}\delta^4 y_n'' + etc.) \qquad \text{.... (6.4.7)}$$

or

$$y_{n+1} = 2y_n - y_{n-1} + \frac{(\delta x)^2}{12}(y_{n+1}'' + 10y_n'' + y_{n-1}'') - \tfrac{1}{240}(\delta x)^6 y_{max}^{(6)} \qquad \text{.... (6.4.7a)}$$

This result may be used as a corrector and the less accurate:

$$y_{n+1} = y_n + y_{n-2} - y_{n-3}$$
$$+ \frac{(\delta x)^2}{4} (5y_n'' + 2y_{n-1}'' + 5y_{n-2}'') + \tfrac{17}{240}(\delta x)^6 y_{max}^{(6)} \quad \dots (6.4.8)$$

as a predictor. As an alternative to equation 6.4.8:

$$y_{n+1} = 2y_{n-1} - y_{n-3} + 4(\delta x)^2 (y_{n-1}'' + \tfrac{1}{3}\delta^2 y_{n-1}'') + \tfrac{16}{240} (\delta x)^6 y_{max}^{(6)}$$
$$\dots (6.4.9)$$

which may be regarded as the analogue of equation 6.4.7, but for double the interval, is perhaps simpler to apply.

When the form of $f(x, y)$ in equation 6.4.1 is such that its calculation for any particular values of $x$ and $y$ is difficult or tedious, a procedure due to Fox and Goodwin often enables a large interval by differencing to be used, with consequent reduction in the number of values of $f(x, y)$ to be calculated. In essence, the method uses a large value of $(\delta x)$ and a simple formula to obtain a rough solution, and then uses the differences obtained from this solution to enable a better approximation to be made.

Thus, suppose that a set of values $y_{(m-1)}$ at interval $(\delta x)$ have been obtained; then, from equation 4.5.3

$$\delta^2 y = (\delta x)^2 (y'' + \tfrac{1}{12}\delta^2 y'' - \tfrac{1}{240}\delta^4 y'' + \dots)$$

and, if we estimate $\delta^2 y''$, $\delta^4 y''$ from the previous approximation,

$$\delta^2 y_{(m)} = (\delta x)^2 (y_{(m)}'' + \tfrac{1}{12}\delta^2 y_{(m-1)}'' - \tfrac{1}{240} \delta^4 y_{(m-1)}'' + \dots)$$

or $\quad \delta^2 y_{(m)} = (\delta x)^2 [f\{x, y_{(m)}\} + \tfrac{1}{12}\delta^2 y_{(m-1)}'' - \tfrac{1}{240}\delta^4 y_{(m-1)}'' \dots]$

Thus, if $y_{(m)n+1}$, $y_{(m)n}$ $y_{(m)n-1}$ are consecutive points in the $m$th approximation:

$$y_{(m)n+1} = 2y_{(m)n} - y_{(m)n-1}$$
$$+ (\delta x)^2 [f\{x, y_{(m)n}\} + \tfrac{1}{12}\delta^2 y_{(m-1)n}'' - \tfrac{1}{240}\delta^4 y_{(m-1)n} \dots ,]$$
$$\dots (6.4.10)$$

a formula which enables the solution to be continued from the $n$th point of the $m$th approximation to the $(n + 1)$th point.

The same general method can be applied to equations of the first order and a comparison of such techniques has been made by Fox and GOODWIN [10]. A particular calculation, in which an economy of labour has been achieved, is the tracing of non-axial rays through an electron lens system where the field distribution is given by Weierstrassian elliptic integrals which are awkward to manipulate. This problem has been extensively studied by JENNINGS [11].

## 6.5 SIMULTANEOUS DIFFERENTIAL EQUATIONS

The typical set of simultaneous differential equations of the first order may be written:

$$y'_m = f_m(x, y_1, y_2 \ldots y_n) \qquad (m = 1 \ldots n) \quad \ldots (6.5.1)$$

The methods of solution are almost identical with those suggested for the ordinary first order equations, and are typified by the following scheme.

(1) Obtain initial values from a Taylor series expansion and the given boundary conditions.

(2) From $y'_{m,\,0},\ y_{m,\,0}$ $(m = 1 \ldots n)$ predict values of $y_{m,1}$ by means of equation 6.3.5 or 6.3.7.

(3) Using the values of $y_{m,1}$ $(m = 1 \ldots n)$ obtained in (2) recalculate $y_{m,1}$ from the differential equations and 6.3.6 or 6.3.8.

(4) If significant changes occur repeat the process from (3) until adequate accuracy has been obtained.

It should be noticed that this technique can be applied, as indicated in section 6.4, to obtain the solution of a second order equation.

In a similar manner, the set of equations of the second order:

$$y''_m = f_m(x, y_1, y_2 \ldots y_n) \qquad (m = 1 \ldots n) \quad \ldots (6.5.2)$$

may be solved, using the repeated integration formulae of equations 6.4.8 and 6.4.9 as predictors, and 6.4.7 as a corrector.

## 6.6 EQUATIONS OF HIGHER ORDER

When such equations, either single or simultaneous, are encountered, the only really practical method of solution appears to be to reduce them to sets of first order simultaneous equations by means of successive transformations of the type in equation 6.4.4. The actual integrations at any step should proceed from the highest order derivative downwards and (6.3.5, 6.3.6) (6.3.7, 6.3.8) or (6.3.11, 6.3.12) are suitable pairs of integration formulae.

## 6.7 MULTI-POINT BOUNDARY CONDITIONS

Although we shall defer consideration of this type of solution until chapter 8, section 6, it is appropriate to indicate here the mode of application of the methods just discussed to this problem.

First consider a second order differential equation

$$y'' = f(y', y, x) \qquad \ldots (6.7.1)$$

If this is to satisfy:

$$y = y_0 \text{ at } x = x_0$$
$$y = y_1 \text{ at } x = x_1$$

there is, of course, insufficient data with which to start a finite difference integration from $x = x_0$. Suppose, however, that 6.7.1 is a linear equation; then if $y = l_1(x)$ and $y = l_2(x)$ are *any* two solutions, $y = Al_1(x) + Bl_2(x)$ is also a solution.

To solve the given equation all that is needed is the following. From $x = x_0$ start any two integrations having $y = y_0$ but *different* values of $y'$ at $x = x_0$. Carry these solutions up to $x = x_1$ and assume these solutions to be $l_1(x)$ and $l_2(x)$. The required solution is then:

$$y = Al_1(x) + Bl_2(x)$$

where $A$ and $B$ are the solutions of:

$$y_0 = Al_1(x_0) + Bl_2(x_0) \quad (i.e.\ A + B = 1)$$
$$y_1 = Al_1(x_1) + Bl_2(x_1).$$

When equation 6.7.1 is not linear this technique will not work, since $Al_1(x) + Bl_2(x)$ is no longer, in general, a solution of the equation. In this event, a possible method of approach is to guess a pair of initial directions which produce solutions straddling the required values at $x = x_1$. Linear interpolation then gives a better initial direction, and the process is repeated until the desired accuracy is attained. Since most of the non-linear equations encountered in practice, have solutions which vary exponentially as some power of the independent variable, this method is, however, seldom applicable over any considerable range.

An extension of this procedure is to take more than two trial solutions and then to use a non-linear interpolation procedure to obtain the correct initial value.

## 6.8. EIGENVALUE PROBLEMS

It is often required to obtain the 'eigenvalues' of a differential operator. By this is meant those values of $\lambda_n$ for which the equation:

$$L\psi_n(x) = \lambda_n\psi_n(x) \qquad \ldots(6.8.1)$$

has solutions which satisfy specified conditions at $x = a$ and $x = b$. A typical form [12] for the operator $L$ is:

$$L \equiv g(x) - \frac{d^2}{dx^2} \qquad \ldots(6.8.2)$$

and $(a, b)$ is often $(0, \infty)$. The trivial solution $\psi_n(x) = 0$ is excluded.

Depending upon the form of $L$, and of the boundary conditions, $\lambda_n$ may have discrete values only, or a complete spectrum. The determination of the values of $\lambda_n$ can be carried out by the process of constructing trial solutions for different assumed values of $\lambda$ and then following the process outlined in section 6.7 to obtain more accurate values.

It should be emphasized that numerical calculation of eigenvalues should never be used as an alternative to a proper analytical investigation of the equation. In many real physical situations such an investigation will lead to a fruitful result.

An alternative approach to the determination of approximate eigenvalues is *via* the equivalent set of simultaneous difference equations, but this will be dealt with more fully in Chapter 8.

### REFERENCES

[1] WHITTAKER, E. T. and ROBINSON, G., 'The Calculus of Observations,' 4th edn. Blackie (1927)

[2] HARTREE, D. R., 'Numerical Analysis,' Oxford (1952)

[3] MILNE, W. E., 'Numerical Calculus,' Princeton (1949)

[4] — 'Numerical Solution of Differential Equations,' Wiley (1953)

[5] LEVY, H. and BAGGOTT, E. A., 'Numerical Studies in Differential Equations,' p. 91 *et seq.* Watts, London (1934)

[6] MILNE, W. E., 'Numerical Solution of Differential Equations,' p. 72 *et seq.* Wiley, New York (1953).

[7] — 'Numerical Solution of Differential Equations,' p. 76 *et seq.* Wiley, New York (1953)

[8] HARTREE, D. R., 'Numerical Analysis,' p. 133 *et seq.* Oxford (1952)

[9] MILNE, W. E., 'Numerical Calculus,' p. 139, Princeton (1949)

[10] FOX, L. and GOODWIN, E. T., *Proc. Camb. Phil. Soc.*, 45 (1949), 373

[11] JENNINGS, J., C.E., *Proc. Phys. Soc.* (in the press)

[12] TICHMARSH, E. C., 'Eigenfunction Expansions,' Oxford (1946)

# SIMULTANEOUS LINEAR EQUATIONS

## 7.1 PRELIMINARY REMARKS

ALTHOUGH simultaneous linear equations arise in a straightforward manner in many problems of physical and engineering science, they have attained a much greater importance in recent years because of their application to the solution of various sorts of differential equation—both ordinary and partial.

Whereas the 'classical' application of simultaneous equations, to such problems as an ordnance survey, rarely results in a set of more than 10 equations in 10 unknowns, many of the more modern approaches to differential equation theory deal with $100 \times 100$ sets as a commonplace and $10^3 \times 10^3$ and upwards as a *desideratum*.

Classical methods of solution by elimination or determinants have, in some hand computing at least, given way to approximate iterative techniques.

The subject, although of great antiquity, is still giving rise to a spate of research papers and there appears little agreement as to a best method of approach. The reader who wishes to pursue the subject can refer to a recent survey and bibliography [1] in which over 450 references to the literature are given.

## 7.2 DEFINITIONS

The set of simultaneous equations:

$$
\left.
\begin{array}{ll}
(1) & a_{11}x_1 + a_{12}x_2 + a_{13}x_3 \ldots \ldots a_{1n}x_n = b_1 \\
(2) & a_{21}x_1 + a_{22}x_2 + a_{23}x_3 \ldots \ldots a_{2n}x_n = b_2 \\
(3) & a_{31}x_1 + \ldots \\
\quad \ldots \ldots \ldots \ldots \ldots \ldots \ldots \ldots \ldots \ldots \ldots \\
\quad \ldots \ldots \ldots \ldots \ldots \ldots \ldots \ldots \ldots \ldots \ldots \\
(r) & a_{r1}x_1 + a_{r2}x_2 + \ldots a_{rr}x_r + a_{rn}x_n = b_r \\
\quad \ldots \ldots \ldots \ldots \ldots \ldots \ldots \ldots \ldots \ldots \ldots \\
\quad \ldots \ldots \ldots \ldots \ldots \ldots \ldots \ldots \ldots \ldots \ldots \\
(n) & a_{n1}x_1 + a_{n2}x_2 + \ldots \ldots + a_{nn}x_n = b_n
\end{array}
\right\} \quad \ldots \ldots (7.2.1)
$$

is taken as the basis. It may be written, in matrix form:

$$A \cdot \boldsymbol{x} = \boldsymbol{b} \qquad \ldots \ldots (7.2.2)$$

where:

$$
A = \begin{bmatrix} a_{11} \cdot a_{12} & \cdots & a_{1n} \\ a_{21} \cdot a_{22} & \cdots & a_{2n} \\ a_{31} & \cdots & a_{3n} \\ \cdots & \cdots & \cdots \\ \cdots & \cdots & \cdots \\ a_{n1} \cdot a_{n2} & \cdots & a_{nn} \end{bmatrix}, \quad \boldsymbol{x} = \begin{bmatrix} x_1 \\ x_2 \\ x_3 \\ \cdot \\ \cdot \\ x_n \end{bmatrix} \quad \boldsymbol{b} = \begin{bmatrix} b_1 \\ b_2 \\ b_3 \\ \cdot \\ \cdot \\ b_n \end{bmatrix} \quad \ldots (7.2.3)
$$

Associated with $A$, are the *determinant* $|A|$, the *transpose* $A'$ [if $A = (a_{ij})$ then $A' = (a_{ji})$] and the *inverse* $A^{-1}$ such that:

$$A^{-1}.A = A.A^{-1} = I \qquad \ldots (7.2.4)$$

where $I$ is the unit matrix:

$$
I = \begin{bmatrix} 1 & 0 & 0 & 0 & \cdots & 0 \\ 0 & 1 & 0 & 0 & \cdots & 0 \\ 0 & 0 & 1 & 0 & \cdots & 0 \\ \cdots & \cdots & \cdots & \cdots & \cdots & \cdots \\ 0 & 0 & 0 & 0 & \cdots & 1 \end{bmatrix} \qquad \ldots (7.2.5)
$$

Formally, we have from equations 7.2.2 and 7.2.4:

$$A^{-1}.A.\boldsymbol{x} = A^{-1}\boldsymbol{b}$$

but

$$A^{-1}.A.\boldsymbol{x} = I.\boldsymbol{x} = \boldsymbol{x}$$

whence

$$\boldsymbol{x} = A^{-1}\boldsymbol{b} \qquad \ldots (7.2.6)$$

It is shown, in works on matrix theory[2], that:

$$
A^{-1} = \begin{bmatrix} A_{11}/|A|, & A_{21}/|A| & \cdots & A_{n1}/|A| \\ A_{12}/|A|, & A_{22}/|A| & \cdots & A_{n2}/|A| \\ \cdots & \cdots & \cdots & \cdots \\ \cdots & \cdots & \cdots & \cdots \\ A_{1n}/|A|, & A_{2n}/|A| & \cdots & A_{nn}/|A| \end{bmatrix} \qquad \ldots (7.2.7)
$$

where $A_{ij}$ is the co-factor of $a_{ij}$ in $|A|$.

In the above, and in the following sections where the condition is necessary, it is assumed that $|A| \neq 0$. When this condition is satisfied, the matrix $A$ is said to be *non-singular*.

When $\boldsymbol{b} = 0$ (*i.e.* $b_r$, $(r = 1 \ldots n) = 0$) the equations 7.2.1 are said to be *homogeneous*; in this case the necessary and sufficient condition for non-zero solutions is $|A| = 0$.

F

Associated with $A$ is the *characteristic equation*:

$$A.\boldsymbol{x} = \lambda.\boldsymbol{x}$$

or:

$$(A - \lambda I)\boldsymbol{x} = 0 \qquad \ldots.(7.2.8)$$

Where the $\lambda$'s are scalar quantities.

Solutions of

$$|A - \lambda I| = \begin{vmatrix} a_{11} - \lambda & a_{12} & a_{13} \cdots & a_{1n} \\ a_{21} & a_{22} - \lambda & a_{23} \cdots & a_{2n} \\ \cdots\cdots\cdots\cdots\cdots\cdots\cdots \\ a_{n1} & a_{n2} & \cdots\cdots & a_{nn} - \lambda \end{vmatrix} = 0 \quad \ldots.(7.2.9)$$

are known as the *latent roots* of $A$ (sometimes called *eigenwerte, eigenvalues,* or *characteristic numbers*).

$\boldsymbol{x}$ and $\boldsymbol{b}$ in equations 7.2.2, 7.2.3 are seen to be composed of $n$ components, $x_1 \ldots x_n$; $b_1 \ldots b_n$, and for this reason are often called *vectors*. Associated with each latent root, $\lambda_i$, say, is a *latent vector* $\boldsymbol{\varphi}_i$ which satisfies:

$$(A - \lambda_i I)\boldsymbol{\varphi}_i = 0 \qquad (i = 1 \ldots n)$$

Finally, with each matrix $A = (a_{ij})$ is associated a *quadratic form*

$$\sum_{i=1}^{n} \sum_{j=1}^{n} a_{ij} x_i x_j \qquad (a_{ij} = a_{ji}) \qquad \ldots.(7.2.10)$$

which is said to be *positive definite* if it is positive for every set of real $(x_i)$ except $(x_1 = x_2 \ldots = x_n = 0)$. (Negative definiteness is defined in a similar manner).

A set of necessary and sufficient conditions for positive-definiteness is:

$$a_{11} > 0, \begin{vmatrix} a_{11} & a_{12} \\ a_{21} & a_{22} \end{vmatrix} > 0 \ldots\ldots \begin{vmatrix} a_{11} & \cdots & a_{1n} \\ \cdots\cdots\cdots \\ a_{n1} & \cdots & a_{nn} \end{vmatrix} > 0 \quad \ldots.(7.2.11)$$

## 7.3 EXACT SOLUTION

The exact solution of the equations 7.2.1 is easily written down; it is:

$$x_r = \begin{vmatrix} a_{11}, a_{12} & \cdot & a_{1,r-1}, b_1, a_{1,r+1} & \cdot & a_{1n} \\ a_{21}, a_{22} & \cdot & a_{2,r-1}, b_2, a_{2,r+1} & \cdot & a_{2n} \\ \cdots\cdots\cdots\cdots\cdots\cdots \\ a_{n1}, a_{n2} & \cdot & a_{n,r-1}, b_n, a_{nr+1} & \cdot & a_{nn} \end{vmatrix} \Bigg/ \begin{vmatrix} a_{11}, a_{12} & \cdot\cdot & a_{1n} \\ a_{21}, a_{22} & \cdot\cdot & a_{2n} \\ \cdots\cdots\cdots \\ a_{n1}, a_{n2} & \cdot\cdot & a_{nn} \end{vmatrix} \quad \ldots.(7.3.1)$$

Although this is formally the complete answer, it is completely use-less for practical computation. The reason for this lies in the fact that, to evaluate a determinant of order $n$ from its algebraic defini-tion requires $(n\,!)(n-1)$ multiplications; it follows that the evalua-tion of all $x_r$ in equation 7.3.1 would need $(n+1).(n\,!)(n-1)$ multiplications and $n$ divisions. Other methods of evaluating the determinants exist, for example that of Doolittle, but these require roughly $n^3/3$ multiplications per determinant, so that the whole solution still requires about $n^4/3$ multiplications. (Notice that in all of these estimates we assume that division and multiplication are roughly equivalent in computational labour, and that $n$ is large compared with unity.)

A more economical method is the following: consider the 1st and $r$th members of the set of equations 7.2.1. Multiply the former by $a_{r1}$ and the latter by $a_{11}$, and then subtract (1) $\times$ $a_{r1}$ from $(r)$ $\times$ $a_{11}$. The result is:

$$(a_{11}a_{r2} - a_{r1}a_{12})x_2 + (a_{11}a_{r3} - a_{r1}a_{13})x_3 \cdots$$
$$+ (a_{11}a_{rn} - a_{r1}a_{1n})x_n = (a_{11}b_r - a_{1r}b_1)$$

or

$$_1l_{r2}x_2 + {}_1l_{r3}x_3 \cdots \cdots {}_1l_{rn}x = {}_1b_r, \text{ say}$$

Repeating this operation for all $r$ in the range $(1 < r \leqslant n)$, a set of $(n-1)$ equations in the $(n-1)$ unknowns $x_2 \ldots x_n$, are obtained and a total of $2n(n-1)$ multiplications is required. (We do *not* need to form $a_{11}a_{r1}$ since this coefficient is eliminated). This sequence of operations is now repeated successively until $x_2 \ldots x_{n-1}$ have each been eliminated; the result is a series of equations:

$$
\left.
\begin{array}{ll}
(1) & a_{11}x_1 + a_{12}x_2 + a_{13}x_3 \cdots \cdots \cdots a_{1n}x_n = b_1 \\
(2) & \qquad\quad {}_1l_{22}x_2 + {}_1l_{23}x_3 \cdots \cdots \cdots {}_1l_{2n}x_n = {}_1b_2 \\
(3) & \qquad\qquad\qquad {}_2l_{33}x_3 + {}_2l_{34}x_4 \cdots {}_2l_{3n}x_n = {}_2b_3 \\
\cdot & \qquad\qquad\qquad\qquad \cdots\cdots\cdots\cdots\cdots \\
\cdot & \qquad\qquad\qquad\qquad \cdots\cdots\cdots\cdots\cdots \\
(n) & \qquad\qquad\qquad\qquad\qquad {}_{(n-1)}l_{nn}x_n = {}_{(n-1)}b_n
\end{array}
\right\} \cdots (7.3.2)
$$

The total number of multiplications involved, up to this point, is

$$2[(n)(n-1) + (n-1)(n-2) \cdots 2.1] = \tfrac{2}{3}n(n^2-1)$$

Starting with the $n$th member of equation 7.3.2 we can find $x_n$, $x_{n-1}, x_{n-2} \ldots x_1$ successively by substitution of the values of $x_r$ already found in the next equation [*i.e.* $x_n$ in $(n-1)$ to get $x_{n-1}$;

$x_n$, $x_{n-1}$ in $(n-2)$ to get $x_{n-2}$ *etc.*]. It will be seen that this process involves $\frac{1}{2}n(n-1)$ multiplications and $n$ divisions, whence the total number of 'equivalent multiplications' for the whole solution is:

$$\tfrac{2}{3}n(n^2-1) + \tfrac{1}{2}n(n-1) + n$$

which is of the order $\frac{2}{3}n^3$ for large values of $n$.

The merit of this process lies in the fact that, if the initial coefficients $a_{ij}$ are small whole numbers, no round-off may be necessary during the initial elimination; thus if integer solutions exist they will be obtained correctly. (This may be important if the equations are 'ill conditioned,' *vide infra*.)

When the initial coefficients are *not* integers a more efficient process is as follows,

(1) Examine the matrix $A = [a_{ij}]$ and find the largest $a_{ij}$, call this $a_{IJ}$.

(2) Multiply the $I$th equation successively by all $a_{iJ}/a_{IJ}$ $(i = 1 \ldots n \neq I)$ and subtract from each of the other equations.

The result of this operation will be a set of $(n-1)$ equations from which $x_J$ has been eliminated, just as occurred in the previous method. The same discrimination–elimination process is applied to the new set of equations and continued until a triangular set of equations of the same type as 7.3.2 is obtained. Back substitution then yields the $x_r$.

The reason for the choice of the *largest* $a_{ij}$ for the divisor at each stage is that the round-off errors, generated at each formation of $a_{iJ}/a_{IJ}$, are thereby reduced in size at the next stage. The method is sometimes described as 'pivotal condensation,' the element $a_{IJ}$ being the pivot.

It is easy to see that $n(n-1)$ multiplications and $(n-1)$ divisions have to be made at the first elimination. This gives $(n^2-1)$ 'equivalent multiplications,' compared to $2n(n-1)$ in the previous process. Thus, for the whole solution, a number of multiplications of order $\frac{1}{3}n^3$ is required.

For hand computation, pivotal condensation is an excellent method since the largest coefficient $a_{IJ}$ can usually be seen at a glance. When an automatic computing machine is in use, however, this discrimination may be troublesome and, for this reason, it has been our practice to use the former method whenever possible.

A third method of solution is usually known as the Choleski process; it depends upon the reduction of the matrix $A$ to the product of a lower triangular matrix $L$, with unit diagonal co-efficients, and an upper triangular matrix $U$.

Thus:

$$Ax = \mathrm{L}.U.x = b$$

whence if

$$L\xi = b$$
$$Ux = \xi$$

and the solution is reduced to a pair of back substitutions. The co-efficients $l_{ij}$ and $u_{ij}$ are readily obtained by forming the product $L.U$ and equating coefficients to those of $A$ in the sequence

$$(a_{11} \ldots a_{1n})(a_{21} \ldots a_{2n}) \ldots (a_{r1} \ldots a_{rn}) \ldots (a_{n1} \ldots a_{nn}).$$

It is stated that an advantage of the Choleski method lies in the fact that few intermediate results have to be written down; it is our experience, however, that the method is too complicated for 'occasional' use, and is not suitable for use on an automatic computor.

## 7.4 THE INVERSION OF MATRICES

When it is desired to solve the equations 7.2.1 for a *fixed* set of $a_{ij}$, but for a number of vectors $b$, it is best to evaluate the inverse matrix $A^{-1}$ and to use equation 7.2.6 to obtain the individual solutions.

The formal inverse (7.2.7) is useless, for the same reasons which cause the rejection of the determinant solution of the original equations. The elimination method may, however, be extended to give the inverse of a matrix. Thus let:

$$A^{-1} = \begin{bmatrix} a_{11}, a_{12} & \cdots & a_{1n} \\ a_{21}, a_{22} & \cdots & a_{2n} \\ \cdots & \cdots & \cdots \\ a_{n1}, a_{n2} & \cdots & a_{nn} \end{bmatrix} \qquad \ldots(7.4.1)$$

Then:

$$\begin{bmatrix} x_1 \\ x_2 \\ \cdot \\ x_n \end{bmatrix} = \begin{bmatrix} a_{11}, a_{12} & \ldots & a_{1n} \\ a_{21}, a_{22} & \ldots & a_{2n} \\ \cdots & \cdots & \cdots \\ \cdots & \cdots & \cdots \\ a_{n1}, a_{n2} & \ldots & a_{nn} \end{bmatrix} \begin{bmatrix} b_1 \\ b_2 \\ \cdot \\ b_n \end{bmatrix} = \begin{bmatrix} a_{11}b_1 + a_{12}b_2 + a_{13}b_3 \ldots + a_{1n}b_n \\ a_{21}b_1 + a_{22}b_2 + a_{23}b_3 \ldots + a_{2n}b_n \\ \cdots \cdots \cdots \cdots \cdots \cdots \\ \cdots \cdots \cdots \cdots \cdots \cdots \\ a_{n1}b_1 + a_{n2}b_2 + a_{n3}b_3 \ldots + a_{nn}b_n \end{bmatrix}$$

$$\ldots(7.4.2)$$

Whence, if we solve the original set of equations for the vectors:

$$\boldsymbol{b} = \begin{bmatrix} 1 \\ 0 \\ 0 \\ 0 \\ \cdot \\ \cdot \\ \cdot \\ 0 \end{bmatrix}, \begin{bmatrix} 0 \\ 1 \\ 0 \\ 0 \\ \cdot \\ \cdot \\ \cdot \\ 0 \end{bmatrix}, \begin{bmatrix} 0 \\ 0 \\ 1 \\ \cdot \\ \cdot \\ \cdot \\ \cdot \\ 0 \end{bmatrix} \cdot \cdot \begin{bmatrix} 0 \\ 0 \\ 0 \\ \cdot \\ \cdot \\ \cdot \\ \cdot \\ 1 \end{bmatrix} \qquad \dots (7.4.3)$$

the solutions, considered as column vectors, are the columns of the inverse matrix.

We note that by using pivotal condensation to solve the sets of equations and arranging the work so that only one triangulation of $A$ is performed $\frac{2}{3}n^3$ multiplications are required.

The Choleski method may also be applied to matrix inversion, for let

$$A = L.U$$

where $L$ and $U$ are triangular matrices of the type defined in section 7.3. Then:

$$A.A^{-1} = I$$

whence:

$$L.U.A^{-1} = I$$

$$L^{-1}LUA^{-1} = UA^{-1} = L^{-1}I = L^{-1}$$

$$U^{-1}UA^{-1} = A^{-1} = U^{-1}L^{-1}.$$

Now it has been seen in section 7.3 that $U$ and $L$ can be determined from $A$; assume that:

$$L^{-1} = \begin{bmatrix} \lambda_{11}.\lambda_{12} & \dots & \lambda_{1n} \\ \lambda_{21}.\lambda_{22} & \dots & \lambda_{2n} \\ \cdot \cdot \cdot \cdot \cdot \cdot \cdot \\ \cdot \cdot \cdot \cdot \cdot \cdot \cdot \\ \lambda_{n1}.\lambda_{n2} & \dots & \lambda_{nn} \end{bmatrix}, \quad L = \begin{bmatrix} 1 & 0\,0\,.\, \dots & 0 \\ l_{21} & 1\,0\,.\, \dots & 0 \\ \cdot \cdot \cdot \cdot \cdot \cdot \cdot \\ \cdot \cdot \cdot \cdot \cdot \cdot \cdot \\ l_{n1}.l_{n2} & \cdot \cdot \cdot l_{n3n-1} & 1 \end{bmatrix}$$

Then, since $L.L^{-1} = I$, we have, equating coefficients:

$$\lambda_{11} = 1, \lambda_{12} = \lambda_{13} = \dots \lambda_{1n} = 0$$

$$\lambda_{11}l_{21} + \lambda_{21} = 0, \quad \lambda_{12}l_{21} + \lambda_{22} = 1,$$

$$\lambda_{13}l_{21} + \lambda_{23} = 0 \dots \lambda_{1j}l_{21} + \lambda_{2j} = 0(j > 2)$$

*etc.* Which enable the $\lambda_{ij}$ to be determined. In a like manner the components $Y_{ij}$ of the inverse $U^{-1}$ may be determined. Thus, multiplying $U^{-1}L^{-1}$, the inverse $A^{-1}$ is obtained. The complexity of this process is self-evident.

Two other methods of finding an inverse are worthy of mention, not so much for their efficiency as far as numbers of multiplications are concerned, but because they are very well adapted to punched card and automatic computing machinery.

The first method is a consequence of the Cayley–Hamilton theorem ('A matrix satisfies its characteristic equation').

Let

$$\lambda^n + a_1\lambda^{n-1} + a_2\lambda^{n-2} \ldots + a_n = 0 \qquad \ldots (7.4.4)$$

be the characteristic equation of a matrix $A$. Then:

$$A^n + a_1A^{n-1} + a_2A^{n-2} + \ldots + a_nI = 0$$

whence :

$$I = -\frac{1}{a_n}\left(A_n + a_1A^{n-1} + a_2A^{n-2} \ldots + a_{n-1}A\right)$$

and:

$$A^{-1}I = A^{-1} = -\frac{1}{a^n}\left(A^{n-1} + a_1A^{n-2} + a_2A^{n-3} + \ldots + a_{n-1}I\right)$$

$$\ldots (7.4.5)$$

Now it may be shown that:

$$\left.\begin{array}{l} a_1 = -s_1 \\ a_2 = -\frac{1}{2}(a_1s_1 + s_2) \\ a_3 = -\frac{1}{3}(a_2s_1 + a_1s_2 + s_3) \\ \cdots\cdots\cdots\cdots\cdots\cdots\cdots \\ a_n = -\frac{1}{n}(a_{n-1}s_1 + a_{n-2}s_2 \ldots + s_n) \end{array}\right\} \qquad \ldots (7.4.6)$$

where:

$$s_r = tr(A^r) \qquad \ldots (7.4.7)$$

$tr$ being the *trace* of the matrix (*i.e.* $\sum\limits_{i=1}^{n} a_{ii}$ the sum of the elements on the principal diagonal).

Since a single matrix multiplication requires $n^3$ scalar multiplications the process of inversion embodied in equations 7.4.5, 7.4.6 and 7.4.7 will require of the order of $n^4$ multiplications.

The second inversion technique is an iterative one based upon the well-known result:

$$x_{n+1} = x_n(2 - ax_n) \qquad \ldots (7.4.8)$$

for which

$$\underset{n\to\infty}{Lt}\, x_n = 1/a$$

Under suitable conditions [3] it may be shown that a similar iteration:

$$X_{n+1} = X_n(2I - A.X_n) \qquad \dots (7.4.9)$$

in which $X_n$ and $A$ are matrices and $I$ is the unit matrix, will converge to $A^{-1}$. A practical experiment [4], in which this method was applied to the inversion of a $16 \times 16$ matrix, showed that 10 iterations were required to produce 4 decimal place accuracy and 20 iterations to produce 6 decimal place accuracy. Actually, the rate of convergence depends upon the goodness of the original approximation, $X_0$, and upon the precise form of $A$. It has been suggested that $X_0 = I$ should be taken as a starting value.

## 7.5 RESIDUALS AND 'CONDITION'

With the exception of the last method described, the procedures so far outlined for solving a set of linear simultaneous equations will give an *exact* solution if the arithmetic operations can be performed with complete accuracy. In practice only an approximation will, in general, be produced, since the arithmetic operations $\times$ and $\div$ will be subject to round-off errors. The iterative methods which will now be described make no pretence at complete accuracy, but merely reduce the errors in an existing approximation. This leads naturally to a consideration of the way in which the accuracy of a given approximation may be measured.

Let us suppose that an approximation $\boldsymbol{\xi}(= \xi_1, \xi_2, \dots \xi_n)$ is given to the solution of the set of equations 7.2.1. If we substitute this in the given equations we obtain:

$$\left.\begin{aligned}
a_{11}\xi_1 + a_{12}\xi_2 + \dots + a_{1n}\xi_n - b_1 &= r_1 \\
a_{21}\xi_1 + a_{22}\xi_2 + \dots + a_{2n}\xi_n - b_2 &= r_2 \\
\cdots\cdots\cdots\cdots\cdots\cdots\cdots\cdots\cdots \\
a_{n1}\xi_1 + a_{n2}\xi_2 + \dots + a_{nn}\xi_n - b_n &= r_n
\end{aligned}\right\} \qquad \dots (7.5.1)$$

The quantities $r_i$ define a vector $\boldsymbol{r}$ $(= r_1, r_2, \dots r_n)$ which is a measure of the inaccuracy of the approximation. To obtain a single number which will express the inaccuracy we may consider the *length* of $\boldsymbol{r}$, or more usefully its square, $R^2$. This is defined as the scalar product of $\boldsymbol{r}$ and itself:

$$R^2 = (\boldsymbol{r}.\boldsymbol{r}) = \sum_{i=1}^{n} r_i^2 = (A\boldsymbol{\xi} - \boldsymbol{b}).(A\boldsymbol{\xi} - \boldsymbol{b}) \qquad \dots (7.5.2)$$

and the quantities $r_i$ are often called 'residuals.'

By means of equation 7.5.1 we may reduce 7.5.2 to a quadratic form in the $\xi_i$:

$$R^2 = \sum_{i=1}^{n} (a_{i1}\xi_1 + a_{i2}\xi_2 \ldots + a_{in}\xi_n - b_i)^2 \qquad \ldots (7.5.3)$$

which is clearly positive-definite.

An alternative measure of accuracy is the quadratic (previously given in 7.2.10):

$$S = \tfrac{1}{2} \sum_{i=1}^{n} \sum_{j=1}^{n} a_{ij}\xi_i\xi_j - \sum_{i=1}^{n} b_i\xi_i \qquad (a_{ij} = a_{ji}) \qquad \ldots (7.5.4)$$

This has the merit of bearing a simple relationship to the original matrix $A$, but the disadvantage that $A$ must be positive definite, so that arguments based upon $S$ may fail if this condition is not satisfied. We note, here, that equation 7.5.4 may be written, vectorially:*

$$S = \tfrac{1}{2}\boldsymbol{\xi}.A\boldsymbol{\xi} - b.\boldsymbol{\xi} \qquad \ldots (7.5.5)$$
$$= \tfrac{1}{2}\boldsymbol{\xi}.(r + b) - b.\boldsymbol{\xi}$$
$$= \tfrac{1}{2}\boldsymbol{\xi}.(r - b)$$
$$= \tfrac{1}{2}(r - b).A^{-1}(r + b) \qquad \ldots (7.5.6)$$

It is clear from equation 7.5.4 that $S$ has a *minimum* when $r = 0$, and the same is true of $R^2$.

The question now arises, how far may an approximate solution $\xi$ deviate from the true solution $x$ for a particular value of $R^2$ or $S$. A measure of this deviation is the square of the length of the difference vector $(\boldsymbol{\xi} - \boldsymbol{x})$, that is

$$(\boldsymbol{\xi} - \boldsymbol{x}).(\boldsymbol{\xi} - \boldsymbol{x}) = (A^{-1}r).(A^{-1}r)$$

This is not easily correlated with either $R^2$ or $S$ but it shows that if $A^{-1}$ has any large component, large differences between true and approximate solutions may be accompanied by small residuals $r_i$ and values of $R^2$ and $S$.

Another approach is to consider the hyper-ellipsoids defined by equations 7.5.3 and 7.5.4, for *fixed* values of $R^2$ and $S$. Considering the latter $(S)$, we first transform to axes through the centre $(x_1, x_2 \ldots x_n)$. Putting

$$\xi_r = x_r + \epsilon_r$$

equation 7.5.4 becomes:

$$S + \tfrac{1}{2} \sum_{i=1}^{n} b_i x_i = \tfrac{1}{2} \sum_{i=1}^{n} \sum_{j=1}^{n} a_{ij}\epsilon_i\epsilon_j \qquad \ldots (7.5.7)$$

* Notice that in equations 7.5.2, 7.5.5, A has the character of a 'Tensor,' or in more modern usage, a 'Dyadic.'

Now it is well known [5] that the quadratic form:

$$\sum_{ij} a_{ij}\epsilon_i\epsilon_j$$

can, by means of a real orthogonal transformation of unit modulus, be reduced to:

$$\sum_{i=1}^{n} \lambda_i E_i^2 \qquad \qquad \ldots (7.5.8)$$

where the $\lambda_i$ are the roots of the characteristic equation 7.2.9. Now

$$S + \tfrac{1}{2}\sum_{i=1}^{n} b_i x_i = \sum_{i=1}^{n} \lambda_i E_i^2$$

represents a hyper-ellipsoid having axes proportional to $1/\sqrt{\lambda_i}$ so that, if any of the $\lambda_i$ are very small, large values of $E_i$ can be

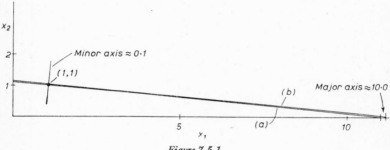

*Figure 7.5.1*

accompanied by small residuals. This is shown, for a two-dimensional case, in *Figure 7.5.1*.

The equations considered are:

$$x_1 + 10x_2 = 11 \quad \ldots \text{ (a)}$$
$$10x_1 + 101x_2 = 111 \quad \ldots \text{ (b)}$$

for which the solution is obviously $x_1 = x_2 = 1$;

*Figure 7.5.1* shows the lie of the curve for $S = 60\cdot 5$, the actual curve being too close to its major axis to be visible on this scale. It will be seen that the axes are approximately $\frac{1}{10}$ and 10 in accord with the ratio $\sqrt{\lambda_1/\lambda_2}$ of the roots of:

$$\begin{vmatrix} 1-\lambda & 10 \\ 10 & 101-\lambda \end{vmatrix} = 0$$

82

or

$$\lambda^2 - 102\lambda + 1 = 0$$

giving

$$\lambda_1 = 101 \cdot 9902, \quad \lambda_2 = 0 \cdot 0098.$$

Also plotted are the lines represented by the equations (a) and (b), and it will be noticed that they are nearly parallel, so that the intersection (1, 1) is very sensitive to the coefficients. The relationship between residuals and parallelism is the basis of the definition of $R^2$ in equation 7.5.2; thus if $p_i$ is the length of the perpendicular from $(\xi_1, \xi_2 \ldots \xi_n)$ on to the hyperplane:

$$a_{i1}x_1 + a_{i2}x_2 + a_{i3}x_3 \ldots a_{in}x_n - b_i = 0$$

we have:

$$p_i = \left( \sum_{j=1}^{n} a_i \xi_{j1} - b_i \right) \bigg/ \sqrt{\sum_{j=1}^{n} a_{ij}^2} \qquad \ldots (7.5.9)$$

$$= r_i \bigg/ \sqrt{\sum_{j=1}^{n} a_{ij}^2}$$

If now we normalize the rows of the matrix $A$

$$\left( i.e., \text{ divide each row by} \sqrt{\sum_{j=1}^{n} a_{ij}^2} \right)$$

we shall not alter the solution of the equations. Assume that this has been done, so that equation 7.5.9 becomes:

$$p_i = r_i \qquad \ldots (7.5.10)$$

Thus equation 7.5.2 may be written:

$$R^2 = \sum_{i=1}^{n} p_i^2$$

and we see that the surfaces of $R^2 = \text{const.}$ are simply those such that the sums of the squares of the perpendiculars from any point $(\xi_1, \xi_2 \ldots \xi_n)$ on the surface on to the hyperplanes

$$a_{i1}x_1 + a_{i2}x_2 \ldots a_{in}x_n - b_i = 0 \quad (i = 1 \ldots n)$$

is constant.

It will be evident, from *Figure 7.5.1*, that in the example quoted, the $R^2 = \text{const.}$ 'surfaces' are similar in shape to those defined by $S = \text{const.}$

The equations (a) and (b) provide an interesting study of the false conclusions which may be drawn from small values of $R^2$. We first

83

normalize by forming (a)$/\sqrt{1^2 + 10^2}$, (b)$/\sqrt{10^2 + 101^2}$ and thus obtain:

$$\frac{x_1}{\sqrt{101}} + \frac{10x_2}{\sqrt{101}} = \frac{11}{\sqrt{101}} \quad \cdots \cdots \quad \text{(a')}$$

$$\frac{10x_1}{\sqrt{10301}} + \frac{101x_2}{\sqrt{10301}} = \frac{111}{\sqrt{10301}} \quad \cdots \quad \text{(b')}$$

The radicals have been purposely retained thus far. If we calculate the components of the residuals for the approximate solution $x_1 = 1 \cdot 001$, $x_2 = 1 \cdot 01$ we find: from (a') $r_1 \simeq \cdot 01$, from (b') $r_2 \simeq \cdot 01$ whence $R^2 \simeq \cdot 0002$.

Next try the values $x_1 = 11 \cdot 1$, $x_2 = 0$, we obtain: $r_1 \simeq \cdot 01$, $r_2 = 0$ whence, this time $R^2 \simeq \cdot 0001$. Most people would conclude from this that $(11 \cdot 1, 0)$ was 'nearer' to the true solution than $(1 \cdot 001, 1 \cdot 01)$ which is manifestly false.

If we had evaluated the radicals and expressed the resulting coefficients in decimal form, the equations (a') and (b') would have appeared as:

$$\cdot 09950x_1 + \cdot 99504x_2 = 1 \cdot 09454 \quad \text{(a'')}$$

$$\cdot 09853x_1 + \cdot 99513x_2 = 1 \cdot 09366 \quad \text{(b'')}$$

and a change of approximately 1 per cent in the coefficient of $x_1$ in (a'') makes the solution $(11 \cdot 1, 0)$ exact.

Thus, the solution of equations of this type is very sensitive to the values of the coefficients, and the term 'ill-conditioned' is applied to them.

Various measures for 'ill-condition' suggest themselves from the preceding discussion. Perhaps the most obvious is the ratio $\lambda_{max}/\lambda_{min}$, which gives a measure of the ratio of greatest to least axes of the hyper-ellipsoid defined by equation 7.5.4. Unfortunately the calculation of $\lambda_{max}$ and $\lambda_{min}$ is an operation of at least the complexity of the solution of the original equations, so that this criterion is of little practical use. Ill condition is accompanied by approximate parallelism of some of the hyperplanes defined by the equations. This can be recognized in simple cases, such as that obtaining in our equations (a) and (b), by observing the ratios of corresponding coefficients, but this, too, is not generally possible.

Yet another measure which has been suggested is the value of the determinant $|A|$, 'small' values being accompanied by ill-condition. In this form the test is without value, since the set of equations can be multiplied by any constant without altering the solution. If the constant is $M$, $|A|$ is multiplied by $M^n$ and so can be made as large as desired; we note that if $|A| = 0$ the equations have *no* unique solution. A better version of this test is first to 'normalize' the equations by division by $\sqrt{\sum_{j=1}^{n} a_{ij}^2}$ for the $i$th equation, and to regard smallness compared to $\pm 1$ as an indication of ill condition. On this basis the 'ideal' equations:

$$a_{11}x_1 = b_1$$
$$a_{22}x_2 = b_2$$

and

$$a_{11}x_1 + a_{12}x_2 = b_1$$
$$a_{21}x_1 - a_{22}x_2 = b_2$$

with

$$a_{11} = a_{12}, \quad a_{21} = a_{22}$$

have $|A| = 1$ $|A| = -1$ respectively, when normalized. On the other hand, our equations (a) (b), in the normal form (a″) (b″), have $|A| \simeq \cdot001$ which gives a clear indication of their ill condition. Yet another example is provided by the much quoted[6] set of ill conditioned equations:

$$5x_1 + 7x_2 + 6x_3 + 5x_4 = 23$$
$$7x_1 + 10x_2 + 8x_3 + 7x_4 = 32$$
$$6x_1 + 8x_2 + 10x_3 + 9x_4 = 33$$
$$5x_1 + 7x_2 + 9x_3 + 10x_4 = 31$$

whose true solution is evidently $(1, 1, 1, 1)$, but for which the values $(+14\cdot6, -7\cdot2, -2\cdot5, +3\cdot1)$ give components $(+\cdot1, -\cdot1, -\cdot1 +\cdot1)$ for the residue vector $r$, and consequently $R^2 = \cdot0004$. The values $(+2\cdot36, +0\cdot18, +0\cdot65, +1\cdot21)$ give residue components $(+\cdot01, -\cdot01, -\cdot01, +\cdot01)$ and consequently $R^2 = \cdot04$. The value of $|A|$ for this set of equations as it stands is 1, but if we normalize by division of the respective equations by

$$\sqrt{5^2 + 7^2 + 6^2 + 5^2}, \qquad \sqrt{7^2 + 10^2 + 8^2 + 7^2},$$
$$\sqrt{6^2 + 8^2 + 10^2 + 9^2} \quad \text{and} \quad \sqrt{5^2 + 7^2 + 9^2 + 10^2},$$

we get $|A|_{\text{norm.}} = \cdot000{,}019{,}9$ which, since it is small compared with unity, indicates clearly the ill condition of the equations.

### 7.6 DETERMINATION OF LATENT ROOTS AND OF CHARACTERISTIC VECTORS

It is possible to determine the latent roots of a matrix directly from the definition 7.2.9, and then to solve the resulting sets of simultaneous equations (one set for each $\lambda_i$) to determine the characteristic vectors. This method, whilst sometimes appropriate for small numbers of equations and unknowns, say less than 5, is not at all feasible when large numbers of variables are involved. This point is therefore an appropriate one at which to consider methods of iteration and successive approximation which will, at the same time, be useful for the solution of simultaneous equations themselves.

When no information is available regarding either latent roots or characteristic vectors, it is usual to start by determining the largest $\lambda_i$ and its associated vector.

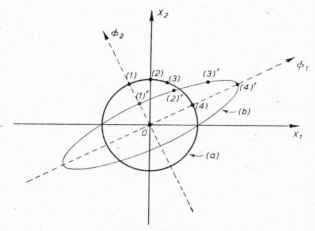

*Figure 7.6.1*

We shall adopt the usual procedure and denote the latent roots by $\lambda_1, \lambda_2 \ldots \lambda_n$, where $|\lambda_1| \geqslant |\lambda_2| \geqslant |\lambda_3| \ldots \geqslant |\lambda_n|$, the associated characteristic vectors are $\varphi_1, \varphi_2 \ldots \varphi_n$ and we recall the definition:

$$(A - \lambda_i I)\varphi_i = 0 \qquad (i = 1 \ldots n) \qquad \ldots (7.6.1)$$

Consider the effect of applying the tensor $A$ to any vector $\mathbf{X}$, that is, of forming $A\mathbf{x}$. The tensor operator can be considered as a set of expansions, or contractions, in an $n$ dimensional hyperspace. These expansions have *directions* given by the principal axes of the quadratic form $\underset{i,j}{\Sigma} a_{ij}x_i x_j$, that is, by the directions of the characteristic vectors; their magnitudes are such that a unit vector in the direction of the $i$th principal axis has its length changed to $\lambda_i$. In two dimensions the effect is shown in *Figure 7.6.1*.

This was constructed for latent roots $\lambda_1 = 2, \lambda_2 = (\frac{1}{2})$ and characteristic vectors $\varphi_1, \varphi_2$ in the directions shown. Points (1), (2), (3), (4) on the unit circle (a) are transformed into (1)′, (2)′, (3)′, (4)′ by the tensor.

Next consider the effect of forming $A\mathbf{x}$, normalizing to form $(A\mathbf{x})_n$, and then reapplying $A$.

This is seen, from *Figure 7.6.2*, to result in a vector in which the component in direction $\boldsymbol{\varphi}_1$ is increased by a factor $\lambda_1$, and that in direction $\boldsymbol{\varphi}_2$ by $\lambda_2$. Thus the transformed vector is more nearly in the direction $\boldsymbol{\varphi}_1$ than was originally the case. The sequence followed by successive applications of the process to a unit vector, initially (1), is shown. $A(1) = (1)′$. This is normalized to give $(1)_n$, $A(1)_n$ gives

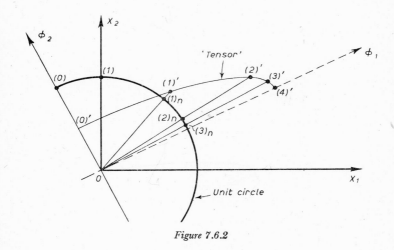

*Figure 7.6.2*

(2)′ and so on. It is clear that a few applications of the process will lead to a vector which lies, sensibly, in direction $\boldsymbol{\varphi}_1$. The figure also shows that, if an initial vector (0) had been chosen *orthogonal* to $\boldsymbol{\varphi}_1$, the operation $A(0)$ would not lead to any convergence to $\boldsymbol{\varphi}_1$, but merely to oscillation along $\boldsymbol{\varphi}_2$. The whole argument can be generalized immediately to an $n$ dimensional hyperspace.

An alternative demonstration of the process just described, and if $A$ is symmetrical (*i.e.* $a_{ij} = a_{ji}$), is as follows. The characteristic vectors are orthogonal, that is $(\boldsymbol{\varphi}_i . \boldsymbol{\varphi}_j) = 0$ $(i \neq j)$; we may therefore express an arbitrary vector $\mathbf{x}$ as a linear combination of the $\boldsymbol{\varphi}_i$:

$$\mathbf{x} = a_1\boldsymbol{\varphi}_1 + a_2\boldsymbol{\varphi}_2 + \ldots + a_n\boldsymbol{\varphi}_n$$

Now apply the operator $A$ and use equation 7.6.1:

$$Ax = a_1\lambda_1\varphi_1 + a_2\lambda_2\varphi_2 + \ldots + a_n\lambda_n\varphi_n$$

$$= \lambda_1\left(a_1\varphi_1 + a_2\frac{\lambda_2}{\lambda_1}\varphi_2 + \ldots + a_n\frac{\lambda_n}{\lambda_1}\varphi_n\right)$$

so that, since $\lambda_1 > \lambda_n (n > 1)$ the result of the operation $A$ is to decrease the proportion of vectors, other than $\varphi_1$, in the system. Thus the process converges, eventually, to $\lambda_1\varphi_1$.

In practice it is usually simpler to take the vector $x$ as having a maximum component unity instead of normalizing properly. This avoids the evaluation of $(\Sigma a_n^2)^{-\frac{1}{2}}$ at each stage, and does not otherwise affect the process.

When multiple roots occur, so that $\lambda_1 = \lambda_2 = \ldots = \lambda_r$ (say), there is no unique value of $\varphi_1$ and, under these circumstances the method breaks down. If, in practical application, it is found that convergence is either slow or absent, it is well, before abandoning the process, to try an initial vector which is orthogonal to that originally taken, in order to eliminate the possibility that the first choice was at right angles to $\varphi_1$.

The figure taken as an illustration in the preceding paragraphs was constructed on the basis of a positive definite quadratic form $\underset{ij}{\Sigma a_{ij}x_ix_j}$, for which all $\lambda_i$ are greater than zero. The same argument is applicable when some $\lambda_i$ are negative, with the exception that the end points $(1)'$, $(2)'$ *etc.* will move from side to side of $\varphi_2$ (assuming $|\lambda_1| > |\lambda_2|$ and $\lambda_1$ negative). The normalizing process now consists not only of reducing the amplitude of $Ax$ to unity, but also in restoring it to its original side of $\varphi_1$.

For non-symmetric matrices, $A$, it is not true to say that the $\varphi_i$ form an orthogonal set of vectors. If, however, the transpose of $A$, $A'$ is taken, then since $|A| = |A'|$ it follows that the latent *roots* of both systems are identical. This is not true of the characteristic *vectors*, and, if we call these $\psi_i$ for $A'$, the $\psi_i$ and $\varphi_i$ are orthogonal, that is the scalar product $(\varphi_i.\psi_j)$ $(i \neq j)$ is zero. Notice that, since for symmetric matrices $A \equiv A'$, $(\varphi_i.\varphi_j) = 0$ $(i \neq j)$ for the latter, the property which was used in the earlier discussion.

When $\lambda_1$ is complex, the above method will fail altogether; a method of determination in this case is to form $AA'$ and then to apply the preceding technique to determine the greatest latent root of this matrix. It is easily shown that the magnitude of this root is equal to the square of the modulus $|\lambda_1|^2$ of the greatest root of $|A|$. Fortunately, in most of the large sets of simultaneous equations resulting from the finite difference solution of partial differential equations, the matrix is symmetrical, so that this difficulty does not arise.

When an approximation is known to any characteristic vector, it is possible to obtain an improved value for the associated latent root by means of the expression:

$$L = \frac{(\boldsymbol{x} . A\boldsymbol{x})}{(\boldsymbol{x} . \boldsymbol{x})} = \frac{\sum\limits_{i,j} a_{ij} x_i x_j}{\sum\limits_{i} x_i{}^2} \qquad \ldots (7.6.2)$$

It is clear that if $\boldsymbol{x} = \boldsymbol{\varphi}_i$, then $(\boldsymbol{x} . A\boldsymbol{x}) = (\boldsymbol{\varphi}_i . A\boldsymbol{\varphi}_i) = \lambda_i(\boldsymbol{\varphi}_i . \boldsymbol{\varphi}_i)$ whence $L = \lambda_i$. Suppose now that $\boldsymbol{x} = \boldsymbol{\varphi}_i + \boldsymbol{\epsilon}$, then:

$$(L - \lambda_i)(\boldsymbol{x} . \boldsymbol{x}) = (\boldsymbol{\varphi}_i + \boldsymbol{\epsilon}) . A(\boldsymbol{\varphi}_i + \boldsymbol{\epsilon}) - \lambda_i(\boldsymbol{\varphi}_i + \boldsymbol{\epsilon}) . (\boldsymbol{\varphi}_i + \boldsymbol{\epsilon})$$

$$= \boldsymbol{\varphi}_i . A\boldsymbol{\varphi}_i + \boldsymbol{\varphi}_i . A\boldsymbol{\epsilon} + \boldsymbol{\epsilon} . A\boldsymbol{\varphi}_i + \boldsymbol{\epsilon} . A\boldsymbol{\epsilon} - \lambda_i \boldsymbol{\varphi}_i . \boldsymbol{\varphi}_i$$

$$- 2\lambda_i . \boldsymbol{\varphi}_i . \boldsymbol{\epsilon} - \lambda_i \boldsymbol{\epsilon} . \boldsymbol{\epsilon}$$

but

$$A\boldsymbol{\varphi}_i = \lambda_i \boldsymbol{\varphi}_i,$$

whence:

$$(L - \lambda_i)(\boldsymbol{x} . \boldsymbol{x}) = \boldsymbol{\varphi}_i . A\boldsymbol{\epsilon} - \lambda_i \boldsymbol{\varphi}_i . \boldsymbol{\epsilon} + \boldsymbol{\epsilon} . A\boldsymbol{\epsilon} - \lambda_i \boldsymbol{\epsilon} . \boldsymbol{\epsilon}$$

$$= \boldsymbol{\varphi}_i . (A - \lambda_i I)\boldsymbol{\epsilon} + \boldsymbol{\epsilon} . (A - \lambda_i I)\boldsymbol{\epsilon}$$

(since $\boldsymbol{\varphi}_i . \boldsymbol{\epsilon}$ is a scalar product and $\boldsymbol{\varphi}_i . \boldsymbol{\epsilon} = \boldsymbol{\epsilon} . \boldsymbol{\varphi}_i$)

Now if $A$ is a symmetric matrix, so is $(A - \lambda_i I)$, and for any symmetric matrix $B$ we have $\boldsymbol{y} . B\boldsymbol{x} = \boldsymbol{x} . B\boldsymbol{y}$, whence:

$$\boldsymbol{\varphi}_i . (A - \lambda_i I)\boldsymbol{\epsilon} = \boldsymbol{\epsilon} . (A - \lambda_i I)\boldsymbol{\varphi}_i = 0$$

Thus:

$$L - \lambda_i = \boldsymbol{\epsilon} . (A - \lambda_i I)\boldsymbol{\epsilon} / \boldsymbol{x} . \boldsymbol{x}$$

and the difference between $L$ and $\lambda_i$ is seen to be of the second order in $\boldsymbol{\epsilon}$.

We may notice, before leaving the quantity $L$, that if $\boldsymbol{x}$ is *any* vector whatever, and $A$ is a real symmetric square matrix, then:

$$\lambda_1 \geqslant L \geqslant \lambda_n \qquad \ldots (7.6.3)$$

Having determined the largest latent root and its associated characteristic vector, it is possible to proceed to the determination of the next smaller root and vector. A crude method is to select any vector $_1\boldsymbol{\varphi}_2$ orthogonal to $\boldsymbol{\varphi}_1$ and then to go through the iterative process $A_1\boldsymbol{\varphi}_2, A(A_1\boldsymbol{\varphi}_2)_n$ *etc*. Since $_1\boldsymbol{\varphi}_2$ is orthogonal to $\boldsymbol{\varphi}_1$ we have seen

G

that convergence to $\varphi_1$, will not occur, and instead the process will, in principle, tend to $\lambda_2 \varphi_2$. Unfortunately, since the arithmetic processes used to form $A_1 \varphi_2$ *etc.* are subject to round off errors, a small proportion of $\varphi_1$ will be introduced into the $_m\varphi_2$ vectors, and this will grow until convergence to $\varphi_1$ instead of $\varphi_2$ results.

This defect is removed in an iterative method which is based upon the Gram-Schmidt process for the construction of orthogonal vectors.

Assume that $\varphi_1$ is known, we then take any vector $_1\varphi_2$ and form:

$$A_1\varphi_2 - a_1\varphi_1$$

so that this vector is orthogonal to $\varphi_1$. Now let:

$$_2\lambda_2 \cdot _2\varphi_2 = A \cdot _1\varphi_2 - a_1\varphi_1$$

and repeat the process to obtain successively:

$$_3\lambda_2 \cdot _3\varphi_2 = A \cdot _2\varphi_2 - a_2\varphi_1$$
$$_4\lambda_2 \cdot _4\varphi_2 = A \cdot _3\varphi_2 - a_3\varphi_1$$
$$\cdots \cdots \cdots \cdots \cdots \cdots$$
$$\cdots \cdots \cdots \cdots \cdots \cdots$$
$$_m\lambda_2 \cdot _m\varphi_2 = A \cdot _{m-1}\varphi_2 - a_{m-1}\varphi_1$$

The scalar multipliers $a_1\, a_2$ *etc.* should be small after the first stage, and serve merely to keep $\varphi_1$ from contaminating the convergents to $\varphi_2$. It is probably sufficient, in most cases, to insert an $a\varphi_1$ term, not at *each* stage, but once every 5 cycles.

When $\lambda_2$ and $\varphi_2$ have been determined with sufficient accuracy, we chose a vector $\varphi_3$ and form:

$$_2\lambda_3 \cdot _2\varphi_3 = A \cdot _1\varphi_3 - a_1\varphi_1 - \beta_1\varphi_2$$
$$_3\lambda_3 \cdot _3\varphi_3 = A \cdot _2\varphi_3 - a_2\varphi_1 - \beta_2\varphi_2$$
$$\cdots \cdots \cdots \cdots \cdots \cdots \cdots$$
$$\cdots \cdots \cdots \cdots \cdots \cdots \cdots$$
$$_m\lambda_3 \cdot _m\varphi_3 = A \cdot _{m-1}\varphi_3 - a_{m-1}\varphi_1 - \beta_{m-1}\varphi_2$$

This determines $\lambda_3$, $\varphi_3$, and a similar process with $\gamma\varphi_3$, $\delta\varphi_4$ *etc.* can be used to obtain the other latent roots and characteristic vectors.

To check the values of the latent roots use may be made of the relations:

$$\sum_{r=1}^{n} \lambda_i = tr|A| \qquad \qquad \ldots(7.6.4)$$

$$\lambda_1 . \lambda_2 . \lambda_3 \ldots . \lambda_n = |A| \qquad \qquad \ldots(7.6.5)$$

which follow at once from the definition of the characteristic equation given in 7.2.9.

To conclude this section we may mention three other methods which have been used for the calculation of latent roots and characteristic vectors. The first is the so-called 'purification' process of RICHARDSON [7], which seeks to remove the contribution of $\varphi_i$ from an arbitrary vector by multiplication by $(A - \lambda_i I)$. This method demands a certain amount of art on the part of the user, and appears unsuitable for use on large systems and with automatic computing machinery. The second method is the so-called 'Escalator' of MORRIS [8], [9] which depends upon the solutions of a characteristic equation of order $(n - 1)$ to obtain the characteristic equation of order $(n)$.

The operation of the escalator is as follows. Consider the quadratic form associated with a matrix $A_{(n)}$ of order $n$; this is:

$$Q_n = \sum_{i,j=1}^{n} a_{ij} x_i x_j \qquad \ldots . (7.6.6)$$

Suppose that we consider the matrix obtained by removing the column $a_{in}$ $(i = 1 \ldots n)$ and the row $a_{nj}$ $(j = 1 \ldots n)$ from $A$,

$$A_{(n)} = \begin{bmatrix} a_{11} & a_{12} & \cdots & a_{1,\,n-1} & a_{1n} \\ a_{21} & a_{22} & \cdots & a_{2,\,n-1} & a_{2n} \\ \cdot & \cdot & \cdots & \cdots & \cdots \\ \cdot & \cdot & \cdots & \cdots & \cdots \\ a_{n-1,\,1} & a_{n-1,\,2} & \cdots & a_{n-1,\,n-1} & a_{n-1,\,n} \\ a_{n1} & a_{n2} & \cdots & a_{n,\,n-1} & a_{nn} \end{bmatrix}$$

$$= \left[ \begin{array}{c|c} & \begin{array}{c} a_{1n} \\ a_{2n} \\ \cdot \\ \cdot \\ a_{n-1,\,n} \end{array} \\ \hline A_{(n-1)} & \\ \hline a_{n1} \; a_{n2} \; \cdots \; a_{n,\,n-1} & a_{nn} \end{array} \right] \qquad \ldots . (7.6.7)$$

Calling this matrix $A_{(n-1)}$ we have the associated quadratic form:

$$Q_{n-1} = \sum_{i,j=1}^{n-1} a_{ij} x_i x_j$$

91

and we may write:

$$Q_n = Q_{n-1} + x_n \sum_{i=1}^{n-1} a_{in}x_i + x_n \sum_{j=1}^{n-1} a_{nj}x_j + a_{nn}x_n^2 \quad \ldots (7.6.8)$$

If we assume that the latent roots $\lambda_r$ $(r = 1 \ldots n - 1)$ and the characteristic vectors $\varphi_r = (\phi_{r1}, \phi_{r2} \ldots \phi_{r,\,n-1})(r = 1 \ldots n - 1)$ are known for $A_{(n-1)}$, then it is well known, from matrix theory, that we can express $Q_{n-1}$ as:

$$Q_{n-1} = \sum_{r=1}^{n-1} \lambda_r \phi_r^2 \qquad \ldots (7.6.9)$$

Now the components $\phi_{rj}$ of $\varphi_r$ are in the directions of the original 'axes' $x_j$ so that we have:

$$\phi_r = l_{r1}x_1 + l_{r2}x_2 \ldots + l_{r,\,n-1}x_{n-1} \qquad (r = 1 \ldots n - 1).$$

and the matrix $L_{(n-1)}$, given by:

$$L_{(n-1)} = \begin{bmatrix} l_{11} & l_{12} & \cdots & l_{1,\,n-1} \\ l_{21} & l_{22} & \cdots & l_{2,\,n-1} \\ \cdot & \cdot & \cdots & \cdot \\ \cdot & \cdot & \cdots & \cdot \\ l_{n-1,\,1} & \cdots & \cdots & l_{n-1,\,n-1} \end{bmatrix} \qquad \ldots (7.6.10)$$

is an ortho-normal one (*i.e.* it corresponds to a change from one set of orthogonal axes to another set related to the first by a simple rotation and without change of scale). $L_{(n-1)}$ is symmetric and obeys:

$$L_{(n-1)} \cdot L'_{(n-1)} = I \qquad \ldots (7.6.11)$$

We can thus express the quantities $x_r$ in terms of the $\varphi_r$:

$$x_r = l_{1r}\phi_1 + l_{2r}\phi_2 \ldots l_{n-1,\,r}\phi_{r-1} \qquad (r = 1 \ldots n - 1)$$

so that, using equation 7.6.9, 7.6.8 becomes:

$$Q_n = \sum_{r=1}^{n-1} \lambda_r \phi_r^2 + x_n \sum_{i=1}^{n-1} a_{in} \sum_{s=1}^{n-1} l_{si}\phi_s + x_n \sum_{j=1}^{n-1} a_{nj} \sum_{s=1}^{n-1} l_{sj}\phi_s + a_{nn}x_n^2$$
$$\ldots (7.6.12)$$

We notice, at this point, that $x_n$ is unchanged by the transformation. It is now evident that the matrix of equation 7.6.12, in terms of $(\varphi_1, \varphi_2 \ldots \varphi_{n-1}, x_n)$ is:

92

$$A_{(n)} = \begin{bmatrix} \lambda_1 & 0 & 0 & \ldots \ldots & 0 & \sum_{r=1}^{n-1} a_{rn}l_{1r} \\ 0 & \lambda_2 & 0 & \ldots \ldots & 0 & \sum_{r=1}^{n-1} a_{rn}l_{2r} \\ 0 & 0 & \lambda_3 & \ldots \ldots & 0 & \ldots \ldots \\ & \ldots & \ldots & \ldots & \ldots & \ldots \ldots \\ & \ldots & \ldots & \ldots & \ldots & \ldots \ldots \\ 0 & 0 & \ldots & \ldots \ldots & \lambda_{n-1} & \sum_{r=1}^{n-1} a_{rn}l_{n-1r} \\ \sum_{r=1}^{n-1} a_{nr}l_{1r} & \sum_{r=1}^{n-1} a_{nr}l_{2r} & \ldots & \sum_{r=1}^{n-1} a_{nr}l_{n-1r} & & a_{nn} \end{bmatrix} \quad \ldots (7.6.13)$$

so that the characteristic equation becomes:

$$|A_{(n)} - \lambda I| = \begin{vmatrix} \lambda_1 - \lambda & 0 & 0 & \ldots \ldots 0 & a_{rn}l_{1r} \\ 0 & \lambda_2 - \lambda & 0 & \ldots \ldots 0 & a_{rn}l_{2r} \\ 0 & 0 & \lambda_3 - \lambda & \ldots \ldots 0 & a_{rn}l_{3r} \\ \ldots & \ldots & \ldots & \ldots & \ldots \\ \ldots & \ldots & \ldots & \ldots & \ldots \\ 0 & 0 & 0 & \ldots \lambda_{n-1} - \lambda & a_{rn}l_{n-1r} \\ a_{nr}l_{1r} & a_{nr}l_{2r} & a_{nr}l_{3r} & \ldots a_{nr}l_{n-1r} & a_{nn} - \lambda \end{vmatrix} = 0$$

$$\ldots (7.6.14)$$

where double suffix notation has been used to avoid writing out the summations.

We now subtract $a_{rn} \cdot l_{1r}/\lambda_1 - \lambda$ times the first column from the last, thus eliminating the first coefficient in column $n$, then $a_{rn} \cdot l_{2r}/\lambda_2 - \lambda$, times the second column and so on. The result is:

$$\begin{vmatrix} \lambda_1 - \lambda & 0 & 0 & \ldots & 0 & 0 \\ 0 & \lambda_2 - \lambda & 0 & \ldots & 0 & 0 \\ 0 & 0 & \lambda_3 - \lambda & \ldots & 0 & 0 \\ \ldots & \ldots & \ldots & \ldots & \ldots & \ldots \\ \ldots & \ldots & \ldots & \ldots & \ldots & \ldots \\ 0 & 0 & 0 & \ldots & \lambda_{n-1} - \lambda & 0 \\ a_{nr}l_{1r} & a_{nr}l_{2r} & a_{nr}l_{3r} & \ldots & a_{nr}l_{n-1r} & a_{nn} - \lambda - \sum_{i=1}^{n-1} \frac{(a_{nr}l_{ir}) \cdot (a_{rn}l_{ir})}{\lambda_i - \lambda} \end{vmatrix}$$

$$= 0.$$

whence, expanding:

$$a_{nn} - \lambda = \sum_{i=1}^{n-1} \frac{(a_{nr}l_{ir})(a_{rn}l_{ir})}{\lambda_i - \lambda}$$

or, since $A$ and $L$ are symmetric:

$$a_{nn} - \lambda = \sum_{i=1}^{n-1} P_i^2/(\lambda_i - \lambda) \qquad \ldots (7.6.15)$$

where

$$P_i = \sum_{r=1}^{n-1} a_{rn}l_{ir} \qquad \ldots (7.6.16)$$

Notice that $P_i$ is simply the sum of the products of the coefficients of the $n$th column in the matrix $A$ with the components of the $i$th characteristic vector in its normalized condition.

Morris has shown that the characteristic vector associated with any solution, $\lambda$, of equation 7.6.15 is given by:

$$\frac{\phi_{\lambda,r}}{\phi_{\lambda,n}} = - \sum_{i=1}^{n-1} l_{ir}P_i/(\lambda_i - \lambda) \ (r = 1 \ \ldots \ n-1) \quad \ldots (7.6.17)$$

where $\phi_{\lambda,r}$ is the $r$th component of the desired vector and $l_{ir}$ is the $r$th component of the characteristic vector associated with $\lambda_i$, the vector being in its normalized condition. Components, $\phi_{\lambda r}$, obtained from equation 7.6.17 have to be normalized to give the desired $l_{\lambda r}$.

The operation of the 'escalator' is as follows:

(1) Solve $a_{11} - \lambda = 0$ to give $\lambda_1$.

(2) Find $\varphi_1$ associated with $\lambda_1$.

(3) Use equation 7.6.15 to find $\lambda_1$ and $\lambda_2$ for next higher step.

(4) Find $\varphi_1$ and $\varphi_2$ using $\lambda_1$, $\lambda_2$ and equation 7.6.17.

(5) Use $\lambda_1$ and $\lambda_2$ with $\varphi_1$ and $\varphi_2$ to find $\lambda_1$, $\lambda_2$, $\lambda_3$ and so on.

The method when applied to an $n$th order matrix, leads to the intermediate calculation of about $n^2/2$ roots and $n^3/3$ components of characteristic vectors, so that the labour involved for large $n$ is considerable. The method does not appear to be well suited to operation on an automatic calculating machine, but for hand computation for reasonable values of $n$ (up to about 10) it appears very convenient, especially when the checks suggested by Morris are applied.

94

Finally, we may mention the use of the relaxation and other successive approximation techniques; these will be described in the next section in relation to the solution of simultaneous equations, but they are equally applicable to the determination both of latent roots and of characteristic vectors.

## 7.7 DESCENT METHODS FOR THE SOLUTION OF LINEAR EQUATIONS

An alternative class of methods for the solution of sets of linear simultaneous equations depends upon the geometry, in hyperspace, of an associated positive definite quadratic form.

Consider first the expression $S$ (equation 7.5.4). We have:

$$S = \tfrac{1}{2}\, \xi.A\xi - b.\xi \qquad \qquad ....(7.7.1)$$

and we have seen, in section 7.5, that the surfaces $S = $ const. represent a set of hyperellipsoids whose common centre has coordinates $(\xi_1 = x_1,\ \xi_2 = x_2\ .\ .\ .\ \xi_n = x_n)$ which define the solution of the set of simultaneous equations 7.2.1.

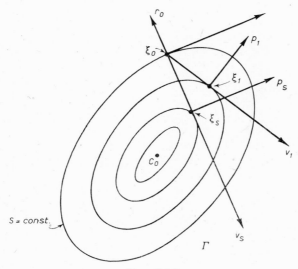

*Figure 7.7.1*

The problem of obtaining a solution of the original equations may now be reduced to the following equivalent: given *any* point $(\xi_0)$, find a process which will lead to a point $(\xi_1)$ for which the value

95

of $S$ is less than that for $(\xi_0)$. A repetition of such a process will eventually lead to some point $(\xi_n)$ from which no possible decrease in the value of $S$ is possible within the limits of accuracy assigned. The point $(\xi_n)$ is then the 'solution' of the equations.

We shall now show that an infinite number of such processes is possible, and shall discuss some of the more significant variants. First take *any* plane $\Gamma$ passing through the point $(\xi_0)$ and containing the residue vector $(r_0)$ (see section 7.5). The surfaces $S = $ const. will intersect this plane in a set of ellipses having a common centre $C_0$ (*Figure 7.7.1*).

Consider *any* vector $(v_1)$ lying in $\Gamma$ and making an angle $> \pi/2$ with the direction of $(r_0)$, then, for points $(\xi_{v_1})$ on this vector and sufficiently near to $(\xi_0)$ $S$ will have a smaller value than that at $(\xi_0)$.

The mode of procedure is clearly to fix upon some $(v_1)$ and proceed along it until $S$ no longer decreases, at $(\xi_1)$ say. To determine $(\xi_1)$ we notice that at $(\xi_1)$, $(v_1)$ and the residue vector $(r_1)$ are at right angles (notice that $r_1$ will not generally lie in $\Gamma$), and this condition may be ensured by making the vectors $v_1$ and $r_1$ have a zero scalar product.

Now any point $(\xi)$ on $(v_1)$ may be written:

$$\xi = \xi_0 + a v_1 \qquad \dots(7.7.2)$$

where $a$ is a scalar. Again, by definition:

$$r = A\xi - b \qquad (7.7.3)$$

whence

$$r_0 = A\xi_0 - b$$

and consequently:

$$r = r_0 + aA \cdot v_1 \qquad \dots(7.7.4)$$

Now at $(r_1)$ we have $(r_1 \cdot v_1) = 0$ whence, from equation 7.7.4 :

$$r_0 \cdot v_1 + a(v_1 \cdot Av_1) = 0$$

or

$$a = -(r_0 \cdot v_1)/(v_1 \cdot Av_1) \qquad \dots(7.7.5)$$

so that our end point $(\xi_1)$ is given by:

$$\xi_1 = \xi_0 - \frac{(r_0 \cdot v_1)}{(v_1 \cdot Av_1)} v_1 \qquad \dots(7.7.6)$$

So far, the vector $(v_1)$ has been completely arbitrary (except for the general condition of making an angle $> \pi/2$ with the direction of $(r_0)$), which demonstrates the truth of our original assertion regarding the infinite number of possible descent processes; we now examine some of the more practical aspects of the choice of $(v_1)$.

Three choices of $(v_1)$ have significant value:

(1) $(v_1)$ is taken parallel to one of the axes $(x_k)$.

(2) $(v_1)$ is taken in the direction of steepest descent from $(\xi_0)$—that is at $180°$ to $(r_0)$.

(3) $(v_1)$ is so chosen as to pass through $C_0$.

The first choice gives the so-called 'relaxation' method for the solution of equations, and if $(x_k)$ is the axis chosen we have:

$$\xi_1 = \xi_0 - \frac{(r_{0k} \cdot x_k)}{(x_k \cdot A x_k)} \cdot x_k$$

$$= \xi_0 - \frac{r_{0k}}{a_{kk}} \cdot \frac{x_k}{|x_k|} \qquad \ldots\ldots(7.7.7)$$

That is, the component of $\xi_0$ in the direction of the $x_k$th axis is decreased by $r_{0k}/a_{kk}$. Notice that by $r_{0k}$ we mean the residual from the $k$th equation at the first approximation.

The virtue of the relaxation method is the simplicity of the formula given in equation 7.7.7. Its defect lies in the fact that $x_k$ has to be chosen by means of some ill-defined criterion, usually by considering the equation which gives the largest residual. In actual computation a skilled operator will often operate on several values of $x_k$ at once, a process known as 'block' or 'group' relaxation. Unfortunately, a high degree of skill is required to make full use of the method in its widest sense, but, even so, the most inexperienced operator can always obtain a result eventually.

For use with an automatic computing machine it is desirable (even if not mandatory) to use a process which calls for no decision based upon the judgement of the user. Such a method is the 'steepest descent,' for which we take $v_1 = -r_0$, and thus obtain:

$$\xi_1 = \xi_0 - \frac{(r_0 \cdot r_0)}{(r_0 \cdot A r_0)} \cdot r_0 \qquad \ldots\ldots(7.7.8)$$

$$= \xi_0 - \left( \frac{\sum\limits_{i=1}^{n} r_0{}^2{}_i}{\sum\limits_{i,\,j=1}^{n} a_{ij} r_{0i} \cdot r_{0j}} \right) \cdot r_0$$

($r_{0i}$ is the $i$th component of $r_0$).

For well-conditioned equations this method is excellent; when, however, it is applied to an ill-conditioned set, the situation shown in *Figure 7.7.2* may arise, in which the minimum $\xi_1$ slightly overshoots a principal diameter of the ellipse system.

Under these circumstances the solution may oscillate from side to side of the principal diameter and, in consequence, require many

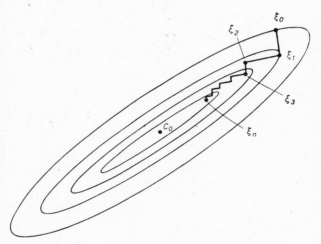

*Figure 7.7.2*

iterations to reach $C_0$. Experience has shown that more rapid convergence may be obtained, for ill-conditioned systems, by taking:

$$\xi_1 = \xi_0 - \frac{\cdot 9(r_0 . r_0)}{(r_0 . A r_0)} . r_0 \qquad \dots (7.7.9)$$

for, say, four iterations and then making a single application of the exact formula 7.7.8.

The third method of procedure may be derived as follows. Suppose that, at the previous stage of the process, there was derived a vector $v_n$ and a point on it, $\xi_n$, such that $(r_n . v_n) = 0$, just as was done in the previous derivations. We now have a pair of orthogonal vectors $v_n$ and $r_n$. Consider the system of ellipses $S = $ const. *in the plane of* $v_n$ *and* $r_n$ shown in *Figure 7.7.3*.

Now *any* vector in the plane $\Gamma$ containing $r_n$ and $v_n$ can be written:

$$v_{n+1} = a r_n + \beta v_n \qquad \dots (7.7.10)$$

98

If $C_{n+1}$ is the centre of the ellipses $S = $ const. then, at $C_{n+1}$, the residue vector $\boldsymbol{r}_{n+1}$ is perpendicular to $\Gamma$, and consequently to *both* $\boldsymbol{r}_n$ and $\boldsymbol{v}_n$, so that $(\boldsymbol{r}_{n+1}.\boldsymbol{r}_n) = (\boldsymbol{r}_{n+1}.\boldsymbol{v}_n) = 0$.

Again:

$$\boldsymbol{\xi}_{n+1} = \boldsymbol{\xi}_n + \boldsymbol{v}_{n+1} = \boldsymbol{\xi}_n + a\boldsymbol{r}_n + \beta\boldsymbol{v}_n \qquad \ldots(7.7.11)$$

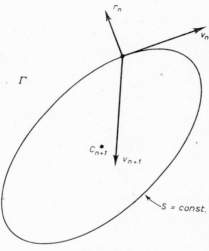

*Figure 7.7.3*

And since

$$\boldsymbol{r} = A\boldsymbol{\xi} - \boldsymbol{b}.$$

$$\boldsymbol{r}_{n+1} = \boldsymbol{r}_n + A(\boldsymbol{\xi}_{n+1} - \boldsymbol{\xi}_n) = \boldsymbol{r}_n + aA\boldsymbol{r}_n + \beta A\boldsymbol{v}_n \quad ..(7.7.12)$$

But, from the orthogonality conditions:

$$(\boldsymbol{r}_n.\boldsymbol{r}_{n+1}) = 0 = (\boldsymbol{r}_n.\boldsymbol{r}_n) + a(\boldsymbol{r}_n.A\boldsymbol{r}_n) + \beta(\boldsymbol{r}_n.A\boldsymbol{v}_n)$$

$$(\boldsymbol{v}_n.\boldsymbol{r}_{n+1}) = 0 = \qquad\qquad a(\boldsymbol{v}_n.A\boldsymbol{r}_n) + \beta(\boldsymbol{v}_n.A\boldsymbol{v}_n)$$

($\boldsymbol{v}_n$ and $\boldsymbol{r}_n$ are *ab initio* orthogonal so that $(\boldsymbol{r}_n.\boldsymbol{v}_n) = 0$)

whence:

$$\left.\begin{array}{l} a = \dfrac{(\boldsymbol{r}_n.\boldsymbol{r}_n)(\boldsymbol{v}_n.A\boldsymbol{v}_n)}{(\boldsymbol{v}_n.A\boldsymbol{r}_n)^2 - (\boldsymbol{r}_n.A\boldsymbol{r}_n)(\boldsymbol{v}_n.A\boldsymbol{v}_n)} \\[3mm] \beta = \dfrac{-(\boldsymbol{r}_n.\boldsymbol{r}_n)(\boldsymbol{v}_n.A\boldsymbol{r}_n)}{(\boldsymbol{v}_n.A\boldsymbol{r}_n)^2 - (\boldsymbol{r}_n.A\boldsymbol{r}_n)(\boldsymbol{v}_n.A\boldsymbol{v}_n)} \end{array}\right\} \quad \ldots(7.7.13)$$

The set of formulae (7.7.11–7.7.13) may be regarded as the two-dimensional analogue of the steepest descent formula (7.7.8); they have the advantage that the solution is obtained in exactly the same number of steps as the equations have variables. This is due to the fact that each new steepest descent vector is orthogonal to all previous descent vectors. Thus, since the hyperspace has only $n$ dimensions, only $n$ such vectors exist and the process is completed at the $n$th vector. In this respect the method is closely related to the Gram–Schmidt orthogonalisation procedure.

### 7.8 A CAUTIONARY PARAGRAPH

We have mentioned, in various places, the fact that the residue criterion based upon:

$$S = \tfrac{1}{2}\boldsymbol{\xi}.A\boldsymbol{\xi} - \boldsymbol{b}.\boldsymbol{\xi}$$

assumes that the matrix $A$ is both symmetric *and* positive definite. It is worth reminding the potential user of 7.7.6–7.8.3 that these equations must only be used when $A$ is known to obey these conditions.

A cautionary example is provided by the equations:

$$x_1 - 2x_2 + 3x_3 + x_4 = 3$$
$$- 2x_1 + x_2 - 2x_3 - x_4 = - 4$$
$$3x_1 - 2x_2 + x_3 + 5x_4 = 7$$
$$x_1 - x_2 + 5x_3 + 3x_4 = 8$$

for which the solution is (1, 1, 1, 1). An application of equation 7.7.8 from the starting point $\boldsymbol{\xi}_0$ (0,0,0,0) for which

$$\boldsymbol{r}_0 = (- 3, + 4, - 7, - 8)$$

leads to

$$\boldsymbol{\xi}_1 = (+ \cdot 34, - \cdot 45, + \cdot 79, + \cdot 90)$$

with

$$\boldsymbol{r}_1 = (+ 1 \cdot 51, + \cdot 39, + \cdot 21, - \cdot 56)$$

which is quite satisfactory $((\boldsymbol{r}_0.\boldsymbol{r}_0) = 138, (\boldsymbol{r}_1.\boldsymbol{r}_1) = 2.7.8)$ A further application of the procedure leads, however, to co-ordinate changes of large magnitude $O(10)$ and to an increase in $(\boldsymbol{r}_2.\boldsymbol{r}_2)$ to $1475 \cdot 49$!

The reason for this behaviour is clear, since when $A$ is not positive-definite, the expression $S$ represents in general hyperelliptic-hyperboloids, and the geometrical assumptions made in section 7.7 no longer hold.

## 7.9 DESCENT METHODS BASED ON $R^2$

By means of the positive definite form:

$$R^2 = (\boldsymbol{r} \cdot \boldsymbol{r}) = (A\boldsymbol{\xi} - \boldsymbol{b})(A\boldsymbol{\xi} - \boldsymbol{b}) \qquad \ldots (7.9.1)$$

we may construct the analogues of the descent formulae previously derived for $S$, but with the advantage that, since $R^2$ is known to be positive definite, this limitation on $A$ is removed. As a penalty for this the formulae are, of course, slightly more complicated.

We again choose an arbitrary vector $(\boldsymbol{v}_1)$ and seek to find the least value of $R^2$ when some multiple $(a\boldsymbol{v}_1)$ is added to $\boldsymbol{\xi}$. Thus:

$$R^2_{(\xi+av)} = [A(\boldsymbol{\xi} + a\boldsymbol{v}_1) - \boldsymbol{b}] \cdot [A(\xi + a\boldsymbol{v}_1) - \boldsymbol{b}]$$
$$= (A\boldsymbol{\xi} \cdot A\boldsymbol{\xi}) + a^2(A\boldsymbol{v}_1 \cdot A\boldsymbol{v}_1) + 2a[(A\boldsymbol{\xi} \cdot A\boldsymbol{v}_1) - (\boldsymbol{b} \cdot A\boldsymbol{v}_1)]$$
$$- 2(\boldsymbol{b} \cdot A\boldsymbol{\xi}) + (\boldsymbol{b} \cdot \boldsymbol{b})$$

At the minimum we have

$$\frac{dR^2}{da} = 0$$

whence:

$$a(A\boldsymbol{v}_1 \cdot A\boldsymbol{v}_1) + [A\boldsymbol{v}_1 \cdot (A\boldsymbol{\xi} - \boldsymbol{b})] = 0$$

or

$$a = -(A\boldsymbol{v}_1 \cdot \boldsymbol{r}_0)/(A\boldsymbol{v}_1 \cdot A\boldsymbol{v}_1)$$

which is easily shown to give a *minimum* value for $R^2$. It follows that the correction formula corresponding to equation 7.7.6 is:

$$\boldsymbol{\xi}_1 = \boldsymbol{\xi}_0 - \frac{(\boldsymbol{r}_0 A \cdot \boldsymbol{v}_1)}{(A\boldsymbol{v}_1 \cdot A\boldsymbol{v}_1)} \cdot \boldsymbol{v}_1 \qquad \ldots (7.9.2)$$

Just as in the previous case we may choose $\boldsymbol{v}_1$ in a number of ways, if it is taken parallel to an axis $\boldsymbol{x}_k$, we obtain the relaxation formula:

$$\boldsymbol{\xi}_1 = \boldsymbol{\xi}_0 - \frac{(\boldsymbol{r}_0 \cdot A\boldsymbol{x}_k)}{(A\boldsymbol{x}_k \cdot A\boldsymbol{x}_k)} \cdot \boldsymbol{x}_k \qquad \ldots (7.9.3)$$

or, in terms of the matrix elements

$$\boldsymbol{\xi}_1 = \boldsymbol{\xi}_0 - \frac{\sum\limits_{i=1}^{n} t_{0i} a_{ik}}{\sum\limits_{i=1}^{n} a_{ik}^2} \boldsymbol{x}_k$$

The steepest descent method is obtained by choosing $(\boldsymbol{v}_1)$ to have the direction in which $R^2$, in the region of $\boldsymbol{\xi}_0$, is changing most rapidly. This is, in vector notation:

$$\boldsymbol{v}_1 = -\operatorname{grad} R^2 \qquad \ldots (7.9.4)$$

101

where the $k$th component of $\boldsymbol{v}_1$, $v_{1k}$, is given by:

$$v_1 k = - \frac{\partial}{\partial \xi_k} (R^2). \qquad \dots (7.9.5)$$

Now an inspection of the quadratic form of $R^2$, given in equation 7.5.3, shows that:

$$\frac{\partial}{\partial \xi_k} (R^2) = \sum_{i=1}^{n} 2a_{ik} \sum_{j=1}^{n} (a_{ij}\xi_j - b_i)$$

$$= \sum_{i=1}^{n} 2a_{ik} r_i \qquad \dots (7.9.6)$$

whence

$$\text{grad } (R^2) = 2A' \boldsymbol{r} \qquad \dots (7.9.7)$$

where $A'$ is the transpose of $A$ and $\boldsymbol{r}$ is the residue vector. We thus obtain

$$\boldsymbol{\xi}_1 = \boldsymbol{\xi}_0 - \frac{(\boldsymbol{r}_0 . AA' \boldsymbol{r}_0)}{[(AA'\boldsymbol{r}_0).(AA'\boldsymbol{r}_0)]} . A' \boldsymbol{r}_0 \qquad \dots (7.9.8)$$

which is the analogue of equation 7.7.8.

Finally, we may find the minimum of $R^2$ over a two dimensional plane containing any pair of non-parallel vectors. It is convenient to choose these to be (grad $R^2$) at $\boldsymbol{\xi}_n$ and the vector $\boldsymbol{v}_n$ used to derive $\boldsymbol{\xi}_n$ from $\boldsymbol{\xi}_{n-1}$—this pair being orthogonal. Thus:

$$\boldsymbol{\xi}_{n+1} = \boldsymbol{\xi}_n + \boldsymbol{v}_{n+1} \qquad \dots (7.9.9.)$$

$$\boldsymbol{v}_{n+1} = a(\text{grad } R^2)_n + \beta \boldsymbol{v}_n = 2aA'\boldsymbol{r}_n + \beta \boldsymbol{v}_n \qquad \dots (7.9.10)$$

where $a$ and $\beta$ are determined so as to make $R^2(\xi_{n+1})$ a minimum. Using 7.9.9, 7.9.10 and the definition of $R^2$ 7.9.1, we have:

$$R^2(\xi_{n+1}) = (A\boldsymbol{\xi}_{n+1} - \boldsymbol{b}) . (A\boldsymbol{\xi}_{n+1} - \boldsymbol{b})$$

$$= [A\boldsymbol{\xi}_n - \boldsymbol{b} + aA(\text{grad } R^2)_n + \beta A\boldsymbol{v}_n].$$

$$[A\boldsymbol{\xi}_n - \boldsymbol{b} + aA(\text{grad } R^2) + \beta A\boldsymbol{v}_n]$$

$$= (\boldsymbol{r}_n + 2aAA'\boldsymbol{r}_n + \beta A\boldsymbol{v}_n) . (\boldsymbol{r}_n + 2aAA'\boldsymbol{r}_n + \beta A\boldsymbol{v}_n)$$

Now we require, for a minimum:

$$\frac{\partial R^2}{\partial a} = \frac{\partial R^2}{\partial \beta} = 0$$

whence:

$$4AA'\boldsymbol{r}_n \cdot (\boldsymbol{r}_n + 2\alpha AA'\boldsymbol{r}_n + \beta A\boldsymbol{v}_n) = 0$$

$$2A\boldsymbol{v}_n \cdot (\boldsymbol{r}_n + 2\alpha AA'\boldsymbol{r}_n + \beta A\boldsymbol{v}_n) = 0$$

giving:

$$\left.\begin{array}{l} 2\alpha = \\ \dfrac{(\boldsymbol{r}_n . A\boldsymbol{v}_n)(A\boldsymbol{v}_n . AA'\boldsymbol{r}_n) - (\boldsymbol{r}_n . AA'\boldsymbol{r}_n)(A\boldsymbol{v}_n . A\boldsymbol{v}_n)}{(AA'\boldsymbol{r}_n . AA'\boldsymbol{r}_n)(A\boldsymbol{v}_n . A\boldsymbol{v}_n) - (A\boldsymbol{v}_n . AA'\boldsymbol{r}_n)(A\boldsymbol{v}_n . AA'\boldsymbol{r}_n)} \\[2mm] \beta = \\ \dfrac{(\boldsymbol{r}_n . AA'\boldsymbol{r}_n)(A\boldsymbol{v}_n . AA'\boldsymbol{r}_n) - (\boldsymbol{r}_n . A\boldsymbol{v}_n)(AA'\boldsymbol{r}_n . AA'\boldsymbol{r}_n)}{(AA'\boldsymbol{r}_n . AA'\boldsymbol{r}_n)(A\boldsymbol{v}_n . A\boldsymbol{v}_n) - (A\boldsymbol{v}_n . AA'\boldsymbol{r}_n)(A\boldsymbol{v}_n . AA'\boldsymbol{r}_n)} \end{array}\right\} \dots (7.9.11)$$

These formulae are far too cumbersome for use by a human computor, but may possibly find application with an automatic digital calculator.

## 7.10 A NUMERICAL EXAMPLE

To illustrate the merits (and otherwise) of the preceding methods, we give their application to the set of equations proposed in section 7.8. It has already been pointed out that methods based upon $S$ will fail for this set of equations since $A$ is not positive definite.

Using the relaxation technique of section 7.9, based on $R^2$ and the initial vector $\boldsymbol{\xi}_0 = (0, 0, 0, 0)$, we obtain *Table 7.10.1* by a direct application of equation 7.9.3.

*Table 7.10.1   Relaxation on set of equations of section 7.8*

| $k$ | $\xi_0$ | $r_0$ | $\xi_1$ | $r_1$ | $\xi_2$ | $r_2$ | $\xi_3$ | $r_3$ | $\xi_4$ | $r_4$ |
|---|---|---|---|---|---|---|---|---|---|---|
| 1 | 0 | $-3$ | 0 | $-1\cdot17$ | 0 | $+\cdot231$ | 0 | $-\cdot633$ | 0 | $-\cdot135$ |
| 2 | 0 | $+4$ | 0 | $+2\cdot17$ | 0 | $+1\cdot235$ | $\cdot432$ | $+1\cdot667$ | $\cdot432$ | $+1\cdot335$ |
| 3 | 0 | $-7$ | 0 | $+2\cdot17$ | $\cdot466$ | $+2\cdot631$ | $\cdot466$ | $+1\cdot767$ | $\cdot632$ | $+1\cdot933$ |
| 4 | 0 | $-8$ | $1\cdot83$ | $-2\cdot50$ | $1\cdot833$ | $-\cdot171$ | $1\cdot833$ | $-\cdot603$ | $1\cdot833$ | $+\cdot227$ |
| | $(\boldsymbol{r}_0.\boldsymbol{r}_0) = 138$ | | $(\boldsymbol{r}_1.\boldsymbol{r}_1) = 17\cdot00$ | | $(\boldsymbol{r}_2.\boldsymbol{r}_2) = 8\cdot53$ | | $(\boldsymbol{r}_3.\boldsymbol{r}_3) = 6\cdot67$ | | $(\boldsymbol{r}_4.\boldsymbol{r}_4) = 5\cdot59$ | |

The residues which indicate the value of $k$ (*i.e.* the co-ordinate number) in equation 7.9.3 have been underlined. We notice that it is not always possible to select the co-ordinate of largest residual at each step since, as happens in $k = 4$ of $\boldsymbol{r}$, a relaxation with respect

103

to this vector has just been performed so that no further improvement can be produced by further alteration to $x_4$ at this stage.

Next we give the results of the same number of steepest descents applied to the same set of equations.

Table 7.10.2.  Steepest descent

| $\xi_0$ $r_0$ $(A'r_0)$ | $\xi_1$ $r_1$ $(A'r_1)$ | $\xi_2$ $r_2$ $(A'r_2)$ | $\xi_3$ $r_3$ $(A'r_3)$ | $\xi_4$ $r_4$ |
|---|---|---|---|---|
| 0 −3 −40 | +·488 +1·416 +·230 | +·392 +·488 +·605 | +·384 +·366 −·603 | +·426 +·478 |
| 0 +4 +32 | −·390 +·267 −1·863 | +·391 +·612 −1·292 | +·409 +·709 −·290 | +·429 +·578 |
| 0 −7 −64 | +·781 +·050 −·246 | +·884 +·413 +1·163 | +·868 +·182 −·623 | +·911 +·216 |
| 0 −8 −66 | +·805 −·802 −1·007 | +1·227 +·102 +2·247 | +1·196 −·097 +·276 | +1·177 +·083 |
| $(r_0.r_0) = 138$ | $(r_1.r_1) = 2\cdot72$ | $(r_2.r_2) = \cdot79$ | $(r_3.r_3) = \cdot68$ | $(r_4.r_4) = \cdot62$ |
| $\xi_1 =$ | $\xi_2 =$ | $\xi_3 =$ | $\xi_4 =$ | |
| $\xi_0 - \cdot0122(A'r_0)$ | $\xi_1 + \cdot419(A'r_1)$ | $\xi_2 + \cdot0136(A'r_2)$ | $\xi_3 + \cdot069(A'r_3)$ | |

It will be noticed that, initially, the convergence of the steepest descent process is faster than that of the relaxation, but that from $\xi_3$ there is an oscillation of the type indicated in *Figure* 7.7.2. This is to be expected in the present set of equations which are quite ill-conditioned.

Finally, *Table 7.10.3* shows the results of four descent to ellipse centre applications based on equations 7.9.9–7.9.11. Since $\xi_1$ is the same as a normal steepest descent and is given in *Table 7.10.2* and since $v_1 = (A'r_0)$ and $r_1$ are also given in the latter table, we do not reproduce them here.

Table 7.10.3

$$(A'r_1) = \begin{bmatrix} + & \cdot230 \\ -1 & \cdot863 \\ - & \cdot246 \\ -1 & \cdot007 \end{bmatrix} \quad (AA'r_1) = \begin{bmatrix} +2 & \cdot211 \\ - & \cdot824 \\ - & \cdot865 \\ -2 & \cdot158 \end{bmatrix} \quad Av_1 \,(=AA'r_0) = \begin{bmatrix} - & 362 \\ + & 306 \\ - & 578 \\ - & 590 \end{bmatrix}$$

$$(r_1.AA'r_1) = +4\cdot60, \quad (AA'r_1.AA'r_1) = +10\cdot973,$$

$$(r_1.Av_1) = +13\cdot39, \quad (Av_1.AA'r_1) = +720\cdot67,$$

$$(Av_1.Av_1) = +906864$$

whence:

$$2a = - \cdot441, \quad \beta = + \cdot000336$$

$$v_2 = \begin{bmatrix} - & \cdot114 \\ + & \cdot833 \\ + & \cdot086 \\ + & \cdot422 \end{bmatrix} \quad \xi_2 = \begin{bmatrix} + & \cdot374 \\ + & \cdot443 \\ + & \cdot867 \\ +1 & \cdot227 \end{bmatrix} \quad r_2 = \begin{bmatrix} + & \cdot316 \\ + & \cdot734 \\ + & \cdot238 \\ - & \cdot053 \end{bmatrix} \quad (r_2.r_2) = \cdot70$$

In a similar manner we obtain:

$$\boldsymbol{v}_3 = \begin{bmatrix} +\cdot080 \\ +\cdot136 \\ +\cdot109 \\ -\cdot074 \end{bmatrix} \quad \boldsymbol{\xi}_3 = \begin{bmatrix} +\cdot454 \\ +\cdot579 \\ +\cdot976 \\ +1\cdot153 \end{bmatrix} \quad \boldsymbol{r}_3 = \begin{bmatrix} +\cdot377 \\ +\cdot566 \\ -\cdot055 \\ +\cdot214 \end{bmatrix} \quad (\boldsymbol{r}_3 \cdot \boldsymbol{r}_3) = \cdot51$$

and:

$$\boldsymbol{v}_4 = \begin{bmatrix} +\cdot097 \\ +\cdot102 \\ -\cdot005 \\ -\cdot057 \end{bmatrix} \quad \boldsymbol{\xi}_4 = \begin{bmatrix} +\cdot551 \\ +\cdot681 \\ +\cdot971 \\ +1\cdot096 \end{bmatrix} \quad \boldsymbol{r}_4 = \begin{bmatrix} +\cdot198 \\ +\cdot541 \\ -\cdot258 \\ +\cdot013 \end{bmatrix} \quad (\boldsymbol{r}_4 \cdot \boldsymbol{r}_4) = \cdot40$$

## 7.11 MATRIX 'ROTATION' AND LATENT ROOTS

A particularly simple and effective method for determining the latent roots of a matrix and, at the same time, the latent vectors has been suggested by VON NEUMANN and GOLDSTINE [10]. It is particularly suitable for use on an automatic computing machine.

The basis of the method is the fact that (see section 7.5) the latent roots of a matrix $A$ are simply the squares of the inverse principal axes of the quadratic form hyper-ellipsoid:

$$\sum_{i,\,j=1}^{n} a_{ij} x_i \cdot x_j = 1 \ (a_{ij} = a_{ji}) \qquad \ldots\ldots(7.11.1)$$

Let $B$ be an orthonormal transformation matrix such that:

$$\boldsymbol{z} = B \cdot \boldsymbol{x} \qquad (B \cdot B' = I) \qquad \ldots\ldots(7.11.2)$$

transforms equation 7.11.1 into:

$$\sum_{i=1}^{n} \lambda_i z_i{}^2 = 1 \qquad \ldots\ldots(7.11.3)$$

then the $\lambda_i$ are the required latent roots of $A$ and the rows of $B$ are the associated latent vectors. Furthermore it is well known [11] that if $C$ is *any* orthonormal transformation matrix defining:

$$\boldsymbol{y} = C' \cdot \boldsymbol{x} \qquad (C \cdot C' = I)$$

then the matrix of the transformed quadratic form, $T$, corresponding to 7.11.1 is

$$T = C' \cdot A \cdot C \qquad \ldots\ldots(7.11.4)$$

Also the sum of the squares of the diagonal elements of $T$ is greatest when $C = B$, that is when the transformed matrix is diagonal.

H

The von Neumann–Goldstine process determines $B$ as the limit of a sequence of simple rotations involving only two of the axes $(x_i)$ at a time, the idea being to eliminate the largest $(a_{ij})$ from $A$ $(i \neq j)$ and then the next largest, and so on.

Suppose that $a_{r,\,s}$ $(= a_{s,\,r})$ is the largest off-diagonal element of $A$, and that we seek to eliminate it by a rotation of axes through an angle $\theta_1$ in the plane of $(x_r, x_s)$. The equations of transformation are:

$$\left.\begin{aligned} x_r &= \cos\theta_1 . y_r - \sin\theta_1 . y_s \\ x_s &= \sin\theta_1 . y_r + \cos\theta_1 . y_s \\ x_i &= y_i \qquad (i \neq r, s) \end{aligned}\right\} \qquad \ldots (7.11.5)$$

and substitution in equation 7.11.1 gives for the coefficient of $(y_r, y_s)$

$$2\cos\theta_1 \sin\theta_1 (a_{rr} - a_{ss}) - 2(\cos^2\theta_1 - \sin^2\theta_1)a_{rs}$$

so that to eliminate this we take:

$$\tan 2\theta_1 = 2a_{rs}/(a_{rr} - a_{ss}) \qquad \ldots (7.11.6)$$

which defines the angle of rotation $(\theta_1)$.

Now the transformation matrix $C_1$ say, corresponding to equation 7.11.5 is:

$$C_1 = \begin{bmatrix} 1 & 0 & 0 & 0 & \ldots & & & & & & & 0 \\ 0 & 1 & 0 & 0 & \ldots & & & & & & & 0 \\ & & & & \ldots & & & & & & & \\ 0 & 0 & 0 & 0 & \ldots & \cos\theta_1 & 0 & 0 & \ldots & 0 & -\sin\theta_1 & \ldots & 0 \\ 0 & 0 & 0 & 0 & \ldots & 0 & 1 & 0 & \ldots & 0 & 0 & \ldots & 0 \\ & & & & \ldots & & & & & & & \\ 0 & 0 & 0 & 0 & \ldots & \sin\theta_1 & 0 & 0 & \ldots & 0 & \cos\theta_1 & \ldots & 0 \\ 0 & 0 & 0 & 0 & \ldots & 0 & 0 & 0 & \ldots & 0 & 0 & 1 & 0 \\ & & & & \ldots & & & & & & & \\ 0 & 0 & 0 & 0 & \ldots & & & & & & & 1 \end{bmatrix} \ldots (7.11.7)$$

*r*th row →    *s*th row →

↑ *r*th column    ↑ *s*th column

and it is easily proved, by direct substitution, that the sum of the squares of the elements on the diagonal of the transformed matrix:

$$T_1 = C_1'AC_1$$

is simply:

$$2a_{rs}^2 + \sum_{i=1}^{n} a_{ii}^2 \qquad \ldots (7.11.8)$$

which shows, since it is greater than $\overset{n}{\underset{i=1}{\Sigma}} a_{ii}^2$, that $T_1$ is nearer (in some sense) to the required diagonal matrix than was $A$.

A repetition of the above process, with the largest off-diagonal element of $T_1$ will lead to a new transformed matrix $T_2$, thus:

$$T_1 = C_1'AC_1$$
$$T_2 = C_2'T_1C_2$$
$$T_3 = C_3'T_2C_3$$
$$\cdots \cdots \cdots$$
$$T_m = C_m'T_{m-1}C_m$$
$$etc.$$

where $T_m$ tends to the matrix $(\lambda_i)$ and the continued product $C_1.C_2.C_3 \ldots$ tends to the diagonalizing matrix $B$ defined in equations 7.11.2 and 7.11.3.

All of the operations involved in the above process are extremely simple, and experience has shown that convergence is rapid. The sole disadvantage, from the point of high speed automatic computors, lies in the fact that the largest off-diagonal element has to be determined at each stage, and this involves an examination of all of the matrix elements.


## 7.12 MONTE CARLO METHODS

The somewhat intriguing title of this section is now applied to methods of numerical analysis which make use of the theory of Games [12]. The suggestion that such methods might be applicable appears to have been due, originally, to von Neumann and Ulam; but statisticians have since claimed that the techniques are simply those of small sample analysis and, as such, have been known for a considerable time.

Monte Carlo methods appear to be applicable to most problems involving *linear* operators, and the present example of a technique for determining the elements of an inverse matrix, was the first actual procedure to be worked out. The reader familiar with the game of solitaire will recognize the basic similarity.

Suppose that it is desired to form the inverse of a matrix $A$, of order $n$. We first form the matrix:

$$E = I - A \qquad \ldots(7.12.1)$$

and assume, for the present purpose, that the relation:

$$|1 - \lambda_M(A)| = |\lambda_M(E)| < 1 \qquad (7.12.2)$$

holds, $\lambda_M$ being the greatest of the latent roots in the respective matrices. Now subject to equation 7.12.2 it can be shown [13] that:

$$A^{-1} = (I - E)^{-1} = I + E + E^2 \ldots + E^k + \ldots = \sum_{k=0}^{\infty} E^k$$
$$\ldots (7.12.3)$$

whence, formally,

$$(A^{-1})_{ij} = \sum_{k=0}^{\infty} (E^k)_{ij} \qquad \ldots (7.12.4)$$

where $(\ )_{ij}$ represents the element of the $i$th row and $j$th column of the matrix $(\ )$.

We now consider a 'random walk' of the following type. Let $P_1$, $P_2 \ldots P_n$ be a set of $(n)$ points, then we start from any point $P_i$ and jump from point to point in such a way that the probability of a direct move from $P_r$ to $P_s$ is $p_{rs}$. At any point $P_r$ there is a probability $p_r = 1 - \sum_{s=1}^{n} p_{rs}$ that the walk ends there. Now, at each transition $P_r \to P_s$, there is a transition value $v_{rs}$ defined by:

$$v_{rs} \cdot p_{rs} = e_{rs} \qquad \ldots (7.12.5)$$

where $e_{rs}$ is the corresponding element of the matrix $E$. If we define the value of the 'walk' to be:

$$W_{ij} = \begin{cases} 0 \text{ if the walk ends at any point } P_k \text{ where } k \neq j \\ v_{i_0 i_1} \cdot v_{i_1 i_2} \ldots v_{i_m k} \cdot p_j^{-1} \text{ when the walk ends at } P_j \end{cases}$$

where the initial value is unity and the points of the walk are $P_{i_0} P_{i_1} \ldots P_{i_m}, P_j$, then the expected value can be shown [14, 15] to be $(A^{-1})_{ij}$; that is the $(ij)$th element of the required inverse of $(A)$. This follows from the relation:

(Expectation)$_{ij}$

$$= \delta_{ij} + \sum_{k=1}^{\infty} \sum_{i_1=1}^{n} \sum_{i_2=1}^{n} \ldots \sum_{i_{k-1}=1}^{n} e_{ii_1} \cdot e_{i_1 i_2} \ldots e_{i_{k-1} j}$$
$$\ldots (\text{from } 7.12.5)$$

$$= I_{ij} + \sum_{k=1}^{\infty} (E^k)_{ij} = \sum_{k=0}^{\infty} (E^k)_{ij} = (A^{-1})_{ij}$$
$$\ldots (\text{from } 7.12.4)$$

where $\delta_{ij}$ is the Kronecker delta function, and arises from the fact that when $i = j$ there is a probability $p_i$ that the walk will *at once* stop at $P_i$, and that the transition value is, in this case, $p_j^{-1}$.

### REFERENCES

[1] PAIGE, L. J. and TAUSSKY, O., 'Simultaneous Linear Equations and the Determination of Eigenvalues,' Bureau of Standards Applied Mathematics Series, No. 29, Washington (1953)

[2] FERRAR, W. L., 'Algebra, a Textbook of Determinants, Matrices and Algebraic Forms,' Oxford (1941)

[3] BARGMANN, V., MURRAY, F. J. and VON NEUMANN, J., 'Solution of Linear Systems of High Order, Princeton (1946)

[4] TODD, J. 'Simultaneous Linear Equations and the Determination of Eigenvalues,' p. 113. *A.M.S.* 29, Washington (1953)

[5] FERRAR, W. L., 'Algebra,' Theorem 49, p. 153. Oxford (1941)

[6] MORRIS, J., *Phil. Mag.* (7) 37 (1946) 106

[7] RICHARDSON, L. F., *Phil. Trans. Roy. Soc.*, 242 (1950), 439

[8] MORRIS, J. and HEAD, J. W., *Phil. Mag.*, 35 (1944), 735

[9] MORRIS, J., 'The Escalator Method in Engineering Vibration Problems,' Wiley, New York (1947)

[10] VON NEUMANN, J. and GOLDSTINE, H. H., *Private commun.* (1950)

[11] FERRAR, W. L., 'Algebra, a Textbook of Determinants, Matrices and Algebraic forms,' Oxford (1941)

[12] VON NEUMANN, J. and MORGANSTERN, O., 'The Theory of Games,' Princeton (1947)

[13] COURANT, R. and HILBERT, D., 'Methods of Mathematical Physics,' vol. 1, Interscience, New York (1953)

[14] FORSYTH, G. E. and LEIBLER, R. A., *Math. Tab., Wash.*, IV (1950), 127

[15] WASOW, W. R., *ibid.*, VI (1952), 78

# 8

# PARTIAL DIFFERENTIAL EQUATIONS

## 8.1 DEFINITIONS AND SCOPE

IN THIS chapter we shall be concerned with the numerical solution of certain simple types of partial differential equation. In the past, it is true to say that only the linear types have received much attention, chiefly because of the technical difficulties of the calculations involved. The present era of high speed automatic digital computors is doing much to remedy this, but the storage capacity of these machines is still too limited to make possible an attack on the more complex types of equation.

The partial differential equations of mathematical physics often fall into the form:

$$A\frac{\partial^2 W}{\partial x^2} + 2H\frac{\partial^2 W}{\partial x \partial y} + B\frac{\partial^2 W}{\partial y^2} + 2G\frac{\partial^2 W}{\partial x \partial z} + 2F\frac{\partial^2 W}{\partial y \partial z} + C\frac{\partial^2 W}{\partial z^2} = I$$

$$\dots (8.1.1)$$

in which $A, B, C, F, G, H, I$ may be constant (including zero) or functions of $(x, y, z)$, $\left(\dfrac{\partial}{\partial x}, \dfrac{\partial}{\partial y}, \dfrac{\partial}{\partial z}\right)$. Thus, when

$$A = B = C = 1, \quad H = G = F = I = 0$$

we obtain the Laplace equation:

$$\frac{\partial^2 W}{\partial x^2} + \frac{\partial^2 W}{\partial y^2} + \frac{\partial^2 W}{\partial z^2} = 0$$

if $I = $ const. 8.1.1 becomes the Poisson equation, and if $W$ is a function of $x$ and $y$ only, these equations reduce to the well-known two dimensional forms. In two dimensions, if

$$H^2 - AB > 0$$

the equation is said to be *hyperbolic*, if

$$H^2 - AB = 0$$

*parabolic*, and if

$$H^2 - AB < 0$$

*elliptic*. These terms are borrowed from the analogous quadratic forms, and are related to convenient subdivisions into which the

110

solutions naturally fall. The methods of solution resemble strongly those which have been discussed for ordinary differential equations, especially in their relation to the boundary conditions which the solution has to satisfy. We shall examine, first, simple equations of parabolic and hyperbolic type which are similar in the nature of their solutions to one-point boundary condition equations in the simpler case of ordinary differential equations.

## 8.2 PARABOLIC AND HYPERBOLIC EQUATIONS IN TWO VARIABLES

The classical example of a parabolic equation represents the one-dimensional flow of heat in a conducting wire, or the diffusion of a liquid or gas along a porous tube, and a study of this equation, from the finite difference viewpoint, lead Courant, Friedrichs and Lewy to their fundamental theorem on the relationship between the space and time intervals. The usual form of the diffusion equation is:

$$c^2 \frac{\partial^2 W}{\partial x^2} = \frac{\partial W}{\partial t} \qquad \ldots (8.2.1)$$

with initial condition $W = f(x)$ at $t = 0$, and *two* boundary conditions of the general type $W + a \dfrac{\partial W}{\partial x} = b(t)$ at $x = l_1$, and $x = l_2$, say.

We will assume that the equation is to be solved by replacing both of the derivatives by finite difference approximations at intervals $(\delta x)$ and $(\delta t)$ respectively. Using the simple relationships:

$$\frac{\partial^2 W}{\partial x^2} \simeq \frac{\delta^2 W}{(\delta x)^2} = \frac{W(x + \delta x, t) - 2W(x, b) + W(x - \delta x, t)}{(\delta x)^2}$$
$$\ldots (8.2.2)$$

and: 
$$\frac{\partial W}{\partial t} \simeq \frac{\Delta W}{(\delta t)} = \frac{W(x, t + \delta t) - W(x, t)}{(\delta t)} \qquad \ldots (8.2.3)$$

we obtain, by substitution in equation 8.2.1:

$$W(x, t + \delta t) \simeq \gamma W(x + \delta x, t) + (1 - 2\gamma) W(x, t) + \gamma W(x - \delta x, t)$$
$$\ldots (8.2.4)$$

where 
$$\gamma = c^2 \delta t / (\delta x)^2 \qquad \ldots (8.2.5)$$

Equation 8.2.4 enables $W(x, n\delta t)$ to be calculated for any value of $n$ by successive build up via

$$W[x, (n - 1)\delta t)] \ W[x,(n - 2)\delta t] \ \ldots \ W(x, 0).$$

If the value of $W(x, t)$ is required at some particular time $T$ we must take:

$$n\delta t = T$$

which may be considered to determine the interval $(\delta t)$ in terms of the total time $T$ and the number of steps $(n)$ required. Thus:

$$\gamma = c^2 T / n(\delta x)^2$$

In a like manner $(\delta x)$ must be an integral sub-multiple of the length of the $(x)$ boundary.

The important contribution of Courant and his co-workers was to show that it is not possible to choose $(\delta x)$ and $(\delta t)$ arbitrarily if a stable solution is to be obtained. By considering the difference, $\epsilon(x, t)$, between the solution of the *differential* equation 8.2.1 and that of the *difference* equation 8.2.4, it was shown that this error is bounded only if $\gamma \leqslant \frac{1}{2}$, and that it grows exponentially with $t$ when $\gamma > \frac{1}{2}$. It follows that, when solving an equation of the general type 8.2.1, $(\delta t)$ and $(\delta x)$ must be so chosen as to make $c^2\delta t/(\delta x)^2 \leqslant \frac{1}{2}$ and that, in consequence, unlimited decrease in the value of $(\delta x)$ will not lead to improved accuracy unless accompanied by a suitable decrease in $(\delta t)$.

Milne has shown that if $W(x,t)$ has continuous partial derivatives of order 6 in $x$ and of order 3 in $t$, then the difference between the true solution of equation 8.2.1 and the solution of the difference equation 8.2.4 satisfies:

$$|\epsilon(x, t)| < \frac{c^2 T (\delta x)^4}{135} \left(\frac{\partial^6 W}{\partial x^6}\right)_{\max} \qquad \ldots\ldots(8.2.6)$$

where the value of the partial derivative is taken in the $(x, t)$ region covered by the solution, and the optimum value $\frac{1}{6}$ is taken for $\gamma$.

An alternative procedure to the above is to replace only *one* of the partial derivatives by a finite difference approximation and thus obtain either:

$$c^2 \frac{d^2}{dx^2} [W(x, t + \delta t) + W(x, t)]$$

$$= \frac{2}{(\delta t)} [W(x, t + \delta t) + W(x, t)] - \frac{4W(x, t)}{(\delta t)} \qquad \ldots\ldots(8.2.7)$$

which is an ordinary differential equation in $x$ for $W(x, t + \delta t)$ in terms of the known values $W(x, t)$, or:

$$\frac{c^2}{(\delta x)^2} [W(x + \delta x, t) - 2W(x, t) + W(x - \delta x, t)] = \frac{dW(x, t)}{dt}$$

$$\ldots\ldots(8.2.8)$$

which is an ordinary differential equation in $t$.

The methods described in Chapter 6 can be applied to solve these equations which present no special problems. It may be mentioned that the process defined by equation 8.2.7 is often called the 'Hartree-Womersley' method[1].

A typical hyperbolic equation which occurs in practice is the wave equation:

$$c^2 \frac{\partial^2 W}{\partial x^2} = \frac{\partial^2 W}{\partial t^2} \qquad \ldots (8.2.9)$$

This time the central difference formulae for the derivatives may be applied to *both* sides with the result:

$$W(x, t + \delta t) = \beta[W(x + \delta x, t) + W(x - \delta x, t) - W(x, t - \delta t)]$$
$$+ 2(1 - \beta)W(x, t) \qquad \ldots (8.2.10)$$

where
$$\beta = c^2 \left(\frac{\delta t}{\delta x}\right)^2 \qquad \ldots (8.2.11)$$

Thus, by taking $\beta = c^2 \left(\dfrac{\delta t}{\delta x}\right)^2 = 1$, equation 8.2.10 reduces to

$$W(x, t + \delta t) = W(x + \delta x, t) + W(x - \delta x, t) - W(x, t - \delta t)$$
$$\ldots (8.2.12)$$

which has exactly the same solution[2], $W = f(x + ct) + g(x - ct)$, as equation 8.2.9. It follows that solutions obtained by replacing equation 8.2.9 by 8.2.10–8.2.12 will be exact. This procedure is particularly useful in dealing with the subsequent motion of a vibrating string whose initial form and velocity are prescribed. In this situation the numerical solution, *via* 8.2.10–8.2.12, is considerably easier to compute than the results of the exact analysis using Fourier series.

The methods just described can be applied in largely unmodified form to parabolic and hyperbolic partial equations of more complicated types, with the exception that the derivatives which occur must be replaced by suitable difference approximations. In a less measure the same remark applies to non-linear equations, although here great care is needed to ensure stability. The reader requiring further information is referred to the excellent paper of BLANCH[3].

## 8.3 HIGHER DIFFERENCES AND CHECKING

A possible method of obtaining a more accurate solution, for the same intervals of differencing, might appear to be to use approximations to the partial derivatives involving higher orders of differences than those considered in section 8.2. This procedure, unfortunately, often leads to the generation of spurious detail in the resulting solution because, in effect, the original equation is being replaced by a difference equation of higher order. A less dangerous procedure is to use higher difference formulae to estimate the error of a result obtained by the use of the simpler methods.

Thus, in place of equation 8.2.4 we may obtain a more exact relationship *via* the central difference formulae in equations 4.2.10, 4.2.11 of Chapter 4.

$$\frac{\partial^2 W}{\partial x^2} = \frac{1}{(\delta x)^2} \left( \delta_x^2 - \tfrac{1}{12}\delta_x^4 + \tfrac{1}{90}\delta_x^6 - etc. \right) W(x, t) \qquad \dots (8.3.1)$$

$$\frac{\partial W}{\partial t} = \frac{1}{(\delta t)} \left[ (\mu\delta)_t - \tfrac{1}{6}\delta_t^2(\mu\delta)_t + \tfrac{1}{30}\delta_t^4(\mu\delta)_t - \tfrac{1}{40}\delta_t^6(\mu\delta)_t \right] W(x, t)$$
$$\dots (8.3.2)$$

where $\delta_x, \delta_t$ indicate that the differences are to be taken for constant $x$ and constant $t$ respectively. It should be noted that, in making the comparison, the optimum value:

$$\gamma = c^2 \delta t / (\delta x)^2 = \tfrac{1}{6} \qquad \dots (8.3.3)$$

should again be used.

## 8.4 EQUATIONS WITH MORE THAN TWO VARIABLES

The extension of our previous finite difference treatment to dimensions outside the $(x, t)$ plane presents no special difficulties. We shall illustrate the method of approach by considering the two dimensional Laplacian operator:

$$\nabla^2 W = \frac{\partial^2 W}{\partial x^2} + \frac{\partial^2 W}{\partial y^2} \qquad \dots (8.4.1)$$

A fairly obvious start is to replace the partial derivatives by their finite difference approximations:

$$\frac{\partial^2 W}{\partial x^2} \simeq \delta_x^2 W / (\delta x)^2 = \frac{1}{(\delta x)^2} \left[ W(x + \delta x, y) - 2W(x, y) + W(x - \delta x, y) \right]$$

$$\frac{\partial^2 W}{\partial y^2} \simeq \delta_y^2 W / (\delta y)^2 = \frac{1}{(\delta y)^2} \left[ W(x, y + \delta y) - 2W(x, y) + W(x, y - \delta y) \right]$$
$$\dots (8.4.2)$$

whence:

$$\nabla^2 W \simeq \frac{1}{(\delta s)^2} \left[ \begin{array}{c} W(x + \delta x, y) + W(x - \delta x, y) + W(x, y + \delta y) \\ + W(x, y - \delta y) - 4\, W(x, y) \end{array} \right]$$
$$\dots (8.4.3)$$

where we have assumed that a square difference grid of side $\delta s = \delta x = \delta y$ is being used.

Equation 8.4.3 can be pictured more vividly by the point pattern shown in *Figure 8.4.1 (a)*, which is conveniently represented by the matrix *Figure 8.4.1 (b)*. If we remember that the Laplacian, $\nabla^2$, of

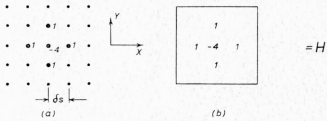

(a)          (b)

*Figure 8.4.1*

a function $W$, at a particular point in space is independent of the particular co-ordinate system chosen, equation 8.43 suggests that an alternative expression could be obtained by rotating the axis system through 45° and working in terms of the corresponding points in

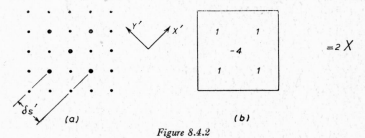

(a)          (b)

*Figure 8.4.2*

this system. Inserting the function values in terms of our original co-ordinate system, and noticing that $\delta s' = \delta s \sqrt{2}$, we obtain:

$$\nabla^2 W \simeq$$

$$\frac{1}{2(\delta s)^2} \left[ \begin{array}{c} W(x - \delta x, y + \delta y) + W(x + \delta x, y + \delta y) \\ + W(x - \delta x, y - \delta y) + W(x + \delta x, y - \delta y) - 4W(x, y) \end{array} \right]$$
$$\dots (8.4.4)$$

115

The preceding arguments have been merely suggestive and we now propose to investigate more closely the nature of the approximations involved; for convenience of writing we shall represent the expressions formed from the function values shown in *Figure 8.4.1 (b)* and *Figure 8.4.2.(b)* respectively, by $H$ and $2X$ ('Horizontal' and 'Cross').

We first introduce the operators $E_x$ and $E_y$ defined by:

$$\left. \begin{array}{l} E_x\,[W(x,y)] = W(x+\delta x, y) \\ E_y\,[W(x,y)] = W(x, y+\delta y) \end{array} \right\} \quad \dots(8.4.5)$$

with symbolic associations, coresponding to equation 3.1.11 of chapter 3,

$$\left. \begin{array}{l} E_x = \exp\,(\delta x)(\partial/\partial x) \\ E_y = \exp\,(\delta y)(\partial/\partial y) \end{array} \right\} \quad \dots(8.4.6)$$

From the expression for H we have:

$$H(W) = (E_x + E_x^{-1} + E_y + E_y^{-1} - 4)(W)$$

or, using equation 8.4.6 and the exponential expansion theorem,

$$H(W) = (\delta s)^2\,\nabla^2(W) + \tfrac{1}{12}(\delta s)^4\,\nabla_0^4(W) + \tfrac{1}{360}(\delta s)^6\,\nabla_0^6(W) + \dots$$
$$\dots(8.4.7)$$

where $\nabla_0^n(W) = \dfrac{\partial^n W}{\partial x^n} + \dfrac{\partial^n W}{\partial y^n}$. We thus see that a more correct form of 8.4.3 is:

$$\nabla^2 W = \frac{1}{(\delta s)^2}\,H(W) - O[(\delta s)^2] \quad \dots(8.4.8)$$

Again, from the expression for $2X$, we have:

$$2X(W) = (E_x^{-1}E_y + E_x.E_y + E_x^{-1}.E_y^{-1} + E_x.E_y^{-1} - 4)(W)$$

which leads to

$$2X(W) = 2(\delta s)^2\,\nabla^2(W) + \tfrac{1}{6}(\delta s)^4\,\nabla_0^4(W)$$
$$+ (\delta s)^4\,\frac{\partial^4 W}{\partial x^2 \partial y^2} + \frac{(\delta s)^6}{180}\,\nabla_0^6(W) + \frac{(\delta s)^6}{12}\,\frac{\partial^4}{\partial x^2 \partial y^2}\,[\nabla^2(W)] + \dots$$
$$\dots(8.4.9)$$

whence:

$$\nabla^2(W) = \frac{1}{2(\delta s)^2}\,[2X(W)] - O[(\delta s)^2] \quad \dots(8.4.10)$$

and we notice that as is to be expected from the effectively larger interval of differencing involved in calculating $(2X)$, the error term, although $O[(\delta s)^2]$, has a larger coefficient than in equation 8.4.8.

In the special case of the Laplace equation where $\nabla^2(W) = 0$ we have

$$\frac{\partial^4 W}{\partial^2 x \partial^2 y} = -\frac{\partial^4 W}{\partial x^4} = -\frac{\partial^4 W}{\partial y^4} = -\tfrac{1}{2}\nabla_0^4(W)$$

so that equation 8.4.9 becomes:

$$2X(W) = 2(\delta s)^2\nabla^2(W) - \tfrac{1}{3}(\delta s)^4\nabla_0^4(W) + \frac{(\delta s)^6}{180}\nabla_0^6(W)$$

whence, using 8.4.7:

$$(4H + 2X)(W) = 6(\delta s)^2\nabla^2(W) + \frac{(\delta s)^6}{60}\nabla_0^6(W)$$

or $$\nabla^2(W) = \frac{1}{6(\delta s)^2}(4H + 2X)W - O((\delta s)^4) \quad \ldots\ldots(8.4.11)$$

The operator $(4H + 2X)$ is easily remembered as:

$$
\begin{array}{ccccc}
\cdot & \cdot & \cdot & \cdot & \cdot \\
\cdot & \cdot & \cdot & \cdot & \cdot \\
\cdot & \cdot & \cdot & \cdot & \cdot \\
\cdot & \cdot & \cdot & \cdot & \cdot \\
\cdot & \cdot & \cdot & \cdot & \cdot \\
\end{array}
\;=\;
\begin{array}{|rrr|}
\hline
1 & 4 & 1 \\
4 & -20 & 4 \\
1 & 4 & 1 \\
\hline
\end{array}
\;=\; K \qquad \ldots\ldots(8.4.12)
$$

the symbol $K$ being suggested by MILNE [4] who, by introducing the symbolic operator $N^2$, defined by:

$$N^2 = 2X - 2H = 
\begin{array}{|rrr|}
\hline
1 & -2 & 1 \\
-2 & 4 & -2 \\
1 & -2 & 1 \\
\hline
\end{array}
= (\delta s)^4\frac{\partial^4}{\partial x^2 \partial y^2} + O[(\delta s)^6]$$

$$\ldots\ldots(8.4.13)$$

shows that $\nabla^2 \equiv$

$$\frac{1}{6(\delta s)^2}\left(K - \frac{K^2}{72} + \frac{K^3}{3240} - \frac{KN^2}{180} - \frac{K^4}{120960} + \frac{K^2N^2}{3780} - \frac{N^4}{504} + \cdots\right)$$

$$\ldots\ldots(8.4.14)$$

The foregoing analysis enables us to obtain numerical procedures for solving the two-dimensional equivalents of the diffusion and wave equations considered in section 8.2.

Thus, corresponding to equation 8.2.1 we have:

$$\frac{\partial W}{\partial t} = c^2 \nabla^2 W \qquad\qquad \ldots (8.4.15)$$

and obtain at once:

$$W(x, y, t + \delta t) = (\delta t)c^2 \nabla^2 W + W(x, y, t).$$

We now replace $\nabla^2 W$ by a suitable finite difference approximation; if the range of $(t)$ over which the solution is to be continued is *not* large it will be sufficient to use equation 8.4.8. Thus:

$$W(x, y, t + \delta t) = c^2 \frac{\delta t}{(\delta s)^2} HW + W$$

and, if the optimum value $\gamma = c^2 \dfrac{\delta t}{(\delta s)^2} = \frac{1}{6}$ is chosen, this becomes:

$$W(x, y, t + \delta t) = (\tfrac{1}{6}H + 1)W \qquad \ldots (8.4.16)$$

or, symbolically:

$$W(x, y, t + \delta t) = \tfrac{1}{6} \begin{array}{|ccc|} \hline & 1 & \\ 1 & 2 & 1 \\ & 1 & \\ \hline \end{array} \; W(x, y, t) \qquad \ldots (8.4.17)$$

If greater accuracy is required we may use equation 8.4.11 and thus obtain $\left(\text{again with } \gamma = \dfrac{c^2 \delta t}{(\delta s)^2} = \frac{1}{6}\right)$:

$$W(x, y, t + \delta t) = (\tfrac{1}{36}K + 1)W = \tfrac{1}{36} \begin{array}{|ccc|} \hline 1 & 4 & 1 \\ 4 & 16 & 4 \\ 1 & 4 & 1 \\ \hline \end{array} \; W(x, y, t)$$

$$\ldots (8.4.18)$$

The matrix $(K + 36)$ is peculiar in that it can be expressed as:

$$\begin{array}{|ccc|} \hline 1 & 4 & 1 \\ \hline \end{array} \times \begin{array}{|c|} \hline 1 \\ 4 \\ 1 \\ \hline \end{array}$$

which, as mentioned in a paper by Yowell, quoted by Milne (*loc. cit.*) enables the iterative process defined by equation 8.4.18 to be adapted to calculation on punched card or other fixed scanning sequence computing machines.

The two-dimensional wave equation can be similarly treated, thus:

$$\frac{\partial^2 W}{\partial t^2} = c^2 \nabla^2 W \qquad \qquad \dots (8.4.19)$$

becomes, on replacing the differentials by differences:

$$W(x, y, t + \delta t) = \frac{c^2}{6} \frac{(\delta t)^2}{(\delta s)^2} KW(x, y, t) + 2W(x, y, t) - W(x, y, t - \delta t)$$
$$\dots (8.4.20)$$

Milne has shown that, for convergence, we must take

$$\beta = c^2 (\delta t)^2 / (\delta s)^2 \leqslant \tfrac{5}{8}$$

and proposes the value $\beta = \tfrac{6}{10}$, he thus obtains (actually by using equation 8.4.14 to replace $\nabla^2$)

$$W(x, y, t + \delta t) = \left( \frac{K}{10} - \frac{K^2}{1800} \right) W(x, y, t) + 2W(x, y, t) - W(x, y, t - \delta t)$$
$$+ O[(\delta s)^6] \qquad \dots (8.4.21)$$

$K^2$ is to be obtained by *two* successive applications of $K$, a procedure which avoids trouble at the boundaries.

Hyperbolic and parabolic partial differential equations are closely analogous to one-point boundary condition ordinary differential equations, in that all the information regarding the solution is known initially, so that the solution can proceed on a step-by-step basis. We have not considered initial conditions of the more complicated types involving first derivatives of the function with respect to space or time co-ordinates, but these can be introduced without any great difficulty, and the diversity of types and situations would make too long an account for the present purpose. In the same way we have considered only hyperbolic and parabolic equations of the most elementary kinds; the method of approach to more complicated examples is still *via* finite difference approximations, but the conditions for convergence are far more difficult to ascertain. Often, in situations representing real problems, a knowledge of the physics of the system will give a clear indication of any marked inaccuracy in the solution; in the absence of such guidance, however, the best that can be done is a check on the solution, as indicated in section 8.3, by means of a more accurate approximation to the equation, using differences of higher order than those used to obtain the solution originally. It cannot be too strongly remarked, however, that such higher difference formulae should *not* be used in the original calculation, since they are equivalent to replacing the original differential equation by one of higher order, and may thus introduce spurious detail into the solution. A better method is to decrease the size of the interval in the 'open' direction, although here again care must be taken to compensate, if necessary, with a decrease in other intervals. Unfortunately, more general versions of Courant's results are not always available but the known forms may give some idea of the *dimensions* involved.

### 8.5 CLASSIFICATION CHARACTERISTICS AND CANONICAL FORM

It was mentioned in section 8.1 that partial differential equations of the type 8.1.1 were divided into classes according to certain criteria; we shall now show how these criteria arise, and how they are related to the canonical forms to which the equation may be reduced.

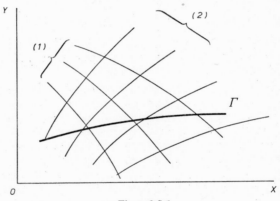

*Figure 8.5.1*

In the first place we introduce the symbols:

$$p = \frac{\partial W}{\partial x} \qquad q = \frac{\partial W}{\partial y}$$

$$r = \frac{\partial^2 W}{\partial x^2} \qquad s = \frac{\partial^2 W}{\partial y \partial x} = \frac{\partial^2 W}{\partial x \partial y} \qquad t = \frac{\partial^2 W}{\partial y^2}$$

which are common in the theory of surfaces. In terms of these symbols equation 8.1.1 may be written:

$$Ar + 2Hs + Bt = \Phi \qquad \qquad \dots (8.5.1)$$

where $\Phi$ may be a function of the remaining quantities in 8.1.1.

120

Now the following relationships obtain:

$$dp = \frac{\partial p}{\partial x}\,dx + \frac{\partial p}{\partial y}\,dy = r\,dx + s\,dy \qquad \ldots\ldots(8.5.2)$$

$$dq = \frac{\partial q}{\partial x}\,dx + \frac{\partial q}{\partial y}\,dy = s\,dx + t\,dy \qquad \ldots\ldots(8.5.3)$$

Next assume that the values of $\dfrac{\partial W}{\partial x}\ (=p)$ and $\dfrac{\partial W}{\partial y}\ (=q)$ are given on some curve $\Gamma$ in the $(x, y)$ plane (*Figure 8.5.1*). Equations 8.5.1–8.5.3 thus constitute a set of simultaneous equations for the determination of $(r, s, t)$ and will have a determinate solution only if:

$$\Delta = \begin{vmatrix} dx & dy & 0 \\ 0 & dx & dy \\ A & 2H & B \end{vmatrix} \neq 0$$

The equation $\Delta = 0$ or:

$$A\left(\frac{dy}{dx}\right)^2 - 2H\left(\frac{dy}{dx}\right) + B = 0 \qquad \ldots\ldots(8.5.4)$$

defines two sets of curves. These will be real and distinct only if $H^2 - AB > 0$; only one curve will exist if $H^2 - AB = 0$, and no real curves will exist if $H^2 - AB < 0$; the curves are known as the 'characteristics' of the given equation.

If the two families of characteristics corresponding to the solutions of 8.5.4 are called:

$$\phi(x, y) = \text{const.} \quad \text{and} \quad \psi(x, y) = \text{const.}$$

it may be shown [5] that the substitution :

$$\xi + i\eta = \phi(x, y), \quad \xi - i\eta = \psi(x, y) \qquad \ldots\ldots(8.5.5)$$

reduces equation 8.1.1 to the canonical *elliptic* form:

$$\frac{\partial^2 W}{\partial \xi^2} + \frac{\partial^2 W}{\partial \eta^2} = X\left(W, \frac{\partial W}{\partial \xi} \ldots, \xi \ldots\right) \qquad \ldots\ldots(8.5.6)$$

whilst the substitution:

$$\xi = \phi(x, y), \quad \eta = \psi(x, y) \qquad \ldots\ldots(8.5.7)$$

gives the canonical *hyperbolic* form:

$$\frac{\partial^2 W}{\partial \xi \partial \eta} = X\left(W, \frac{\partial W}{\phi \xi} \ldots, \xi \ldots\right) \qquad \ldots\ldots(8.5.8)$$

121

I

The *parabolic* form is obtained when:

$$\xi = \phi(x, y) = \psi(x, y), \quad \eta = x \qquad \dots (8.5.9)$$

and is

$$\frac{\partial^2 W}{\partial \eta^2} = X\left( W, \frac{\partial W}{\partial \xi} \dots, \xi \dots \right) \qquad \dots (8.5.10)$$

Characteristics thus specify, in some sense, a set of co-ordinates in which the general equation reduces to the simpler canonical form. It thus becomes appropriate in certain cases to take as a grid for finite differences the characteristics themselves. This technique is likely to be useful only in simple cases in which equation 8.5.4 can be handled by direct analytical methods; it has found some applications in aerodynamics.[6]

## 8.6 MULTI-POINT BOUNDARY CONDITIONS AND ELLIPTIC PARTIAL DIFFERENTIAL EQUATIONS

Although it may appear curious to include a discussion of *ordinary* differential equations in a chapter on *partial* equations, this position is really the most suitable for those of the former class which have to satisfy multi-point boundary conditions. The essential identity of the principal method of solution for elliptic partial differential equations and that for the ordinary variety will, we hope, be clear after reading this section.

We will start by considering the simplest possible ordinary differential equation of the second order:

$$y'' = 0 \qquad (8.6.1)$$

and we will assume that the solution has to satisfy the two-point conditions $(y = y_0, \ x = 0)$ $(y = y_n, \ x = n\delta x)$. Now equation 8.6.1 can be approximated by:

$$\delta^2 y_m = 0 \qquad (m = 1, 2 \dots n - 1)$$

that is by the set of simultaneous equations:

$$\left.\begin{aligned}
y_0 - 2y_1 + y_2 &= 0 \\
y_1 - 2y_2 + y_3 &= 0 \\
y_2 - 2y_3 + y_4 &= 0 \\
\overline{\phantom{y_{n-3} - 2y_{n-2} + y_{n-1}}} \\
y_{n-3} - 2y_{n-2} + y_{n-1} &= 0 \\
y_{n-2} - 2y_{n-1} + y_n &= 0
\end{aligned}\right\} \ \dots (8.6.2)$$

These equations may be rearranged into the matrix form

$$
\begin{bmatrix}
2 & -1 & 0 & 0 & - & - & - & - & - & - & 0 \\
-1 & 2 & -1 & 0 & - & - & - & - & - & - & 0 \\
0 & -1 & 2 & -1 & - & - & - & - & - & - & 0 \\
- & - & - & - & - & - & - & - & - & - & - \\
- & - & - & - & - & - & - & - & - & - & - \\
0 & 0 & 0 & 0 & - & -1 & 2 & -1 \\
0 & 0 & 0 & 0 & - & 0 & -1 & 2
\end{bmatrix}
\begin{bmatrix}
y_1 \\ y_2 \\ y_3 \\ - \\ - \\ y_{n-2} \\ y_{n-1}
\end{bmatrix}
=
\begin{bmatrix}
y_0 \\ 0 \\ 0 \\ - \\ - \\ 0 \\ y_n
\end{bmatrix}
\quad \ldots(8.6.3)
$$

or $A.\boldsymbol{y} = \boldsymbol{b}$ say, whence, if we can find $A^{-1}$, we can obtain the solution to 8.6.1 as $\qquad \boldsymbol{y} = A^{-1}.\boldsymbol{b}$.

Now, in the case of the matrix $A$ of equation 8.6.3 the inverse is easily shown to be:

$A^{-1} =$

$$
\begin{bmatrix}
(1 - 1/n) & (1 - 2/n) & (1 - 3/n) & (1 - 4/n) & - & - & 2/n & 1/n \\
(1 - 2/n) & 2(1 - 2/n) & 2(1 - 3/n) & 2(1 - 4/n) & - & - & 2.2/n & 2.1/n \\
(1 - 3/n) & 2(1 - 3/n) & 3(1 - 3/n) & 3(1 - 4/n) & - & - & 3.2/n & 3.1/n \\
(1 - 4/n) & 2(1 - 4/n) & 3(1 - 4/n) & 4(1 - 4/n) & - & - & 4.2/n & 4.1/n \\
- & - & - & - & - & - & - & - \\
1/n & 2/n & 3/n & 4/n & - & - & - & (n-1).1/n
\end{bmatrix}
$$
$$\ldots(8.6.4)$$

so that we obtain as our finite difference solution to equation 8.6.1, subject to the given boundary conditions:

$$
(\boldsymbol{y}) =
\begin{bmatrix}
y_1 \\ y_2 \\ - \\ - \\ - \\ - \\ - \\ y_{n-1}
\end{bmatrix}
= A^{-1}.
\begin{bmatrix}
y_0 \\ 0 \\ 0 \\ 0 \\ - \\ 0 \\ 0 \\ y_n
\end{bmatrix}
=
\begin{bmatrix}
(1 - 1/n)y_0 + y_n/n \\
(1 - 2/n)y_0 + 2y_n/n \\
(1 - 3/n)y_0 + 3y_n/n \\
- - - - - - - - - \\
- - - - - - - - - \\
- - - - - - - - - \\
- - - - - - - - - \\
(1/n)y_0 + (n - 1)y_n/n
\end{bmatrix}
\quad \ldots(8.6.5)
$$

Since the analytical solution of equation 8.6.1, subject to the boundary conditions, is

$$
y = \frac{(y_n - y_0)}{n\delta x} x + y_0
$$

we see that the solution given by 8.6.5 is, in this case, *exact*.

123

The same method can be adopted for the more general equation:

$$y'' = f(x)$$

with similar boundary conditions. In this case the set of difference equations becomes:

$$\delta^2 y_m = f(m\delta x).(\delta x)^2 \quad (m = 1, 2 \ldots n - 1)$$

and the solution may be written:

$$[y] = \begin{bmatrix} y_1 \\ y_2 \\ - \\ - \\ - \\ y_{n-1} \end{bmatrix} = A^{-1}. \begin{bmatrix} y_0 - f(\delta x)(\delta x)^2 \\ - f(2\delta x)(\delta x)^2 \\ - f(3\delta x)(\delta x)^2 \\ - - - - - - - \\ - - - - - - - \\ y_n - f[(n-1)\delta x](\delta x)^2 \end{bmatrix} \quad \ldots (8.6.6)$$

where $A^{-1}$ is the matrix defined by equation 8.6.4.

These simple examples will give the idea behind a general method for solving multi-point boundary condition differential equations. The solution proceeds in three parts:

(1) Represent the given equation by a finite difference approximtion *of the same order.*

(2) Set up the system of simultaneous equations defined by the finite difference approximations at each point $(m\delta x)$ $[m = 1 \ldots (n-1)]$ at which a solution is required, using the boundary conditions to define $y_0$ and $y_n$ in the case of second order equations; for higher orders the boundary conditions may define $y_0, y_1$ etc. $\ldots y_{n-1}, y_n$.

(3) Solve the simultaneous equations to give the required solution of the original differential equation.

It is evident that the fortunate accident of $A$ having a known inverse will not, in general, happen, so that the set of simultaneous equations, corresponding to 8.6.2, will have to be solved by one of the methods described in Chapter 7. Much existing work in solving two-point boundary condition differential equations has been carried out by the use of the relaxation method (Chapter 7, sections 7.7, 7.9), and the computational layout for such cases has been well described by SOUTHWELL.[7] When a high speed automatic digital calculator is available, however, modern practice would favour the use of pivotal condensation (Chapter 7, section 7.3). As a check in the work, a finite difference approximation of higher order may be used. This, however, must not be made the basis of the original solution.

Non-linear equations can be solved by the same method, but since these will lead to non-linear simultaneous equations the work of solving the latter may be prohibitive.

A natural extension of the preceding discussion allows the solution of elliptic partial differential equations. We shall consider first the most common form of these—the Laplace equation in two dimensions:

$$\nabla^2 W = 0 \qquad \ldots (8.6.7)$$

with $W = W_\Gamma$ on some boundary $\Gamma$. To start with, it will be assumed that $\Gamma$ consists only of elements parallel to the co-ordinate axes $(x, y)$.

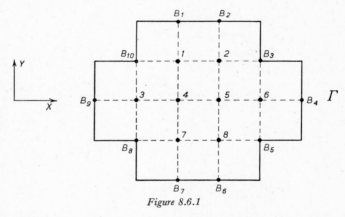

Figure 8.6.1

We divide the interior of $\Gamma$ over which a solution to equation 8.6.7 is required, by means of a co-ordinate grid of equispaced lines, and call the *interior* points of this grid, 1, 2 . . . 8 (*Figure 8.6.1*). At each such point the equation 8.6.7 may be approximated by $H(W) = 0$ (8.4.8) so that, for the region shown in *Figure 8.6.1*, we obtain the set of relations:

$$H(W_r) = 0 \quad (r = 1 \ldots 8)$$

and, if the boundary values are $B_1 \ldots B_{10}$ as shown, these become:

$$
\begin{aligned}
4W_1 - W_2 \qquad\quad - W_4 \qquad\qquad\qquad\qquad\quad &= B_1 + B_{10} \\
- W_1 + 4W_2 \qquad\qquad\quad - W_5 \qquad\qquad\qquad &= B_2 + B_3 \\
4W_3 - W_4 \qquad\qquad\qquad\qquad &= B_8 + B_9 + B_{10} \\
- W_1 \qquad\quad - W_3 + 4W_4 - W_5 \qquad - W_7 \qquad &= 0 \\
- W_2 \qquad\quad - W_4 + 4W_5 - W_6 \qquad\qquad - W_8 &= 0 \\
- W_5 + 4W_6 \qquad\qquad\qquad &= B_3 + B_4 + B_5 \\
- W_4 \qquad\qquad\qquad + 4W_7 - W_8 &= B_7 + B_8 \\
- W_5 \qquad\qquad\qquad - W_7 + 4W_8 &= B_5 + B_6
\end{aligned}
$$

$$\ldots (8.6.8)$$

In matrix form this set of equations may be written:

$$G . W = b \qquad \qquad \dots (8.6.9)$$

where:

$$G = \begin{bmatrix}
4 & -1 & 0 & -1 & 0 & 0 & 0 & 0 \\
-1 & 4 & 0 & 0 & -1 & 0 & 0 & 0 \\
0 & 0 & 4 & -1 & 0 & 0 & 0 & 0 \\
-1 & 0 & -1 & 4 & -1 & 0 & -1 & 0 \\
0 & -1 & 0 & -1 & 4 & -1 & 0 & -1 \\
0 & 0 & 0 & 0 & -1 & 4 & 0 & 0 \\
0 & 0 & 0 & -1 & 0 & 0 & 4 & -1 \\
0 & 0 & 0 & 0 & -1 & 0 & -1 & 4
\end{bmatrix} \qquad \dots (8.6.10)$$

and $b$ is the column vector whose components are the right-hand elements of equations 8.6.8. It is evident, from the form of equations 8.6.8, 8.6.9, that the matrix $G$ is independent of the boundary values themselves, and also that $G$ is always symmetrical. Further investigation [8] shows that $G$ is non-singular, and has latent roots which lie in the range $0 < \lambda_i < 8$, these roots being symmetrically located with respect to $\lambda = 4$.

The solution of the Laplace equation 8.6.7 subject to the given boundary conditions is therefore approximated by the solution to 8.6.9:

$$W = G^{-1} . b \qquad \qquad \dots (8.6.11)$$

so that the methods of chapter 7, and in particular the relaxation method, can be used to solve this problem. If a solution to the Laplace equation is required for the same boundary *shape* but a number of different boundary *values*, it may be more expeditious to evaluate $G^{-1}$ and then to use equation 8.6.11 rather than to solve the given equations by relaxation each time.

Exactly the same method can be applied to the solution of Poisson's equation:

$$\nabla^2 W = \rho(x, y) \qquad \qquad \dots (8.6.12)$$

except that the individual difference equations will now become:

$$H(W_r) = (\delta s)^2 \rho_r$$

where $\rho_r$ indicates that the value of $\rho$ is to be taken at the lattice point corresponding to $W_r$.

Thus, in the example of *Figure 8.6.1*, the resulting equations are:

$$G.\boldsymbol{W} = \begin{bmatrix} B_1 + B_{10} + (\delta s)^2 \rho_1 \\ B_2 + B_3 + (\delta s)^2 \rho_2 \\ B_8 + B_9 + B_{10} + (\delta s)^2 \rho_3 \\ etc. \\ B_5 + B_6 + (\delta s)^2 \rho_8 \end{bmatrix} \qquad ..(8.6.13)$$

where $G$ is the matrix of equation 8.6.10.

We now consider the question of lattice dimensions and boundaries which are not straight lines. In the first place, it is clear that $(\delta s)$

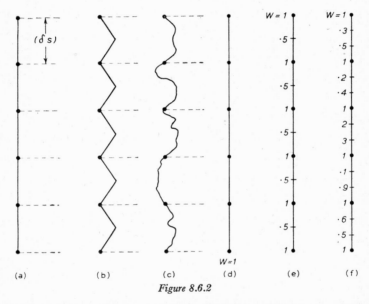

*Figure 8.6.2*

must be chosen so that variations in boundary shape and value *can* make themselves felt on the solution. Thus, with the mesh $(\delta s)$ shown in *Figure 8.6.2*, boundaries $(a)$, $(b)$ and $(c)$ and boundary values $(d)$, $(e)$ and $(f)$ will lead to identical solutions of the finite difference equations approximating 8.6.7 or 8.6.12 although it is quite evident that the true solutions are by no means identical. It is clear, therefore, that the interval $(\delta s)$ must be so chosen as to allow adequate representation of the detail of the solution as revealed by the known boundary values.

On the other hand, physical considerations, for example, of the related problems of charged conductors, suggest that far from the

127

boundaries much of this detail will be lost, so that an overall decrease in mesh size would be wasteful in computing time. To overcome this difficulty it is usual to take a small mesh size near to sharp discontinuities and to increase this towards the body of the region of solution. This is illustrated in the enlarged view of the region $B_1 B_{10}$, $B_9$ of *Figure 8.6.1* given in *Figure 8.6.3* where it is seen that a mesh of different size has been adopted in the region of the discontinuities.

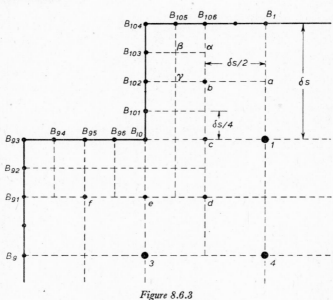

*Figure 8.6.3*

The joining up of such small meshes to the main one is carried out in steps; for example, in *Figure 8.6.3* we should:

(1) Evaluate the solution using only the coarse mesh shown in *Figure 8.6.1*.

(2) Use linear interpolation from (1) and the boundary values $B_1$ $B_{10}$, $B_{104}$ to find approximate values of $W$ at $(a)$ and $(b)$. Thus
$W_{(a)} \simeq \frac{1}{2}(W_1 + W_{B1})$  $W_{(b)} \simeq \frac{1}{4}(W_1 + W_{B1} + W_{B10} + W_{B104})$.
Similarly for $W_{(c)} \ldots W_{(f)}$.

(3) Apply relaxation or other techniques to refine these approximations, noticing that alterations in $W_{(a)} \ldots W_{(f)}$ will produce changes in the main net $W_1 - W_8$ so that this will require further treatment at the same time.

128

(4) When adequately small residuals have been obtained for $W_{(a)}$ . . . $W_{(f)}$ $W_1$ . . . $W_8$, add the next finer mesh ($\alpha$) ($\beta$) ($\gamma$) *etc.* and proceed as before.

As the intervals decrease near the boundary it should be found that less and less alteration is required in the main structure.

The above types of procedure are well adapted to straight boundaries of the sort illustrated, but with curved boundaries, and

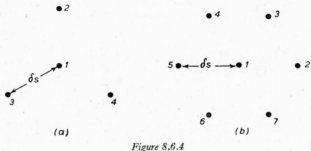

*Figure 8.6.4*

for straight boundaries which suggest hexagonal or related structures it is sometimes more convenient to adopt one of the finite difference approximations [9]:

$$3W_1 - W_2 - W_3 - W_4 = -\tfrac{3}{4}(\delta s)^2\rho_1 \qquad \ldots (8.6.14)$$

for the triangular mesh shown in *Figure 8.6.4 (a)*, or

$$6W_1 - W_2 - W_3 - W_4 - W_5 - W_6 - W_7$$
$$= -\tfrac{3}{2}(\delta s)^2[\rho_1 + \tfrac{1}{16}(\delta s)^2\nabla^2\rho_1] \qquad \ldots (8.6.15)$$

for the hexagonal mesh of *Figure 8.6.4 (b)*.

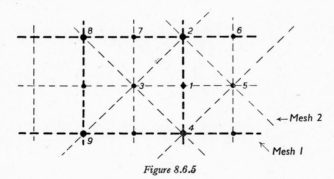

*Figure 8.6.5*

We may remark, in passing, that it has been recommended that, in decreasing the mesh size, a two stage process of the type shown in *Figure 8.6.5* should be adopted:

First the large grid, one element of which is (2, 4, 8, 9), should be refined. Then the diagonal grid (2, 3, 4, 5) should be adopted, the value of $W_3$ being taken as $\frac{1}{4}(W_2 + W_4 + W_8 + W_9)$. After refinement of this the small grid (1, 2, 7, 3) may be taken with the value $W_1$ estimated as $\frac{1}{4}(W_2 + W_3 + W_4 + W_5)$. In our experience this cautious approach is not usually justified, and the direct process of halving the mesh edge at each stage is to be preferred.

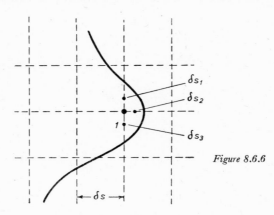

Figure 8.6.6

The general treatment of curved boundaries is difficult; formulae can be constructed to introduce the boundary values in a general situation such as that shown in *Figure 8.6.6* for which

$$\nabla^2 W =$$

$$\frac{2}{\delta s + \delta s_2} \left[ \frac{W(x + \delta s_2, y) - W(x, y)}{\delta s_2} + \frac{W(x - \delta s, y) - W(x, y)}{\delta s} \right] +$$

$$\frac{2}{\delta s_1 + \delta s_3} \left[ \frac{W(x, y + \delta s_1) - W(x, y)}{\delta s_1} + \frac{W(x, y - \delta s_3) - W(x, y)}{\delta s_3} \right]$$
$$- O(\delta s) \quad \dots (8.6.16)$$

and from which it is seen that the error is considerably greater than is the case with the symmetrical formula 8.4.8. Asymmetrical formulae can be constructed [10] to have an error $O[(\delta s)^2]$ but they are very complicated and we prefer to adopt a locally finer grid in the boundary region and use equation 8.6.16.

130

## 8.7 PRACTICAL ASPECTS OF THE RELAXATION METHOD

It seems likely that the large-scale solution of the simultaneous difference equations which result from attempts to solve elliptic partial differential equations will soon be a process which is exclusively performed on high speed computing machines. The best method of solution in this case is one in which a standard procedure is followed in all examples, as, for instance, in the elimination method of section 7.3 or the steepest descent methods of sections 7.7, 7.9.

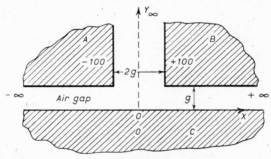

*Figure 8.7.1*

Occasionally, however, it will always be necessary to solve given problems by hand and in this event the relaxation method seems to offer the simplest procedure and, at the same time, the greatest scope for intuition and experience on the part of the human computer. We therefore propose in this section, to mention briefly, one or two practical aspects of relaxation technique as applied to the solution of equations involving the Laplacian operator.

To illustrate the method we shall examine the two dimensional potential problem represented by the system shown in *Figure 8.7.1*.

In one physical interpretation of this situation $A$ and $B$ represent the pole faces of a magnetic recording head and $C$ represents the recording medium; all are *assumed* to define equipotentials.

In obtaining a numerical solution of the Laplace equation

$$\nabla^2 V = 0$$

in the air gap region of *Figure 8.7.1* a difficulty arises at once from the fact that the air region extends to infinity in the directions shown. This is overcome in practice by assuming that at some finite distance the solution becomes indistinguishable from the solution at infinity. For the system shown this is the linear function:

$$V_\infty = 100y/g$$

131

at infinity in a direction parallel to $C$, and the similar function:

$$V_\infty = 100x/g$$

at infinity in a direction parallel to $A$ and $B$, the $y$ axis being taken to lie midway between $A$ and $B$.

For the present purpose we will assume that we are interested in a solution of accuracy 1 unit of potential, and experience suggests that the field will be sensibly that at infinity when $OX = 5g$ and similarly for $OY$. We thus replace *Figure 8.7.1* by the system shown in *Figure 8.7.2*.

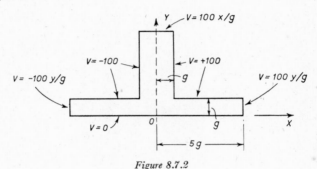

*Figure 8.7.2*

Next we notice that the distribution will be anti-symmetrical about $OY$ so that $OY$ is at potential zero and *Figure 8.7.2* can be reduced to *Figure 8.7.3*.

Finally we observe that the solution will be symmetrical about $OGZ$ (making an angle of 45° with $OX$) so that our computations can be confined to the region $OGLX$.

The next consideration is the choice of a finite difference grid upon which to carry out the calculations. Normally, for the accuracy required, we would take a mesh of side $\delta s = g/10$ but for the purpose of this example we shall start with a very coarse mesh $(g/2)$ and decrease this progressively to illustrate the technique.

We thus have the system shown in *Figure 8.7.4*.

The mesh points concerned are $(a \ldots i)$ and we *might* start by taking the initial values of $V$ at these to be zero. If the residuals are now calculated [taking them to be $H(V)$ where $H$ is defined by *Figure 8.4.1*] we find $H(V_a) = 0$, $H(V_b) \ldots H(V_h) = 100$, and $H(V_i) = 150$. Now a situation of this kind in which a number of adjacent mesh points have large residuals of the same sign is usually treated by a technique known as 'block' or 'group' relaxation, a

132

term which means simply that *all* of the values of $V$ are changed simultaneously and in the same direction until the residuals are reduced as far as possible.

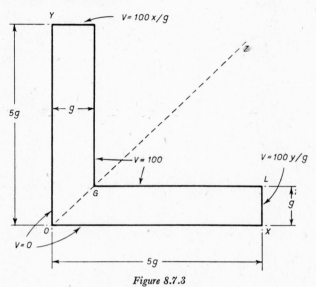

*Figure 8.7.3*

SOUTHWELL[11] has given a physical picture which is often helpful in seeing what sort of movement is required in block relaxation. He shows that the solution is equivalent to finding the equilibrium position of the points $a$ . . . $i$ if they were connected together, and to the boundaries, by means of light elastic strings. The boundaries are assumed to be at levels (perpendicular to the plane of the paper) proportional to their potentials.

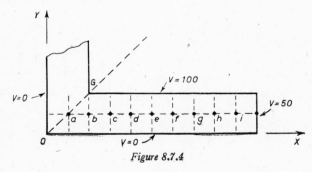

*Figure 8.7.4*

Thus, for *Figure 8.7.4*, a more plausible starting point would be to take the 'levels' of $a \ldots i$ at height 50, *i.e.* midway between those of the two boundaries. If this is done we find $H(V_a) = -150$, $H(V_b) \ldots H(V_i) = 0$ which is considerably more satisfactory.

The first relaxation net is now as shown in *Figure 8.7.5* which also gives the inscriptions which are inserted as the relaxation proceeds.

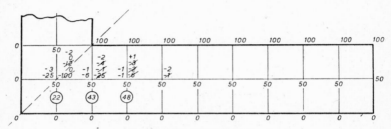

*Figure 8.7.5. Relaxation No. 1*

It is our practice to write the initial value under each lattice point and then inscribe residuals in a vertical column to the right of the point; corrections, if any, are written on the left. One point of procedure may be mentioned: *remember to correct residuals at adjacent points after altering any lattice-value*, neglect of this obvious warning has often led to error. Numbers are always chosen so that only integers

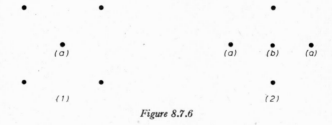

*Figure 8.7.6*

appear on the computation sheet, this means that it is not worth reducing residuals to below 2 units in magnitude. At this point the corrections are added into the initial values and the residuals recalculated to ensure removal of casual errors, then the process is restarted with the residuals multiplied by 10 or 100.

For the present example we do not yet perform this scaling up of residuals, we first divide the mesh interval by 2, obtaining

*Figure 8.7.7*, and then refine this as far as possible. The procedure for obtaining initial values at the new points is shown in the figure

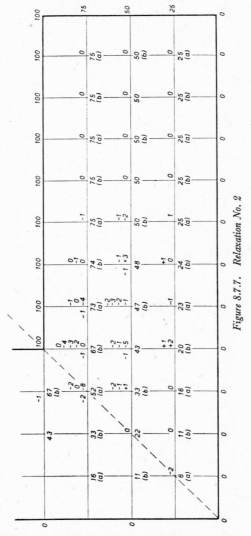

Figure 8.7.7. Relaxation No. 2

first those values marked (*a*) are derived by taking $\frac{1}{4} \times$ sum of the adjacent net points (and boundary values if necessary) obtained in the first approximation as shown in *Figure 8.7.6* (1). When all

135

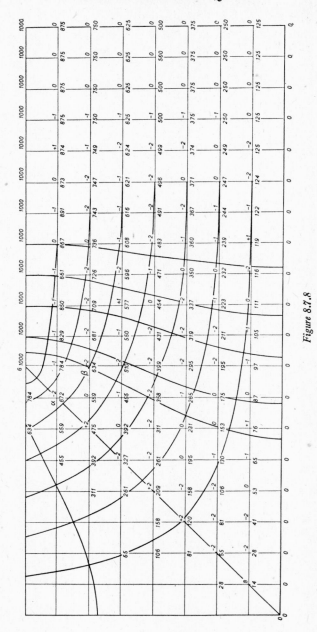

*Figure 8.7.8*

136

$(a)$-type points have been evaluated these are used, with the original values, to obtain intermediate points $(b)$ shown in *Figure 8.7.6* (2). The advantage of this procedure is that the $(b)$ points have a maximum residual of $\pm 2$ when we work to the nearest whole number. When the new approximation is complete it is 'relaxed' as before to reduce *all* residuals to 2 or less.

At this point the interval is again halved and the values corrected, by relaxation, to have residuals less than or equal to two. The results of this process are shown in *Figure 8.7.8*.

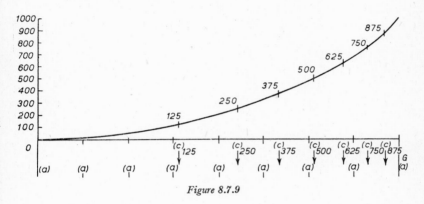

*Figure 8.7.9*

For the present purpose this approximation is sufficiently exact, but if greater precision were needed the mesh size could again be halved and the process repeated. In *Figure 8.7.8* have been drawn a set of equipotentials and, as these frequently are required, we may remark that these can be located with sufficient accuracy by drawing a simple graph of the potential values along each net line and finding the intersections of this curve with ordinates whose values are those of the potentials required. An example of such a graph, for the symmetry axis $OG$, is shown in *Figure 8.7.9*. In this example, where equipotentials intersect $OG$ normally, it is a good plan to find the intersections with this line although, in general, such an oblique line would not be needed. As a practical point in technique it should be noticed that the graph for an oblique line such as $OG$, can be most conveniently drawn by placing the ruled paper with its edge along $OG$ and marking the lattice point intersections as shown in $(a) \ldots (a)$. The contour crossings are also marked on the graph at $(c) \ldots (c)$ and can be inserted on the grid by replacing the completed graph on $OG$.

137                                        K

## 8.8. CHECKING

An advantage of the relaxation method is the fact that errors are automatically corrected although, of course, they hold up the convergence of the process. It is particularly necessary to recompute the residuals *ab initio* periodically since it is rather easy to make mistakes in writing down corrections to adjacent residuals after altering any point.

The estimation of the overall accuracy of the solution is more difficult, it is *not* sufficient to assume that when residuals have been reduced to $\pm 2$ units this is the overall accuracy of the solution, since no account has been taken of the intrinsic errors due to the finite difference approximation. A good guide is available when several grids, of different mesh sizes ($\delta s$), have been used in the calculation; generally the error of the final solution at any point is less than the difference between the values obtained, at that point, on the final and penultimate nets.

An analytic estimate of error can be obtained by computing the value of the operator $K$ (8.4.12) at each point, the value $-K/20$ will then give the correction to be applied if $K$ (instead of $H$) were the relaxation operator, since $K$ is a better approximation to $\nabla^2$ than $H$ (8.4.11), this correction is a measure of the error.

Thus, in our previous example (*Figure 8.7.8*), the application of $K$ at the points $\alpha$ and $\beta$ leads to values $R_\alpha = +47$, $R_\beta = -38$ suggesting corrections $+2$, $-2$. Since these are in accord with our previous estimates we may take the values given in *Figure 8.7.8* as certainly reliable to 1 per cent. as required.

Other measures of the accuracy of a solution can be derived. For example, if we assume that errors are of two kinds:

(1) Those due to the approximations involved in solving the finite difference equations.

(2) Those due to approximating the operator $\nabla^2$ by the operators $H$ or $K$,

then it can be shown [12] that, if the region over which the solution is computed can be enclosed in a circle of radius $R$, then the maximum error in the approximate solution of the difference equations is:

$$\epsilon_{(1)} \leqslant |r_m| R^2/e(\delta s)^2 \qquad \ldots (8.8.1)$$

where $r_m$ is the maximum value of the residual at any point, ($\delta s$) is the mesh size, and $e = 4$ for the operator $H$ and $e = 24$ for the operator $K$.

Errors due to cause (2) are more difficult to estimate, but the formula

$$\epsilon_{(2)} \leqslant \frac{R^2}{24(\delta s)^2} |N^2 W|_{max} \qquad \ldots (8.8.2)$$

(where $N^2$ is the operator defined in equation 8.4.13) gives an order of magnitude in the case of operator $H$ whilst for $K$

$$\epsilon_{(2)} \leqslant \frac{R^2}{21096(\delta s)^2} |N^4 W|_{max} \qquad \ldots (8.8.3)$$

is appropriate. Neither result is valid for boundary points; 8.8.2 holds, in general, for both the Laplace and the Poisson equations, and 8.8.3 for the Laplace equation only. For the special value $\rho(x, y) = $ const., in equation 8.6.12, 8.8.3 may also be used.

## 8.9 MONTE CARLO METHODS

Monte Carlo methods can be derived for the solution of linear partial differential equations and have the advantage that, by their aid, the

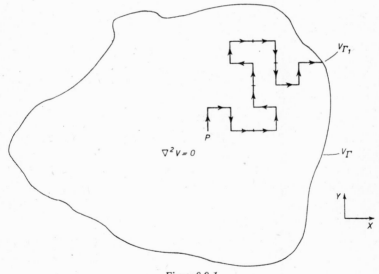

*Figure 8.9.1*

solution can be obtained at a single point without the need for working over the whole field. We give as an example the solution of the Laplace equation.

139

Assume that the solution of $\nabla^2 V = 0$ is required at some point $P$, inside a boundary $\Gamma$ upon which the values of $V$ are prescribed. Starting at $P$ we make a random walk in which the steps, of length $(\delta s)$ and in a positive or negative direction, are made parallel to the $X$ or $Y$ axes. The walk continues until it reaches $\Gamma$ when it is terminated, and the value of $V$, $V_\Gamma$, say, is recorded. This process is repeated many times $(n)$ and it may be shown [13] that:

$$\operatorname*{Lt}_{n \to \infty} \sum_1^n V_{\Gamma_r}/n \to Vp. \qquad \ldots (8.9.1)$$

The method can be extended to more than two dimensions and also to the case of the Poisson equation; it seems more appropriate to the determination of the values of $V$ at a single point than to its evaluation over the whole interior of $\Gamma$, since the number of steps in each walk is of the order $(R/\delta s)^2$ where $R$ is the radius of a circle completely enclosing $\Gamma$, and the rate of convergence is proportional only to $1/\sqrt{n}$.

## 8.10 MORE COMPLICATED PARTIAL DIFFERENTIAL EQUATIONS

The methods outlined in this chapter can be extended, formally, to more complicated equations without difficulty. For example the equations:

$$\frac{\partial w}{\partial t} = c^2 e^x \left( \frac{\partial^2 w}{\partial x^2} + \frac{\partial w}{\partial x} \right) \qquad \ldots (8.10.1)$$

$$\frac{\partial w}{\partial t} = \frac{\partial^2}{\partial x^2} (we^{-w}) \qquad \ldots (8.10.2)$$

$$\frac{\partial w}{\partial t} = c^2 \left( \frac{\partial^2 w}{\partial x^2} + \frac{\partial^2 w}{\partial y^2} + \frac{\partial^2 w}{\partial z^2} \right) \qquad \ldots (8.10.3)$$

$$\nabla^2 \nabla^2 w = 0 \qquad \ldots (8.10.4)$$

$$\frac{\partial}{\partial x} \left( \chi \frac{\partial \psi}{\partial x} \right) + \frac{\partial}{\partial y} \left( \chi \frac{d\psi}{\partial y} \right) + Z(x,y) = 0 \; [\chi = \chi(x,y)] \qquad \ldots (8.10.5)$$

$$\left. \begin{array}{ll} \dfrac{\partial v}{\partial t} = \dfrac{\partial^2 v}{\partial x^2} + e^{-1/v} & x \geqslant 0,\, t > 0 \\[2mm] -\dfrac{\partial v}{\partial x} = H[v_g(t) - v] & x = 0,\, t > 0 \\[2mm] \dfrac{\partial v}{\partial x} \to 0 & x \to \infty,\, t \geqslant 0 \\[2mm] v = v^{(0)} & x \geqslant 0,\, t = 0 \end{array} \right\} \qquad \ldots (8.10.6)$$

140

$$H \frac{\partial u}{\partial x} + K\left(\frac{\partial u}{\partial r} + \frac{\partial v}{\partial x}\right) + L \frac{\partial v}{\partial r} + P = 0$$

$$\frac{\partial v}{\partial x} - \frac{\partial u}{\partial r} = 0 \qquad \left.\right\} \quad \ldots (8.10.7)$$

$$H = a^2 - u^2, \quad K = -uv, \quad L = a^2 - v^2, \quad P = av^2/r$$

$$a^2 = \tfrac{1}{2}(g - 1)(1 - u^2 - v^2)$$

appear in the literature and methods of approach can be worked out for almost any equation or system of equations which may be suggested. The difficulty is not in evolving systematic means of iterative 'solution', but of ensuring that the results obtained do, in fact, bear some relation to the true answer.

The reader interested in following up the equations just quoted will find them in the references given below:

8.10.1– MILNE, W. E., 'Numerical Solution of Differential Equations,' Wiley,
8.10.4 New York (1953)
8.10.5 SOUTHWELL, R. V., 'Relaxation Methods in Theoretical Physics', Oxford
(1946)
8.10.6 LANDAU, H. G. and HICKS, B. L., *Math. Tab. Wash.*, III (1948) 207
8.10.7 LOTKIN, M., *ibid.*, III (1948) 209

REFERENCES

[1] HARTREE, D. R., and WOMERSLEY, J. R., *Proc. Roy. Soc.* A, 161 (1937), 363
[2] BOOLE, G., 'Calculus of Finite Differences,' 2nd Edn. p. 270. Macmillan, London (1872)
[3] BLANCH, G., *J. Res. Nat. Bur. Stand.*, 50 (1953) 343
[4] MILNE, W. E., 'Numerical Solution of Differential Equations,' p. 133, Wiley, New York (1953)
[5] SOMMERFELD, A., 'Partial Differential Equations of Physics,' p. 38 Academic Press, New York (1949)
[6] SHAPIRO, A. H. and EDELMAN, G. M., *J. Appl. Mech.* A14 (1947) 154
[7] SOUTHWELL, R. V., 'Relaxation Methods in Engineering Science,' Oxford (1940)
[8] MILNE, W. E., 'Numerical Solution of Differential Equations,' Wiley, New York (1953)
[9] SOUTHWELL, R. V., 'Relaxation Methods in Theoretical Physics,' Oxford (1946)
[10] MILNE, W. E., 'Numerical Solution of Differential Equations,' p. 150, Wiley, New York (1953)
[11] SOUTHWELL, R. V., 'Relaxation Methods in Theoretical Physics,' Oxford (1946)
[12] MILNE, W. E., 'Numerical Solution of Differential Equations,' p. 217, Wiley, New York (1953)
[13] CURTISS, J. H. 'Monte Carlo Methods for the Iteration of Linear Operators', *Nat. Bur. Stand.* Rep. 2365, Washington (1953)

# NON-LINEAR ALGEBRAIC EQUATIONS

## 9.1 PRELIMINARY IDEAS

THE subject of this chapter is the solution of those types of non-linear equation, both simple and simultaneous, which do *not* involve the operations of the differential or integral calculus. The problem may be expressed as:

'Find the solutions of the set of $(n)$ simultaneous equations

$$f_i (x_1, x_2 \ldots x_r \ldots x_n) = 0 \quad (i = 1 \ldots n) \quad \ldots . (9.1.1)$$

where the function $f_i$ may vary from equation to equation.

If we take a single function, $f$ say, of a single variable, $x$, the problem is simply:

$$\text{'solve } f(x) = 0\text{'} \quad \ldots . (9.1.2)$$

Clearly equation 9.1.1 embraces 9.1.2 and also the case in which the $f_i$ are simple linear combinations of the $x_i$, the latter case leading to the simultaneous linear equations of Chapter 7.

It will be appropriate to consider, too, those cases in which the equations 9.1.1. form both under- and over-determined sets, a situation which is common in various branches of physical science.

## 9.2 GRAPHICAL METHODS

The solution of non-linear algebraic equations in a single variable can generally be best performed in two stages. The first may be called a *survey* in which the general characteristics of the system are investigated and in which the roots are located approximately. The second stage may be called the *refinement*, in which the roots are found to the desired degree of accuracy.

It cannot be too strongly urged that even in the simplest problems the survey should be carried out, since the *feel* of the problem, thus obtained, will invariably lead to a better use of the available resources at the refinement stage.

Since the advent of high speed digital calculators the technique of survey has been slightly altered and, in some cases, the mathematical work which had to be carried out as a preliminary to the old methods has been thereby eliminated. Nevertheless the availability of the new machines should not be made the excuse for rushing into computation rather than contemplating the problem.

To take a concrete example we may consider the solution of the cubic equation:

$$ax^3 + bx^2 + cx + d = 0 \qquad\qquad (9.2.1)$$

First we notice that this can be reduced to the form:

$$x^3 + b'x^2 + c'x + d' = 0 \qquad\qquad \ldots\,(9.2.2)$$

by division through by $a$, and for a computing machine such a preliminary reduction would almost always be wise. If the survey is to be conducted by hand, however, we should consider the nature of the original coefficients $a$, $b$, $c$, $d$; should these be simple whole numbers they may be far easier to manipulate than the, possibly, infinite decimals of equation 9.2.2. We assume that, in the present case, the latter form is appropriate, and consider the next step. On an automatic machine this might consist of a simple evaluation of 9.2.2 for a range of values of $x$. Considerations of the relative sizes of $b'$, $c'$, $d'$ will limit this to manageable proportions, and may give some clue as to the interval of tabulation required. As a minor point of procedure it may be noted that 9.2.2 should *not* be calculated by forming (on an automatic computer) successively $x^3$, $b'x^2$, $c'x$ and adding these to $d'$, but by means of the sequence:

$$x + b', \quad x(x + b') + c', \quad x[x(x + b') + c'] + d'$$

the reason being that the former process requires four multiplications to form $x^3$, $b'x^2$ and $c'x$, whereas the latter requires only two.

When an automatic machine is *not* available, however, the above method is not to be recommended. A better approach is to notice that the roots of 9.2.2 are the same as the $x$ co-ordinates of the intersections of

$$\left. \begin{aligned} y &= -\,c'x - d' \\ y &= x^3 + b'x^2 \end{aligned} \right\} \qquad \ldots\,(9.2.3)$$

The first of these equations represents a straight line, which may be conveniently drawn through the two points: $(0, -d')$ $(-d'/c', 0)$ whilst the second equation is most easily plotted by means of a table of squares and a slide rule—the first to find $x^2$ and the second to multiply this by $(x + b')$ which is formed mentally.

143

*Figure 9.2.1* (a) (b), illustrates the two methods of approach applied to the simple cubic equation:

$$x^3 - 3x^2 + 4x - 2 = 0.$$

Graph (a) is obtained by a direct plot of:

$$y = x^3 - 3x^2 + 4x - 2$$

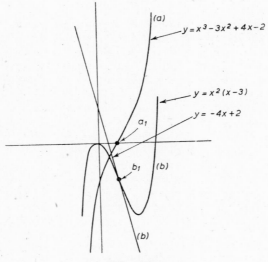

Figure 9.2.1

at interval $x = 0 \cdot 5$, whilst the pair of graphs (b) give

$$y = -4x + 2$$
$$y = x^2(x - 3)$$

and were plotted from points at the same interval, both reveal the real root at $x = 1$.

The above example is an extremely simple one and does not show the wealth of detail which can sometimes result from the preliminary survey; a more interesting illustration is provided by the equation:

$$ax = \tan x \qquad\qquad \ldots\ldots(9.2.4)$$

144

which occurs in the design of gears. We replace the single equation by:

$$\left.\begin{array}{l} y = ax \\ y = \tan x \end{array}\right\} \qquad \ldots\ldots(9.2.5)$$

and thus obtain the graph of *Figure 9.2.2*.

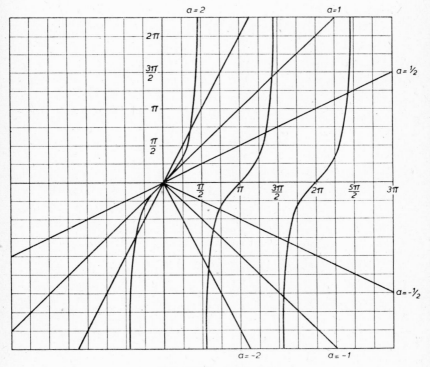

Figure 9.2.2.    tan $x = ax$

The intersections, for various values of $a$, give the approximate positions of the required roots which can be refined by the processes to be described in section 9.3. In addition to this data, the graphs show that there are no positive real roots (other than $x = 0$) in the range $(0, \pi)$ when $0 < a \leqslant +1$, and no roots in the range $(0, \pi/2)$ when $a < 0$. Furthermore, it is clear that for large $x$ the roots tend asymptotically to $(n + \frac{1}{2})\pi$ for all values of $|a| > 0$.

An example of a survey applied to a set of simultaneous equations is provided by x-ray crystal structure analysis. It became necessary

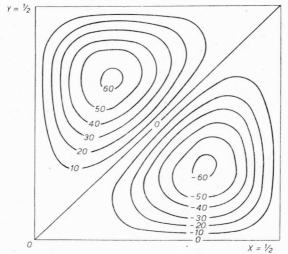

*Figure 9.2.3* (a) $40 [\sin (4\pi x).\sin (2\pi y) - \sin (2\pi x).\sin (4\pi y)]$

to obtain the solution of the simultaneous equations:

$$\left.\begin{array}{r}40[\sin (4\pi x).\sin (2\pi y) - \sin (2\pi x).\sin (4\pi y)] = -30 \\ 40[\cos (8\pi x) + \cos (8\pi y)] = +10\end{array}\right\} \quad \dots (9.2.6)$$

and for these the two dimensional contour maps shown in *Figure 9.2.3* (a) (b) are plotted. By superimposing the two maps, as in *Figure 9.2.4* it is possible to read off the approximate roots of the equations 9.2.6, and also to see exactly how the various alternative pairs of $(x, y)$ values arise, a point which is by no means clear from a direct analytic solution.

For systems of equations which involve more than two variables the graphical survey is generally impossible. In these cases, apart from any information as to the locations of roots which may result from a knowledge of the experimental system in which they arise, there will usually be no alternative but to take some arbitrary starting point and use one of the successive refinement methods to be described in the remainder of this chapter. A word of warning is perhaps appropriate in this connection; it is that refinement methods usually postulate that the trial point is near to the true solution. If

146

this condition is not satisfied, they may either not converge at all or, more probably, converge to a false solution which is in the nature

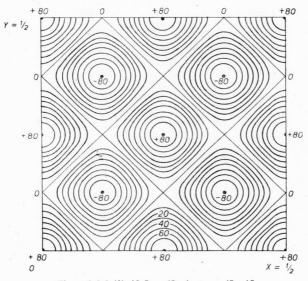

*Figure 9.2.3 (b)* 40 [cos (8$\pi x$) + cos (8$\pi y$)]

of a 'col', or depression, in a mountain range, instead of the true valley which is sought.

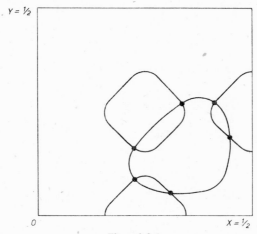

*Figure 9.2.4*

147

NON-LINEAR ALGEBRAIC EQUATIONS

## 9.3 ITERATIVE PROCESSES—ONE VARIABLE

We may, as in section 9.1, write the general non-linear equation in one variable as:

$$f(x) = 0 \qquad \dots (9.3.1)$$

and the problem which we shall consider in this section is the solution of this form. We may remark that when $f(x)$ is a polynomial, say:

$$f(x) = x^n + a_1 x^{n-1} + a_2 x^{n-2} \dots + a_n = 0 \quad \dots (9.3.2)$$

classical methods of solution, depending upon the theory of equations, are available. We shall not mention them further except to remark that they are the methods of Horner and Graeffe [1, 2] and that they find little favour with modern numerical analysts. The analytic solutions of the cubic and diquadratic equations, known as Ferrari's, Tartaglia's and Cardan's methods, are of little utility in numerical work.

An iterative process for the solution of an equation of the type 9.3.1 may be defined by the statement that, if $x_0$ is an approximation to the solution of equation 9.3.1, it enables a quantity $x_1$ to be calculated by means of some relation:

$$x_1 = I(x_0) \qquad \dots (9.3.3)$$

in such a manner that $x_1$ is a closer approximation to the required solution than was $x_0$.

If $x_0$ differs from the true root by a small quantity, of order $(\epsilon)$, say, then the iterative process 9.3.3 is said to be $n$th order if the error in $x_1$ is of order $(\epsilon^n)$. Most of the best iterative processes are second order; third and higher order processes exist and can always be constructed from those of lower order, but often they involve greater *total* computing labour for a given final accuracy than those of the second order.

As an example of a first order process we may consider the so-called *regula falsi* or rule of false position which is possibly the oldest known iterative procedure.

Suppose it is required to find the root of:

$$y = f(x) = 0$$

corresponding to the intersection $R$ shown in *Figure 9.3.1*. Any point $(x_0, y_0)$ on the curve is taken and also any other point $(x_1, y_1)$—preferably on the opposite side of $OX$ from $(x_0, y_0)$. Effectively the process consists of finding the intersection of the line joining $(x_0, y_0)(x_1, y_1)$ with $OX$ and then taking this abscissa, $x_2$ say, to determine a new point $(x_2, y_2)$ on the curve. The operation sequence is repeated using $(x_0, y_0)$ and $(x_2, y_2)$, and it is clear that convergence to the root, $R$ say, takes place. Analytically the method is equivalent to a sequence of linear interpolations, and the relation between successive convergents is easily shown to be:

$$x_{n+1} = (x_0 y_n - x_n y_0)/(y_n - y_0) \qquad \ldots . (9.3.4)$$

To investigate the relation between the errors of the $n$th and $(n + 1)$th approximation assume the root to be $x = X$ and let:

$$x_0 = X + \epsilon_0$$
$$x_n = X + \epsilon_n$$

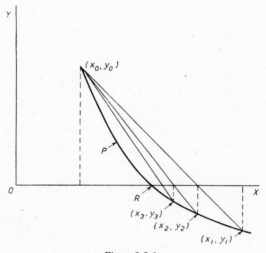

Figure 9.3.1

Then Taylor's theorem gives:

$$y_0 = \epsilon_0 f'(X) + \tfrac{1}{2}\epsilon_0^2 f''(X) + \ldots .$$
$$y_n = \epsilon_n f'(X) + \tfrac{1}{2}\epsilon_n^2 f''(X) + \ldots .$$

(since, by definition $f(X) = 0$) and substitution in 9.3.4 and simplification leads to:

$$x_{n+1} \simeq X + \tfrac{1}{2}\epsilon_0 \cdot \epsilon_n f''(X)/f'(X)$$

whence

$$\epsilon_{n+1} \simeq \tfrac{1}{2}\epsilon_0 \cdot \epsilon_n f''(X)/f'(X) \qquad \ldots . (9.3.5)$$

thus, if $\epsilon_0$ is such that $\left| \tfrac{1}{2}\epsilon_0 f''(X)/f'(X) \right| < 1$, the process will

149

converge. Actually convergence may be quite rapid if the initial point is well chosen, but it should be noticed that each iteration of the process will only produce an improvement of the order of one place of decimals.

A general technique of construction for second order processes is that known as the Newton-Raphson method. Assume that an approximation $(x_n)$ has been calculated which has an error $(\epsilon_n)$, then since:

$$f(x_n + \epsilon_n) = 0$$

we have, by Taylor's theorem:

$$f(x_n + \epsilon_n) = 0 = f(x_n) + \epsilon_n f'(x_n) + \frac{\epsilon_n^2}{2} f''(x_n) + \cdots$$

so that, if we choose

$$x_{n+1} = x_n - f(x_n)/f'(x_n) \qquad \dots (9.3.6)$$

the error in $x_{n+1}$ is of order $(\epsilon_n)^2$.

It should be noticed that there is no *unique* iteration of the second order leading to a given result. Thus, suppose that a process for determining the square root of a quantity $b$ is required, the equation:

$$x^2 - b = 0 \qquad \dots (9.3.7)$$

has the required solution $x = \pm \sqrt{b}$.

From equation 9.3.6 the iteration:

$$x_{n+1} = x_n - (x_n^2 - b)/2x_n = \tfrac{1}{2}(x_n + b/x_n) \qquad \dots (9.3.8)$$

is obtained. On the other hand, 9.3.7 may be written:

$$1/x^2 - 1/b = 0$$

and this leads to:

$$x_{n+1} = x_n - (1/x_n^2 - 1/b)/(-2/x_n^3) = x_n[1 + (b - x_n^2)/2b]$$
$$\dots (9.3.9)$$

It can be shown that, although equations 9.3.8. and 9.3.9 are both second order processes, equation 9.3.8 converges rather more rapidly since the coefficient of $\epsilon_n^2$ is less. On the other hand, 9.3.9 requires only one division (to form $1/2b$) and this may be an advantage if it is to be used on an automatic digital calculator which, as is often the case, has no automatic divider.

Simple rearrangement of the original equation is not the only method for obtaining second order processes. Thus we may multiply the original equation $f(x) = 0$ by an arbitrary function $g(x)$ and apply the Newton-Raphson process to the combined system. If we take $g(x) = x$ and apply this to equation 9.3.7 there results:

$$x^3 - bx = 0$$

for which the iterative solution formula is:

$$x_{n+1} = x_n - \frac{x_n^3 - bx_n}{3x_n^2 - b} = 2x_n^3/(3x_n^2 - b) \quad \ldots\ldots(9.3.10)$$

Now although both equations 9.3.7 and 9.3.10 are second order processes it is easy to show that, if:

$$x_n = \sqrt{b} + \epsilon$$

equation 9.3.7 leads to:

$$x_{n+1} = \sqrt{b} + \tfrac{1}{2}\epsilon^2/\sqrt{b} - \tfrac{1}{2}\epsilon^3/b + etc.$$

and equation 9.3.10 to:

$$x_{n+1} = \sqrt{b} + \tfrac{3}{2}\epsilon^2/\sqrt{b} - \tfrac{7}{2}\epsilon^3/b + etc.$$

Whence, by taking the iteration defined by:

$$\tfrac{3}{2}(9.3.7) - \tfrac{1}{2}(9.3.10)$$

the term in $\epsilon^2/\sqrt{b}$ is eliminated and we obtain the third order process: [3]

$$x_{n+1} = (5x_n^4 + 6bx_n^2 - 3b^2)/4x_n(3x_n^2 - b) + \epsilon^3/b + etc. \quad \ldots\ldots(9.3.11)$$

Similarly from: $\tfrac{3}{4}(9.3.7) + \tfrac{1}{4}(9.3.9)$

we obtain the third order process:

$$x_{n+1} = (3b^2 + 6bx_n^2 - x_n^4)/8bx_n - \tfrac{3}{4}\epsilon^3/b + etc. \quad \ldots\ldots(9.3.12)$$

and 9.3.11 and 9.3.12 could be combined to give a fourth order process. It is quite apparent from the complexity of 9.3.11 and 9.3.12 that they are of little utility in practical computation.

We may notice, before leaving the subject of second order processes for simple functions, the formula:

$$x_{n+1} = x_n(2 - bx_n) \quad \ldots\ldots(9.3.13)$$

which converges to $1/b$ and is derived from the equation:

$$1/x - b = 0;$$

and also the iteration:

$$x_{n+1} = x_n[(p + 1) - bx_n^p]/p \quad \ldots\ldots(9.3.14)$$

which converges to $1/x^{1/p}$ and is derived from:

$$1/x^{\,p} - b = 0$$

**151**

## 9.4 COMPLEX ROOTS

The Newton-Raphson process, described above, is usually considered to be applicable only to the determination of real roots, and various other methods have been suggested for determining complex roots. Thus, in attempting to find the solution of a polynomial equation:

$$y = x^n + a_1 x^{n-1} + a_2 x^{n-2} \ldots + a_n = 0 \quad \ldots (9.4.1)$$

it is usually recommended that all real roots be first found, say $a_1$, $a_2 \ldots a_r$, and then the polynomial divided through by the product $(x - a_1)(x - a_2) \ldots (x - a_r)$ to give a polynomial of degree $(n - r)$:

$$z = x^{n-r} + b_1 x^{n-r-1} + b_2 x^{n-r-2} \ldots b_{n-r} = 0 \quad \ldots (9.4.2)$$

all of whose roots are now known to be complex.

At this stage an attempt is made to find the real quadratic factors of equation 9.4.2 by a process which involves a combination of two trial divisions by an assumed approximation:

$$x^2 + cx + e$$

and a second order treatment of the results to give a better approximation. [4]

Actually it is quite feasible to use the Newton-Raphson process for evaluating complex roots, and since this is applicable to quite general equations and is second order, it will now be described.

Assume that it is desired to find a solution $z = a + ib$ to the equation:

$$f(z) = 0 \quad \ldots (9.4.3)$$

Let $z = z_0 + \eta$, where $\eta = \epsilon + i\delta$, and $\epsilon$ and $\delta$ are assumed to be of the first order of small quantities. Then Taylor's theorem gives:

$$f(z) = 0 = f(z_0 + \eta) = f(z_0) + \eta f'(z_0) + \tfrac{1}{2}\eta^2 f''(z_0) + \ldots$$

whence, to the second order:

$$\eta = -f(z_0)/f'(z_0) \quad \ldots (9.4.4)$$

which is identical with the ordinary Newton-Raphson formula for real roots. We now note that:

$$\epsilon = \text{real part of } [-f(z_0)/f'(z_0)]$$

$$\delta = \text{imaginary part of } [-f(z_0)/f'(z_0)]$$

152

and that, to start the iteration, it is necessary to take a complex value of $(z_0)$ which in the absence of other information can be taken to be (i).

As an example of the convergence of this process the following figures, obtained in solving:

$$z^2 - 2z + 2 = 0$$

from the initial value $z_0 = i$, show it in a favourable light:

| | |
|---|---|
| $z_0 = i$ | $\eta_0 = \frac{1}{4}(3 - i)$ |
| $z_1 = \frac{3}{4}(1 + i)$ | $\eta_1 = \frac{1}{40}(13 + 9i)$ |
| $z_2 = \frac{1}{40}(43 + 39i)$ | $\eta_2 = - \cdot 07673 + \cdot 02230i$ |
| $\quad (= 1\cdot075 + \cdot975i)$ | |
| $z_3 = \cdot99827 + \cdot99730i$ | |

The true solution is evidently $(1 + i)$ and the errors: $|1 + i - z_r|$ are 1, $\cdot35$, $\cdot08$ and $\cdot0032$ respectively.

On the other hand, if an attempt is made to find directly a complex root of the equation:

$$z^3 - 3z^2 + 4z - 2 = 0$$

discussed in section 9.2, starting from the same initial approximation (i) the successive convergents are:

| | |
|---|---|
| $z_0 = i$ | $\eta_0 = \cdot46 - \cdot24i$ |
| $z_1 = \cdot46 + \cdot76i$ | $\eta_1 = \cdot43 - \cdot12i$ |
| $z_2 = \cdot85 + \cdot64i$ | $\eta_2 = \cdot825 + \cdot28i$ |
| $z_3 = 1\cdot54 + \cdot78i$ | |

with errors 1, $\cdot59$, $\cdot39$ and $\cdot58$, so that $z_3$ is a less good approximation than $z_2$. The reason for this behaviour lies in the fact that the derivative of

$$z^3 - 3z^2 + 4z - 2 = 0$$

that is:

$$3z^2 - 6z + 4$$

has a pair of complex roots $1 \pm \cdot577i$ and that the value

$$z_2 = \cdot85 + \cdot64i$$

is fairly close to one of these.

## 9.5 EQUAL ROOTS

When an equation is such that it is satisfied for values of the variable which tend to equality, with some parameter in the equation, the Newton-Raphson process will, in general, break down. Geometrically the situation is simply that the curve:

$$y = f(x)$$

is nearly parallel to the $x$ axis in the region of the roots (or, in the limit touches the $x$ axis), and this should have become evident in the preliminary survey.

When *exactly* equal roots occur they can be found by the simple process of extracting the highest common factor of $f(x)$ and $f'(x)$. When exact equality is not present, however, the first step should be to find the root of $f'(x) = 0$, say $(x_m)$. Then assume that the roots of $f(x) = 0$ are $(x_m \pm \epsilon)$ so that:

$$f(x_m \pm \epsilon) = 0 = f(x_m) \pm \epsilon f'(x_m) + \tfrac{1}{2}\epsilon^2 f''(x_m) \pm \cdots$$

or, since by definition $f'(x_m) = 0$,

$$\epsilon = \pm \sqrt{\frac{-2f(x_m)}{f''(x_m)}} \qquad \ldots (9.5.1)$$

From this point it should be possible to revert to the normal Newton-Raphson process with some hope of convergence.

Alternatively, when a pair of equal roots is known to exist, an approximating value, $x_0$, may be improved as follows. Assume that the correct solution is $(x_0 + \epsilon)$, then Taylor's theorem gives:

$$f(x_0 + \epsilon) = f(x_0) + \epsilon f'(x_0) + \tfrac{1}{2}\epsilon^2 f''(x_0) + \cdots$$

Since a multiple root occurs at $(x_0 + \epsilon)$ this must correspond to the *minimum* of $f(x_0 + \epsilon)$ with respect to $\epsilon$.

$$\frac{df}{d\epsilon} = 0 \simeq f'(x_0) + \epsilon f''(x_0)$$

Whence: $\qquad\qquad \epsilon = -f'(x_0)/f''(x_0) \qquad \ldots (9.5.2)$

## 9.6 SIMULTANEOUS NON-LINEAR EQUATIONS

We return now to the solution of the general set of non-linear simultaneous equations envisaged in section 9.1

$$f_i(x_1, x_2 \ldots x_n) = 0 \quad (i = 1 \ldots m) \qquad \ldots (9.6.1)$$

that is, a set of $m$ equations in $n$ unknowns. When $m = n$ we have the classical case in which a finite multiplicity of solutions may exist. The more general situations, in which $m < n$ or $m > n$ are also encountered in physical problems and, in these circumstances there may be no *unique* solution in the former event, and no solution in the latter.

To unify the method of approach we shall define a solution of equations 9.6.1 to be any set of parameters $(x_i)$ which makes the positive definite form:

$$\Phi = \sum_{i=1}^{n} G_i(f_i) \qquad \qquad \dots (9.6.2)$$

a minimum, $G_i(z)$ being a function so chosen as to be always positive for all values of $z$, real or complex.

For convenience and simplicity it is usual to take either:

$$G_i(z) = z . \bar{z}$$

or

$$G_i(z) = |z|$$

where $\bar{z}$ is understood to mean the complex conjugate of $z$.

The general approach to the solution of a set of equations of type 9.6.1 should again be in two parts, first a survey to detect the rough location of the roots, and second a refinement process to evaluate the roots more exactly. Unfortunately the survey process is almost impossible when more than two variables are involved and in this event a refinement by successive approximation may have to be attempted.

When only a small number of equations and variables are involved (up to three) it may be feasible to use the Newton-Raphson process to find a solution to the required accuracy. Thus suppose that the required solution is at $(x_1 + \epsilon_1, x_2 + \epsilon_2 \ldots x_n + \epsilon_n)$, then the $n$ variable form of Taylor's theorem gives:

$$f_i(x_1 + \epsilon_1, x_2 + \epsilon_2 \ldots x_n + \epsilon_n)$$

$$= f_i(x_1, x_2 \ldots x_n) + \sum_{r=1}^{n} \epsilon_r \frac{\partial f_i}{\partial x_r} + O(\epsilon^2) \qquad (i = 1 \ldots n)$$

whence, for a second order process, we take $(\epsilon_1 \ldots \epsilon_n)$ to be the solution of the set of *linear* simultaneous equations:

$$\epsilon_1 \frac{\partial f_i}{\partial x_1} + \epsilon_2 \frac{\partial f_i}{\partial x_2} \ldots + \epsilon_n \frac{\partial f_i}{\partial x_n} = -f_i \qquad (i = 1 \ldots n) \qquad \dots (9.6.3)$$

which correspond exactly to the one-dimensional Newton-Raphson process of equation 9.3.6.

When large numbers of variables and equations are involved this process will, in general, be too complicated to apply, and under these circumstances the analogue of one of the successive approximation methods of Chapter 7, sections 7.7. and 7.9 is to be preferred.

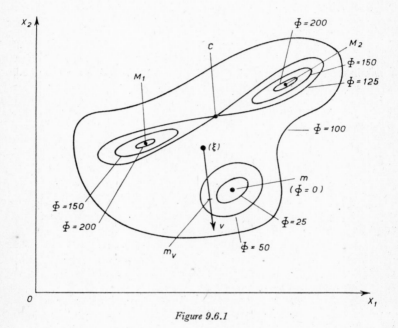

*Figure 9.6.1*

If the function $\Phi(x_1, x_2 \ldots x_n)$, defined in equation 9.6.2, is taken as the basis of a minimization process, the analysis can be conducted in a manner which closely parallels that of sections 7.7 and 7.9 with the exception that the $n$ dimensional surfaces:

$$\Phi = \text{const.}$$

are no longer, in general, hyper-ellipsoids.

To take a two-dimensional example, the contour map of *Figure 9.6.1* might be encountered. In this two maxima are shown at $M_1$ and $M_2$, a minimum at $m$ and a 'col', or pass between mountains, at $C$.

We seek to progress from an initial point of vector $\boldsymbol{\xi}$ ($= x_1 x_2 \ldots x_n$) to a vector ($\boldsymbol{\xi} + a\boldsymbol{v}$) which makes $\Phi(\boldsymbol{\xi} + a\boldsymbol{v})$ less than $\Phi(\boldsymbol{\xi})$. The Taylor expansion gives, at once,

$$\Phi(\boldsymbol{\xi} + a\boldsymbol{v}) = \Phi(\boldsymbol{\xi}) + \sum_{r=1}^{n} av_r \frac{\partial \Phi}{\partial x_r} + \sum_{r,s=1}^{n} \tfrac{1}{2} a^2 v_r v_s \frac{\partial^2 \Phi}{\partial x_r \partial x_s} + O(a^3)$$

$$\ldots\ldots (9.6.4)$$

Here $\boldsymbol{v}$ is any vector and $v_r$ is its component in direction $x_r$. Assume now that it is adequate to represent the variation of $\Phi$ along the vector $\boldsymbol{v}$ by means of the terms of degree less than *three* in $a$ in equation 9.6.4. We then obtain for the least value of $\Phi$ the multiplier $a$ by means of:

$$\frac{\mathrm{d}\Phi}{\mathrm{d}a} = 0$$

That is, from equation 9.6.4,

$$a = - \sum_{r=1}^{n} v_r \frac{\partial \Phi}{\partial x_r} \bigg/ \sum_{r,s=1}^{n} v_r \cdot v_s \frac{\partial^2 \Phi}{\partial x_r \partial x_s} \qquad \ldots\ldots (9.6.5)$$

Just as in Chapter 7, there are several national choices for the vector $\boldsymbol{v}$. If it is taken parallel to one of the axes of co-ordinates, $x_k$ say, equation 9.7.5 becomes:

$$a = - \frac{\partial \Phi}{\partial x_k} \bigg/ \frac{\partial^2 \Phi}{\partial x_k^2} \qquad \ldots\ldots (9.6.6)$$

and this corresponds to the relaxation technique of the linear case.

For a steepest descent, $\boldsymbol{v}$ is defined by:

$$\boldsymbol{v} = \mathrm{grad}\ \Phi = \sum_{r=1}^{n} \boldsymbol{e}_r \frac{\partial \Phi}{\partial x_r} \qquad \ldots\ldots (9.6.7)$$

where $\boldsymbol{e}_r$ represents the unit vector parallel to the axis of $x_r$. Substituting in 9.6.5 we obtain:

$$a = - \sum_{r=1}^{n} \left(\frac{\partial \Phi}{\partial x_r}\right)^2 \bigg/ \sum_{r,s=1}^{n} \frac{\partial \Phi}{\partial x_r} \cdot \frac{\partial \Phi}{\partial x_s} \cdot \frac{\partial^2 \Phi}{\partial x_r \partial x_s} \qquad \ldots\ldots (9.6.8)$$

so that the actual change in any co-ordinate $x_k$ is:

$$a \frac{\partial \Phi}{\partial x_k} = - \frac{\partial \Phi}{\partial x_k} \cdot \sum_{r=1}^{n} \left(\frac{\partial \Phi}{\partial x_r}\right)^2 \bigg/ \sum_{r,s=1}^{n} \frac{\partial \Phi}{\partial x_r} \cdot \frac{\partial \Phi}{\partial x_s} \cdot \frac{\partial^2 \Phi}{\partial x_r . \partial x_s} \qquad \ldots\ldots (9.6.9)$$

This formula is really too complex for use in actual computation and although it has been applied,[5] is not so simple as a variant which will now be described.

Let the value of $\Phi$ along $\boldsymbol{v}$ be as shown in *Figure 9.6.2*.

We first take the intersection of the tangent to the $\Phi$, $a$ curve with the line $\Phi = 0$, $T$ say. $OT$ is simply determined by means of equation 9.6.4 by neglecting terms in $a^2$ and so on. Thus:

$$a_T = -\ \Phi(\xi) \bigg/ \sum_{r=1}^{n} v_r \frac{\partial\Phi}{\partial x_r} \qquad \ldots . (9.6.10)$$

Next we calculate the values of $\Phi$ at the points $(\xi + a_T\boldsymbol{v})$ and $(\xi + \tfrac{1}{2}a_T\boldsymbol{v})$ and call these $\Phi_1$, and $\Phi_{\frac{1}{2}}$ respectively.

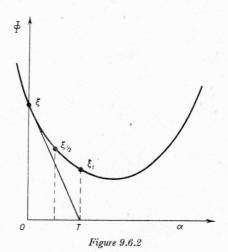

*Figure 9.6.2*

The minimum is then calculated by the simple process of forming the quadratic approximation to $\Phi$ which passes through $\Phi$, $\Phi_{\frac{1}{2}}$ and $\Phi_1$, and then differentiating it with respect to $a$. Thus:

$$\Phi a \simeq \Phi + \frac{2a}{a_T}\Delta\Phi + \frac{a}{a_T}\left(\frac{2a}{a_T} - 1\right)\Delta^2\Phi$$

whence, since $\dfrac{\mathrm{d}\Phi a}{\mathrm{d}a} = 0$,

$$\frac{a}{a_T} = (\Delta^2\Phi - 2\Delta\Phi)/4\Delta^2\Phi \qquad \ldots . (9.6.11)$$

Thus the individual component changes, $av_r$, are for the steepest descent, simply:

$$-\frac{(\Phi_1 - 4\Phi_{\frac{1}{2}} + 3\Phi)}{4(\Phi_1 - 2\Phi_{\frac{1}{2}} + \Phi)} \cdot \frac{\Phi \cdot \partial \Phi / \partial x_r}{\left[ \sum_{r=1}^{n} \left( \frac{\partial \Phi}{\partial x_r} \right)^2 \right]} \qquad \dots (9.6.12)$$

It will be noticed that the use of this version of the steepest descent process requires the calculation of three values of $\Phi$, and all $\frac{\partial \Phi}{\partial x_r}$, $(n + 3)$ values in all, as compared with about $\frac{n^2}{2}$ values of

$$\frac{\partial \Phi}{\partial x_r} + \frac{\partial^2 \Phi}{\partial x_r \partial x_s}$$

for the analytic expression 9.6.9.

The method of minimizing $\Phi$ with respect to variations along a single vector $v$ can be extended to cover the case of two vectors $v$ and $w$. This requires the minimization of $\Phi(\xi + av + \beta w)$ with respect to $a$ and $\beta$ and follows the same lines as those used in deriving equation 9.6.5. Just as in Chapter 7, section 7.7 the vectors $v$ and $w$ are taken to be the current direction of steepest descent and the direction of the last descent; the formulae are, however, so complex as to be practically useless.

To conclude this section we may mention some of the difficulties which accompany the solution of non-linear algebraic equations by minimization methods. These stem from the fact that the surfaces $\Phi =$ const. are not simple hyper-ellipsoids having a single common centre corresponding to the minimum of $\Phi$. As shown in *Figure 6.9.1* *maxima* may occur, as at $M_1$ and $M_2$, relative minima are possible, and 'cols' are of common occurrence. Each singularity of this type is a possible *stationary* value of $\Phi$ and care must be taken to ensure that any 'solution' obtained by descent methods is a true minimum and not one of these spurious addenda. This is particularly true in the case of redundant sets of equations where an actual zero of $\Phi$ is not to be hoped for.

It may be noted that, whilst maxima and 'cols' are easily detected by virtue of the fact that for the regions near to these the quadratic form:

$$\sum_{r, s} \frac{\partial^2 \Phi}{\partial x_r \partial x_s} \cdot x_r x_s$$

159

is *not* positive definite, a relative minimum is quite indistinguishable by any purely mathematical test from the true minimum which defines the desired solution.

REFERENCES

[1] OLVER, F. W. J. *Phil. Trans. Roy. Soc.*, A 244 (1952) 385
[2] WHITTAKER, E. T. and ROBINSON, G., 'The Calculus of Observations,' 4th edn., p. 106 (1949)
[3] HARTREE, D. R., *Proc. Camb. Phil. Soc.*, 45 (1948) 230
[4] — 'Numerical Analysis,' p. 201, Oxford (1952)
[5] BOOTH, A. D., *Quart. J. mech.*, II (1949) 460

# 10

# APPROXIMATING FUNCTIONS

## 10.1 DEVELOPMENT IN SERIES

THE advent of automatic digital calculators has resulted in the frequent necessity for means of generating various common functions using only the operations of elementary arithmetic. Thus it is useless, from the computing machine viewpoint, to say 'calculate sin $x$' since the machine will not normally understand a direct command of this type.

In practice a statement such as that made in the previous paragraph could be replaced by the equivalent:

Form
$$\left( x - \frac{x^3}{3!} + \frac{x^5}{5!} - \frac{x^7}{7!} \cdots \right)$$

taking sufficient terms so that the result is correct to the number of places required. In order to minimize the amount of work required to calculate the value of a given function it is thus appropriate to consider whether a better approximation than the Taylor series can be found for a given amount of work.

To make this more precise we may consider the following proposition: determine the $(N + 1)$ coefficients $a_r$ so that the maximum *difference* between $f(x)$ and $\sum_{r=0}^{N} a_r x^r$ is as small as possible for a given range of values of $x$. Or again; determine the values of $a_r$ so that the difference between $f(x)$ and $\sum_{r=0}^{N} a_r x^r$ has the least possible mean square value for a given range of $x$.

Which of these definitions will be best in any given context depends essentially upon the ultimate use to which the approximations to $f(x)$ are to be put. Clearly if only a single value is required the maximum divergence should be made as small as possible, on the other hand, if a number of such values are to be associated, either directly as:

$$\sum_{s=1}^{M} f(x_s) \qquad \qquad \dots (10.1.1)$$

161

or with a weighting function $w(x_s)$

$$\sum_{s=1}^{M} w(x_s)f(x_s) \qquad \ldots (10.1.2)$$

then some approximation of least integral square deviation will be best.

In this chapter we shall consider several useful approximations of both categories.

## 10.2 LEAST SQUARE APPROXIMATIONS

Consider any set of functions $O_n(x)$ ($n = 0 \ldots \infty$) ortho-normal in the interval $(a, b)$. We shall show that if an arbitrary function, $f(x)$, is expanded in a Fourier series of these functions, then the first $(n + 1)$ terms of that series constitute the best $(n + 1)$ term approximation to $f(x)$ in the least square sense.

For suppose that the expansion is:

$$f(x) \simeq \sum_{r=0}^{n} a_r O_r(x) \qquad \ldots (10.2.1)$$

then it is required that:

$$L = \int_{a}^{b} \left[ f(x) - \sum_{r=0}^{n} a_r O_r(x) \right]^2 dx \qquad \ldots (10.2.2)$$

is a minimum. Now for a minimum:

$$\frac{\partial L}{\partial a_r} = 0 \qquad (r = 0 \ldots n) \qquad \ldots (10.2.3)$$

whence:

$$\int_{a}^{b} O_s(x) \left[ f(x) - \sum_{r=0}^{n} a_r O_r(x) \right] dx = 0 \qquad (s = 0 \ldots n)$$
$$\ldots (10.2.4)$$

but, since the functions $O_r(x)$ are ortho-normal in $(a, b)$

$$\int_{a}^{b} O_r(x) O_s(x) dx = \delta_{rs} \qquad (\ldots 10.2.5)$$

where $\delta_{rs}$ is the Kronecker delta function defined by:

$$\delta_{rs} \begin{array}{l} = 0 \, (r \neq s) \\ = 1 \, (r = s) \end{array}$$

whence equation 10.2.4 may be written:

$$\int_a^b O_s(x)f(x)\mathrm{d}x = \sum_{r=0}^n a_r\delta_{rs} = a_s \qquad \ldots (10.2.6)$$

but this is simply the definition of the coefficient of $O_s(x)$ in the normal Fourier expansion of $f(x)$.

The approximation can be generalized to include a weight function $w(x)$. Thus the functions $O_n(x)$ satisfy:

$$\int_a^b O_r(x)O_s(x)w(x)\mathrm{d}x = \delta_{rs} \qquad \ldots (10.2.7)$$

and

$$L_w = \int_a^b w(x)\left[f(x) - \sum_{r=0}^n a_rO_r(x)\right]^2\mathrm{d}x \qquad \ldots (10.2.8)$$

is a minimum when

$$a_s = \int_a^b w(x)O_s(x)f(x)\mathrm{d}x \qquad \ldots (10.2.9)$$

which is, again, the normal Fourier coefficient.

### 10.3 SOME USEFUL FUNCTIONS FOR LEAST SQUARE APPROXIMATION

From the classical viewpoint the most important set of orthogonal functions are sin $(nx)$ and cos $(nx)$, which lead to the well-known Fourier expansions in $(0, \pi)$ and $(0, 2\pi)$. These will not be further considered here save to remark that, under suitable circumstances, not only is the mean square difference between function and approximation minimized, but that the same is true of derivatives.

The most important polynomial expansions, for unit weight function, are these in terms of the Legendre polynomials $P_n(x)$. These are defined by:

$$P_n(x) = \frac{1}{2^nn!}\frac{\mathrm{d}^n}{\mathrm{d}x^n}(x^2 - 1)^n \qquad \ldots (10.3.1)$$

$$P_{n+1}(x) = [(2n + 1)xP_n(x) - nP_{n-1}(x)]/n + 1 \ldots \qquad \ldots (10.3.2)$$

with orthogonality relations:

$$\int_{-1}^{+1} P_n(x)P_m(x)\mathrm{d}x = 2\delta_{mn}/(2n + 1) \qquad \ldots (10.3.3)$$

For intervals other than $(-1, +1)$ it is easy to transform the Legendre polynomials by means of:

$$x = \frac{2}{b-a}z - \frac{b+a}{b-a} \qquad \ldots (10.3.4)$$

which gives a set of polynomials $Q_n(z)$, say, orthogonal in $(a, b)$ and with orthogonality relations:

$$\int_a^b Q_n(z)Q_m(z)\mathrm{d}z = (b-a)\delta_{mn}/(2n+1) \qquad \ldots (10.3.5)$$

The first eleven Legendre polynomials for interval $(-1, +1)$ are given in *Table 10.3.1*.

*Table 10.3.1. Legendre polynomials for interval $(-1, +1)$*

| $n$ | $P_n(x)$ | $n$ | $P_n(x)$ |
|---|---|---|---|
| 0 | $1$ | 6 | $\frac{1}{16}(231x^6 - 315x^4 + 105x^2 - 5)$ |
| 1 | $x$ | 7 | $\frac{1}{16}(429x^7 - 693x^5 + 315x^3 - 35x)$ |
| 2 | $\frac{1}{2}(3x^2 - 1)$ | 8 | $\frac{1}{128}(6435x^8 - 12012x^6 + 6930x^4 - 1260x^2 + 35)$ |
| 3 | $\frac{1}{2}(5x^3 - 3x)$ | 9 | $\frac{1}{128}(12155x^9 - 25740x^7 + 18018x^5 - 4620x^3 + 315x)$ |
| 4 | $\frac{1}{8}(35x^4 - 30x^2 + 3)$ | 10 | $\frac{1}{256}(46189x^{10} - 109395x^8 + 90090x^6$ |
| 5 | $\frac{1}{8}(63x^5 - 70x^3 + 15x)$ | | $\qquad\qquad - 30030x^4 + 3465x^2 - 63)$ |

Useful expansions are:

$$x^{2n} = \frac{1}{(2n+1)}\left[ 1.P_o(x) + 5.\frac{2n}{2n+3}.P_2(x) \right.$$
$$\left. + 9.\frac{2n(2n-2)}{(2n+3)(2n+5)}.P_4(x) + \ldots \right]$$

$$x^{2n+1} = \frac{1}{(2n+3)}\left[ 3.P_1(x) + 7.\frac{2n}{2n+5}P_3(x) \right.$$
$$\left. + 11\frac{2n(2n-2)}{(2n+5)(2n+7)}P_5(x) + \ldots \right]$$

$$(1-x^2)^{\frac{1}{2}} = \frac{\pi}{2}\left[ \frac{1}{2}P_0(x) - 5.\frac{1}{4}\left(\frac{1}{2}\right)^2 P_2(x) \right.$$
$$\left. - 9.\frac{3}{6}\left(\frac{1}{2.4}\right)^2 P_4(x) - 13.\frac{5}{8}\left(\frac{1.3}{2.4.6}\right)^2 P_6(x) - \ldots \right]$$

164

$$(1 - x^2)^{-\frac{1}{2}} = \frac{\pi}{2}\bigg[ P_0(x) + 5 \cdot (\tfrac{1}{2})^2 P_2(x)$$

$$+ 9 \cdot \left(\frac{1 \cdot 3}{2 \cdot 4}\right)^2 P_4(x) + 13 \cdot \left(\frac{1 \cdot 3 \cdot 5}{2 \cdot 4 \cdot 6}\right)^2 P_6(x) + \ldots \bigg]$$

$$\sin^{-1}(x) = \frac{\pi}{8}\bigg[ 3 \cdot P_1(x) + 7 \cdot (\tfrac{1}{4})^2 P_3(x) + 11 \cdot \left(\frac{1 \cdot 3}{4 \cdot 6}\right)^2 P_5(x) + \ldots \bigg]$$

$$\sin\left(\frac{\pi}{2} x\right) = 3 \cdot J_{\frac{3}{2}}(\pi/2) P_1(x) - 7 \cdot J_{\frac{7}{2}}(\pi/2) P_3(x)$$

$$+ 11 \cdot J_{\frac{11}{2}}(\pi/2) P_5(x) - \ldots$$

$$\cos\left(\frac{\pi}{2} x\right) = 1 \cdot J_{\frac{1}{2}}(\pi/2) P_0(x) - 5 \cdot J_{\frac{5}{2}}(\pi/2) P_2(x)$$

$$+ 9 \cdot J_{\frac{9}{2}}(\pi/2) P_4(x) - \ldots$$

where $J_\nu(x)$ is the $\nu$th order Bessel function.

Polynomials appropriate to $(0,\infty)$ and for weight function $e^{-x}$ are those of Laguerre, they are given by:

$$L_n(x) = e^x \frac{d^n}{dx^n} (x^n e^{-x}) \qquad \ldots (10.3.6)$$

$$L_{n+1}(x) = (2n + 1 - x)L_n(x) - n^2 L_{n-1}(x) \qquad \ldots (10.3.7)$$

and satisfy:

$$\int_0^\infty L_n(x) L_m(x) e^{-x} dx = (n!)^2 \delta_{mn} \qquad \ldots (10.3.8)$$

Finally, for interval $(-\infty, +\infty)$, there are Hermite polynomials, which are defined by:

$$H_n(x) = (-1)^n e^{x^2} \frac{d^n}{dx^n} (e^{-x^2}) \qquad \ldots (10.3.9)$$

$$H_{n+1}(x) = 2x H_n(x) - 2n H_{n-1}(x) \qquad \ldots (10.3.10)$$

and have orthogonality relations:

$$\int_{-\infty}^\infty H_n(x) H_m(x) e^{-x^2} dx = 2^n \cdot n! \sqrt{\pi} \, \delta_{mn} \qquad \ldots (10.3.11)$$

165

The expressions for some of the above polynomials are given in *Table 10.3.2.*

Table 10.3.2. *Laguerre and Hermite polynomials*

| $n$ | $L_n(x)$ | $H_n(x)$ |
|---|---|---|
| 0 | 1 | 1 |
| 1 | $-x+1$ | $2x$ |
| 2 | $x^2-4x+2$ | $4x^2-2$ |
| 3 | $-x^3+9x^2-18x+6$ | $8x^3-12x$ |
| 4 | $x^4-16x^3+72x^2-96x+24$ | $16x^4-48x^2+12$ |
| 5 | $-x_5+25x^4-200x^3+600x^2-600x+120$ | $32x^5-160x^3+120x$ |

## 10.4 LEAST ABSOLUTE DEVIATION APPROXIMATION

A remarkable set of orthogonal polynomials is that derived by Chebyshev, these are defined by:

$$T_0^* = 1, \quad T_n^*(x) = \frac{1}{2^{n-1}} \cos(n \cos^{-1} x) \quad (n \geqslant 1) \quad \ldots(10.4.1)$$

$$T_{n+1}^*(x) = xT_n^*(x) - \tfrac{1}{4}T_{n-1}^*(x) \qquad \ldots(10.4.2)$$

and have orthogonality relations:

$$\int_{-1}^{+1} T_n^*(x)T_m^*(x)\frac{\mathrm{d}x}{\sqrt{1-x^2}} = \frac{\pi}{2^{2n-1}}\delta_{mn} \quad \ldots(10.4.3)$$

Their importance lies in the fact that, of all polynomials of degree $n$, $T_n^*(x)$ has the least maximum value in $(-1, +1)$ when the coefficient of $x^n$ is taken to be unity. For consider the function defined by equation 10.4.1, it is easily seen that the maxima and minima occur at:

$$x_k = \cos k\pi/n$$

where $k = 0, 1 \ldots n$, and that for these points:

$$T_n^*(x_k) = (-1)^k/2^{n-1}$$

Let

$$M_n(x) = x^n + a_1x^{n-1} + a_2x^{n-2} + \ldots + a_n$$

be a function, not everywhere zero, whose deviation from zero in $(-1, +1)$ is, if possible, less than that of $T_n^*(x)$. Then:

$$T_n^*(x_0) - M_n(x_0) > 0, \; T_n^*(x_1) - M_n(x_1) < 0, \; T_n^*(x_2) - M_n(x_2) > 0 \; etc.$$

that is, the function $T_n^*(x) - M_n(x)$ has roots between $(x_0, x_1)$ $(x_1, x_2)$ ... $(x_{n-1}, x_n)$. There are $n$ of these, and since $T_n^* - M_n$ is of degree $(n-1)$ at most, we are led to a contradiction, it follows that the assumption that $M_n(x)$ is different from zero and $T_n^*(x)$ is false.

Modern usage[1] favours the slightly modified definition:

$$T_0 = 1 \quad T_n(x) = \cos\,(n\,\cos^{-1}x) \qquad \ldots\,(10.4.4)$$

$$T_{n+1} = 2xT_n(x) - T_{n-1}x \qquad \ldots\,(10.4.5)$$

$$\left.\begin{aligned}\int_{-1}^{+1} T_n(x)\,T_m(x)\,\frac{\mathrm{d}x}{\sqrt{1-x^2}} &= \frac{\pi}{2}\,\delta_{mn} \quad (m \neq 0)\\[4pt] &= \pi \quad (m = n = 0)\end{aligned}\right\} \ldots\,(10.4.6)$$

which has the advantage of avoiding fractions in the values of $T_n(x)$, the first eleven of which are given in *Table 10.4.1*.

Table 10.4.1.  Chebyshev polynomials

| $n$ | $T_n(x)$ | $n$ | $T_n(x)$ |
|---|---|---|---|
| 0 | 1 | 6 | $32x^6 - 48x^4 + 18x^2 - 1$ |
| 1 | $x$ | 7 | $64x^7 - 112x^5 + 56x^3 - 7x$ |
| 2 | $2x^2 - 1$ | 8 | $128x^8 - 256x^6 + 160x^4 - 32x^2 + 1$ |
| 3 | $4x^3 - 3x$ | 9 | $256x^9 - 576x^7 + 432x^5 - 120x^3 + 9x$ |
| 4 | $8x^4 - 8x^2 + 1$ | 10 | $512x^{10} - 1280x^8 + 1120x^6 - 400x^4 + 50x^2 - 1$ |
| 5 | $16x^5 - 20x^3 + 5x$ | | |

Useful expansions are:

$$x^n = \frac{1}{2^{n-1}} \sum_{k=0}^{[\frac{1}{2}n]} \binom{n}{k} T_{n-2k}(x)$$

where $[\frac{1}{2}n]$ represents the largest integer in $(\frac{1}{2}n)$ and the coefficient of $T_0(x)$ (if present) is halved,

and: $$\sin\left(\frac{\pi}{2}x\right) = 2 \sum_{r=0}^{\infty} (-1)^r J_{2r+1}\left(\frac{\pi}{2}\right).\,T_{2r+1}(x)$$

$$\cos\left(\frac{\pi}{2}x\right) = J_0\left(\frac{\pi}{2}\right) + 2\sum_{r=1}^{\infty} (-1)^r J_{2r}\left(\frac{\pi}{2}\right).\,T_{2r}(x)$$

where $J_r(x)$ is the $r$th order Bessel function.

167

These Bessel functions, and also those required in the Legendre Polynomial expansions, do not appear to be readily available; we give their values in *Table 10.4.2.*

*Table 10.4.2.   Bessel functions for Legendre and Chebyshev interpolation*

| $n$ | $J_n(\pi/2)$ | $J_{(n + \frac{1}{2})}(\pi/2)$ |
|---|---|---|
| 0 | 0·47200 12157 7 | 0·63661 97723 7 |
| 1 | 0·56682 40889 1 | 0·40528 47345 7 |
| 2 | 0·24970 16291 4 | 0·13741 70540 3 |
| 3 | 0·06903 58882 9 | 0·03212 73337 1 |
| 4 | 0·01399 60398 1 | 0·00575 32170 8 |
| 5 | 0·00224 53571 2 | 0·00083 61720 0 |
| 6 | 0·00029 83476 0 | 0·00010 23428 0 |
| 7 | 0·00003 38506 4 | 0·00001 08228 5 |
| 8 | 0·00000 33522 0 | 0·00000 10077 8 |
| 9 | 0·00000 02945 7 | 0·00000 00838 4 |
| 10 | 0·00000 00232 7 | 0·00000 00063 0 |
| 11 | 0·00000 00016 7 | 0·00000 00004 3 |
| 12 | 0·00000 00001 1 | 0·00000 00000 3 |

## 10.5 GENERATING FUNCTIONS AND DIFFERENTIAL EQUATIONS

In deriving expansions using the various polynomials discussed above it is sometimes convenient to have them expressed in terms of a generating function. The most useful of these are:

*Legendre Polynomials:*

$$\frac{1}{\sqrt{1 - 2hx + h^2}} = \sum_{n=0}^{\infty} h^n P_n(x) \qquad \ldots(10.5.1)$$

*Laguerre Polynomials:*

$$\frac{e^{-xh/(1-h)}}{(1 - h)} = \sum_{n=0}^{\infty} \frac{h^n}{n!} L_n(x) \qquad \ldots(10.5.2)$$

*Hermite Polynomials:*

$$e^{[x^2 - (h-x)^2]} = \sum_{n=0}^{\infty} \frac{h^n}{n!} H_n(x) \qquad \ldots(10.5.3)$$

*Chebyshev Polynomials:*

$$\frac{1 - xh}{1 - 2xh + h^2} = \sum_{n=0}^{\infty} h^n T_n(x) \qquad \ldots(10.5.4)$$

The differential equations satisfied by $P_n$, $L_n$, $H_n$ and $T_n$ are [2], respectively:

$$(x^2 - 1)P_n''(x) + 2xP_n'(x) - n(n + 1)P_n(x) = 0 \quad \ldots (10.5.5)$$

$$xL_n''(x) + (1 - x)L_n'(x) + nL_n(x) = 0 \quad \ldots (10.5.6)$$

$$H_n''(x) - 2xH_n'(x) + 2nH_n(x) = 0 \quad \ldots (10.5.7)$$

and

$$(1 - x^2)T_n''(x) - xT_n'(x) + n^2T_n(x) = 0 \quad \ldots (10.5.8)$$

## 10.6 A COMPARISON OF ACCURACY

We conclude this brief account of the use of approximating polynomials by giving a table, due to GOODWIN [3], showing the relative number of terms required for the ordinary Taylor series and of the Chebyshev approximating polynomial in certain cases.

| Function | Range | Terms in Taylor expansion | Terms in Chebyshev expansion |
|---|---|---|---|
| $e^x$ | $(0, + 1)$ | 14 | 9 |
| $\cos x$ | $(-\pi/2, \pi/2)$ | 8 | 7 |
| $\sin^{-1} x$ | $(- 1, + 1)$ | 25 | 10 |
| $\ln (1 + x)$ | $(0, + 1)$ | $10^{10}$ | 14 |

In each case the required accuracy is ten decimal places.

### REFERENCES

[1] LANCZOS, C., 'Tables of Chebyshev Polynomials,' *Nat. Bur. Stand.* Applied Mathematics Series, No. 9, Washington (1952)
[2] COURANT, R. and HILBERT, D., 'Methods of Mathematical Physics,' vol. 1, Chap. II, New York (1953)
[3] GOODWIN, E. T., 'The Use of Mathematical Tables in a High-speed Digital Computer,' N.P.L. Symposium on automatic digital computation. Paper No. 21. Teddington (1953)

M

# 11

# FOURIER SYNTHESIS AND ANALYSIS

## 11.1 FOURIER SYNTHESIS

ONE of the chief sources of numerical work in modern physics lies in
the deduction of molecular structure from observations of the x-ray
diffraction spectra which arise when a monochromatic beam of
x-rays is incident, at the appropriate BRAGG[1] angle, on a single
crystal. This leads to a Fourier synthesis, a type of calculation
which occurs also in tide prediction and in astrophysics.

For the purposes of the numerical analyst it is sufficient to note
that Fourier synthesis calls for the evaluation of functions $\rho(x, y, z)$
defined by:

$$\rho(x, y, z) = \frac{1}{V} \underset{h \ k \ l}{\Sigma\Sigma\Sigma} |F(h, k, l)| \cos \left[ 2\pi \left( h\frac{x}{a} + k\frac{y}{b} + l\frac{z}{c} \right) - a_{hkl} \right]$$

$$\dots (11.1.)$$

Typical cases have 60 values of $x$, $y$ and $z$, and thus involve the
evaluation of $(60)^3$ values of $\rho(x, y, z)$. The observed coefficients
$|F(h, k, l)|$ are frequently up to 1000 in number and, in some recent
work, have been as many as 10,000.

Under these circumstances it is not practicable, even with a high
speed automatic digital calculator, to evaluate the $\rho(x, y, z)$ individu-
ally, and means have been devised for the simultaneous evaluation
of whole groups of $\rho(x, y, z)$; usually for fixed values of two of the
variables and a range of values of the third.

A very large number of different summation methods have been
evolved, but we shall confine our attention to the method in most
common use, which is due to BEEVERS and LIPSON.[2, 3]

The Beevers-Lipson method depends upon the breaking down of
the three dimensional synthesis (11.1.1) into a series of one dimensional syntheses of the type:

$$\rho(x) = \sum_{h=-H_1}^{+H_2} \pm A_h \begin{Bmatrix} \sin \\ \cos \end{Bmatrix} \left( 2\pi h\frac{x}{a} \right) \qquad \dots (11.1.2)$$

which, as we shall presently show, can be done.

To effect the summation (11.1.2), for a range of values of $(x)$,
Beevers and Lipson prepared a set of 'strips', one to each value of

$A_h$ in the integer range 1–99 and for each value of $h$ in the range 0–20. The sine and cosine functions are catered for separately. Each strip bears, upon its front surface, the information:

(Value of $A$)          (Sine or Cosine)          (Frequency $h$)

$$\left(16 \text{ Values of } A \begin{Bmatrix} \sin \\ \cos \end{Bmatrix} \frac{2\pi}{60} \, n.h\right)$$

where $n$ runs through the integers 0–15; the reverse side of the strip contains the same information, but for $-A$. A typical strip is shown in *Figure 11.1.1*.

*Figure 11.1.1 Beevers-Lipson strip for* $32 \sin 2\pi . 3(x/a)$

| $32\,S\,3$ | 0 | 10 | 19 | 26 | 30 | 32 | 30 | 26 | 19 | 10 | 0 | $\overline{10}$ | $\overline{19}$ | $\overline{26}$ | $\overline{30}$ | $\overline{32}$ |
|---|---|---|---|---|---|---|---|---|---|---|---|---|---|---|---|---|

The reason for the choice of interval $2\pi/60$ is a physical one which is related to the resolving power to be expected from the use of x-rays of a given wavelength.

The use of the strips will be clear from the following simple example, suppose that we require:

$$\Sigma = 12 \cos 2\pi . 1(x/a) + 32 \sin 2\pi . 3(x/a) - 40 \cos 2\pi . 4(x/a)$$
$$\dots (11.1.3)$$

The appropriate strips are selected and laid together in a matrix:

| $x/a =$ | 0 | 1 | 2 | 3 | 4 | 5 | 6 | 7 | 8 | 9 | 10 | 11 | 12 | 13 | 14 | 15 |
|---|---|---|---|---|---|---|---|---|---|---|---|---|---|---|---|---|
| $12\,C\,1$ | 12 | 12 | 12 | 11 | 11 | 10 | 10 | 9 | 8 | 7 | 6 | 5 | 4 | 3 | 1 | 0 |
| $32\,S\,3$ | 0 | 10 | 19 | 26 | 30 | 32 | 30 | 26 | 19 | 10 | 0 | $\overline{10}$ | $\overline{19}$ | $\overline{26}$ | $\overline{30}$ | $\overline{32}$ |
| $\overline{40}C\,4$ | $\overline{40}$ | $\overline{37}$ | $\overline{27}$ | $\overline{12}$ | 4 | 20 | 32 | 39 | 39 | 32 | 20 | 4 | $\overline{12}$ | $\overline{27}$ | $\overline{37}$ | $\overline{40}$ |
| $\Sigma$ | $\overline{28}$ | $\overline{15}$ | 4 | 25 | 45 | 62 | 72 | 74 | 66 | 49 | 26 | $\overline{1}$ | $\overline{27}$ | $\overline{50}$ | $\overline{66}$ | $\overline{72}$ |

If it is desired to extend the range beyond $(\frac{15}{60} \times 2\pi)$ it is merely necessary to reverse the cosine strips of *odd* frequency and the sine strips of *even* frequency, thus in the above case:

| $x/a =$ | 30 | 29 | 28 | 27 | 26 | 25 | 24 | 23 | 22 | 21 | 20 | 19 | 18 | 17 | 16 | 15 |
|---|---|---|---|---|---|---|---|---|---|---|---|---|---|---|---|---|
| $\overline{12}\,C\,1$ | $\overline{12}$ | $\overline{12}$ | $\overline{12}$ | $\overline{11}$ | $\overline{11}$ | $\overline{10}$ | $\overline{10}$ | 9 | 8 | 7 | 6 | 5 | 4 | 3 | $\overline{1}$ | $\overline{0}$ |
| $32\,S\,3$ | 0 | 10 | 19 | 26 | 30 | 32 | 30 | 26 | 19 | 10 | 0 | $\overline{10}$ | $\overline{19}$ | $\overline{26}$ | $\overline{30}$ | $\overline{32}$ |
| $\overline{40}\,C\,4$ | $\overline{40}$ | $\overline{37}$ | $\overline{27}$ | $\overline{12}$ | 4 | 20 | 32 | 39 | 39 | 32 | 20 | 4 | $\overline{12}$ | $\overline{27}$ | $\overline{37}$ | $\overline{40}$ |
| $\Sigma$ | $\overline{52}$ | $\overline{39}$ | $\overline{20}$ | 3 | 23 | 42 | 52 | 56 | 50 | 35 | 14 | $\overline{11}$ | $\overline{35}$ | $\overline{56}$ | $\overline{68}$ | $\overline{72}$ |

171

The ranges (30–45) (45–60) follow in a similar manner from the symmetry properties of the trigonometric functions. In more complicated summations it is more economical to perform the sine-even, sine-odd, cosine-even, cosine-odd summations separately and then to combine the results as required to extend the range.

We now revert to the original summation (11.1.1). This may be written:

$$\rho(x, y, z) = \frac{1}{V} \underset{h, k, l}{\Sigma\Sigma\Sigma} |F| \cos \alpha \cos 2\pi \left( h\frac{x}{a} + k\frac{y}{b} + l\frac{z}{c} \right)$$

$$+ |F| \sin \alpha \sin 2\pi \left( h\frac{x}{a} + k\frac{y}{b} + l\frac{z}{c} \right) \quad \ldots\ldots(11.1.4)$$

where, for simplicity, we have written $|F|$ for $|F(h, k, l)|$ and $\alpha$ for $\alpha_{hkl}$.

In a like manner 11.1.4 may be broken down into:

$$\rho(x, y, z) =$$

$$\frac{1}{V} \underset{h\ k}{\Sigma\Sigma} \cos 2\pi \left( \frac{h}{a}x + k\frac{y}{b} \right) \underset{l}{\Sigma} \left[ |F| \cos \alpha \cos 2\pi l\frac{z}{c} + |F| \sin \alpha \sin 2\pi l\frac{z}{c} \right]$$

$$+ \sin 2\pi \left( \frac{h}{a}x + k\frac{y}{b} \right) \underset{l}{\Sigma} \left[ |F| \sin \alpha \cos 2\pi l\frac{z}{c} - |F| \cos \alpha \sin 2\pi l\frac{z}{c} \right]$$

$$\ldots\ldots(11.1.5)$$

which is of the form:

$$\rho(x, y, z) = \frac{1}{V} \underset{h\ k}{\Sigma\Sigma}{}_{hk}C_z \cos 2\pi \left( h\frac{x}{a} + k\frac{y}{b} \right) + {}_{hk}S_z \sin 2\pi \left( h\frac{x}{a} + k\frac{y}{b} \right)$$

$$\ldots\ldots(11.1.6)$$

where:

$${}_{hk}C_z = \underset{l}{\Sigma} \left[ |F| \cos \alpha \cos 2\pi l\frac{z}{c} + |F| \sin \alpha \sin 2\pi l\frac{z}{c} \right] \quad \ldots\ldots(11.1.7)$$

$${}_{hk}S_z = \underset{l}{\Sigma} \left[ |F| \sin \alpha \cos 2\pi l\frac{z}{c} - |F| \cos \alpha \sin 2\pi l\frac{z}{c} \right] \quad \ldots\ldots(11.1.8)$$

Now the summations for ${}_{hk}C_z$ and ${}_{hk}S_z$ can be performed directly by means of the Beevers-Lipson strips and the resulting sets of coefficients tabulated. The process is then repeated to give:

$$\rho(x, y, z) =$$

$$\frac{1}{V}\sum_h \cos 2\pi\left(h\frac{x}{a}\right)\sum_k\left[{}_{hk}C_z \cos 2\pi\left(k\frac{y}{b}\right) + {}_{hk}S_z \sin 2\pi\left(k\frac{y}{b}\right)\right]$$

$$+ \sin 2\pi\left(h\frac{x}{a}\right)\sum_k\left[{}_{hk}S_z \cos 2\pi\left(k\frac{y}{b}\right) - {}_{hk}C_z \sin 2\pi\left(k\frac{y}{b}\right)\right]$$

or

$$\rho(x, y, z) = \frac{1}{V}\sum_h {}_hC_{yz} \cos 2\pi\left(h\frac{x}{a}\right) + {}_hS_{yz} \sin 2\pi\left(h\frac{x}{a}\right) \quad \ldots(11.1.9)$$

where:

$${}_hC_{yz} = \sum_k\left[{}_{hk}C_z \cos 2\pi\left(k\frac{y}{b}\right) + {}_{hk}S_z \sin 2\pi\left(k\frac{y}{b}\right)\right] \quad \ldots(11.1.10)$$

$${}_hS_{yz} = \sum_k\left[{}_{hk}S_z \cos 2\pi\left(k\frac{y}{b}\right) - {}_{hk}C_z \sin 2\pi\left(k\frac{y}{b}\right)\right] \quad \ldots(11.1.11)$$

Thus, since ${}_hC_{yz}$, ${}_hS_{yz}$ can be evaluated by the Beevers-Lipson technique, and the final summation 11.1.9 is also in the correct form, the problem is solved.

Various points of technique arise in the practical summation of multiple series of the type 11.1.4, notably that of 'multiplicity correction'. This is necessary because the method of reduction used in 11.1.5–11.1.11 has the effect of including terms of the types $(h, k, 0)$ $(h, 0, 0)$ $(0, 0, 0)$ more than once. It is sufficient to state here that the corrections:

$$F(h, k, l) \div 1$$
$$F(h, k, 0) \div 2$$
$$F(h, 0, 0) \div 4$$
$$F(0, 0, 0) \div 8$$

are appropriate, for further details the reader is referred to the specialist monographs.[4, 5]


## 11.2 THE LOCATION OF MAXIMA

One important requirement in dealing with series of the type envisaged in section 11.1 is that of locating accurately the maxima of $\rho(x, y, z)$. This can be conveniently achieved by the methods of differential synthesis [6, 7] which make unnecessary a complete evaluation of $\rho(x, y, z)$ for all values of $(x, y, z)$. The method is essentially that of Newton-Raphson (see Chapter 9, section 9.3) applied to the derivatives of $\rho(x, y, z)$. Thus, at a maximum we have:

$$\frac{\partial \rho}{\partial x} = \frac{\partial \rho}{\partial y} = \frac{\partial \rho}{\partial z} = 0.$$

We denote the synthesis 11.1.1 by the shorthand notation:

$$\rho = \frac{1}{V} \underset{3}{\Sigma} |F| \cos (\theta - a) \qquad \qquad \dots (11.2.1)$$

whence

$$\frac{\partial \rho}{\partial x} = - \frac{2\pi}{aV} \underset{3}{\Sigma} h |F| \sin (\theta - a) = 0$$

$$\frac{\partial \rho}{\partial y} = - \frac{2\pi}{bV} \underset{3}{\Sigma} k |F| \sin (\theta - a) = 0 \qquad \left.\right\} \quad \dots (11.2.2)$$

$$\frac{\partial \rho}{\partial z} = - \frac{2\pi}{cV} \underset{3}{\Sigma} l |F| \sin (\theta - a) = 0$$

Assume that $(x, y, z)$ is an approximation to the maximum and that the true value is $(x + \epsilon_x, y + \epsilon_y, z + \epsilon_z)$, then, to the first order:

$$- \frac{2\pi}{aV} \underset{3}{\Sigma} \{h |F| \sin (\theta - a) + h \epsilon_\theta \cos (\theta - a)\} = 0$$

$$- \frac{2\pi}{bV} \underset{3}{\Sigma} \{k |F| \sin (\theta - a) + k \epsilon_\theta \cos (\theta - a)\} = 0 \quad \left.\right\} \quad \dots (11.2.3)$$

$$- \frac{2\pi}{cV} \underset{3}{\Sigma} \{l |F| \sin (\theta - a) + l \epsilon_\theta \cos (\theta - a)\} = 0$$

where

$$\epsilon_\theta = 2\pi \left( h \frac{\epsilon_x}{a} + k \frac{\epsilon_y}{b} + l \frac{\epsilon_z}{c} \right)$$

From these equations we obtain:

$$\begin{aligned} A_{hh}\epsilon_x + A_{hk}\epsilon_y + A_{hl}\epsilon_z + A_h &= 0 \\ A_{kh}\epsilon_x + A_{kk}\epsilon_y + A_{kl}\epsilon_z + A_k &= 0 \\ A_{lh}\epsilon_x + A_{lk}\epsilon_y + A_{ll}\epsilon_z + A_l &= 0 \end{aligned} \quad \left.\right\} \quad \dots (11.2.4)$$

where:

$$A_h = -\frac{2\pi}{aV} \underset{3}{\Sigma} h|F| \sin(\theta - a)$$

$$A_k = -\frac{2\pi}{bV} \underset{3}{\Sigma} k|F| \sin(\theta - a) \qquad \Bigg\} \quad \dots (11.2.5)$$

$$A_l = -\frac{2\pi}{cV} \underset{3}{\Sigma} l|F| \sin(\theta - a)$$

$$A_{hk} = A_{kh} = -\frac{4\pi^2}{abV} \underset{3}{\Sigma} hk|F| \cos(\theta - a)$$

$$A_{kl} = A_{lk} = -\frac{4\pi^2}{bcV} \underset{3}{\Sigma} kl|F| \cos(\theta - a) \qquad \Bigg\} \quad \dots (11.2.6)$$

$$A_{lh} = A_{hl} = -\frac{4\pi^2}{caV} \underset{3}{\Sigma} lh|F| \cos(\theta - a)$$

$$A_{hh} = -\frac{4\pi^2}{a^2V} \underset{3}{\Sigma} h^2|F| \cos(\theta - a)$$

$$A_{kk} = -\frac{4\pi^2}{b^2V} \underset{3}{\Sigma} k^2|F| \cos(\theta - a) \qquad \Bigg\} \quad \dots (11.2.7)$$

$$A_{ll} = -\frac{4\pi^2}{c^2V} \underset{3}{\Sigma} l^2|F| \cos(\theta - a)$$

The process as described above is second order, in practice it is usual to compute the coefficients $A_{hh}$, $A_{kk}$, $A_{ll}$, $A_{hk}$, $A_{kl}$, $A_{lh}$ only at the start and at the finish of the refinement which makes the process formally only first order; the convergence is, however, still extremely rapid.

## 11.3 RADIAL AND OTHER SYNTHESES

For practical requirements it is sometimes necessary to obtain from the three dimensional x-ray data a radial distribution function. This is defined as the average of $\rho(x, y, z)$ over shells of constant radius from the origin. The series involved is usually:

$$P(u, v, w) = \frac{1}{V} \underset{h, k, l}{\Sigma\Sigma\Sigma} |F(h, k, l)|^2 \cos 2\pi \left( h\frac{u}{a} + k\frac{v}{b} + l\frac{w}{c} \right)$$
$$\dots (11.3.1)$$

175

the so-called PATTERSON function',[8] or to mathematicians the 'convolution' or 'faltung',[9] and the radial distribution function $p_3(r)$ is defined to be:

$$4\pi r^2 p_3(r)\mathrm{d}r = \int_S P(u, v, w)\mathrm{d}S.\,\mathrm{d}r \qquad \ldots (11.3.2)$$

where $\mathrm{d}S$ is an element of the spherical surface, of radius $r$, whose centre is $(0, 0, 0)$.

Now the expression 11.3.2 may be written, by virtue of equation 11.3.1,

$$4\pi r^2 p_3(r)\mathrm{d}r = \frac{1}{V} \underset{h,\,k,\,l}{\Sigma\Sigma\Sigma} |F(h, k, l)|^2 \int_S \cos 2\pi \left( h\,\frac{u}{a} + k\,\frac{v}{b} + l\,\frac{w}{c} \right) \mathrm{d}S.\,\mathrm{d}r$$

and the integrals can be evaluated by transforming to axes normal and perpendicular to the plane:

$$h\,\frac{u}{a} + k\,\frac{v}{b} + l\,\frac{w}{c} = 0.$$

Thus :

$$\int_S \cos 2\pi \left( h\,\frac{u}{a} + k\,\frac{v}{b} + l\,\frac{w}{c} \right) \mathrm{d}S = \int_{-r}^{+r} \cos 2\pi \left( \frac{n}{\mathrm{d}(h, k, l)} \right).\,2\pi r.\,\mathrm{d}n$$

$$= 4\pi r^2 \frac{\sin 2\pi r/\mathrm{d}(h, k, l)}{2\pi r/\mathrm{d}(h, k, l)} \qquad \ldots (11.3.3)$$

where $\mathrm{d}n$ is an element in the direction of the normal to

$$h\,\frac{u}{a} + k\,\frac{v}{b} + l\,\frac{w}{c} = 0$$

and $\mathrm{d}(h, k, l)$ is the length of the perpendicular from the origin on to the plane

$$h\,\frac{u}{a} + k\,\frac{v}{b} + l\,\frac{w}{c} = 1.$$

It follows from 11.3.1, 11.3.2 and 11.3.3 that:

$$p_3(r) = \frac{1}{V} \underset{h,\,k,\,l}{\Sigma\Sigma\Sigma} |F(h, k, l)|^2 \frac{\sin 2\pi r/\mathrm{d}(h, k, l)}{2\pi r/\mathrm{d}(h, k, l)} \qquad \ldots (11.3.4)$$

176

In a similar manner it is sometimes necessary to obtain radial distribution functions for the two dimensional series:

$$P(u, v) = \frac{1}{A} \underset{h,\,k}{\Sigma\Sigma} |F(h, k, 0)|^2 \cos 2\pi \left( h\frac{u}{a} + k\frac{v}{b} \right) \quad \ldots\,(11.3.5)$$

and it is easily shown that the relevant function is defined by:

$$2\pi r p_2(r)\mathrm{d}r = \int_S P(u, v)\mathrm{d}S.\,\mathrm{d}r \quad \ldots\,(11.3.6)$$

where $S$ is now a circle in the $(u, v)$ plane with centre $(0, 0)$. The integration is performed as before to give:

$$p_2(r) = \frac{1}{A} \underset{h\;k}{\Sigma\Sigma} |F(h, k, 0)|^2 J_0 2\pi r / \mathrm{d}(h, k, 0) \quad \ldots\,(11.3.7)$$

where $J_0(z)$ is the zero'th order Bessel function.

Other types of syntheses can be obtained by projecting the density $\rho(x, y, z)$ contained between selected values of $z$, say, on to a plane parallel to $(x, y)$. These, whilst of considerable value to the specialist crystallographer, are not of general interest and require no novelties of technique, the interested reader is referred to the literature. [10]

## 11.4 FOURIER ANALYSIS

The converse process to Fourier synthesis may be expressed, in the one dimensional case, by

$$\rho(x) = \tfrac{1}{2}A_0 + \overset{\infty}{\underset{h=1}{\Sigma}} A_h \cos 2\pi \left( h\frac{x}{a} \right) + B_h \sin 2\pi \left( h\frac{x}{a} \right) \quad \ldots\,(11.4.1)$$

Where $\rho(x)$ is known in the repetition interval $(0, a)$ and it is required to determine the values of the Fourier coefficients $(A_h, B_h)$.

Formally we have at once from the orthogonality of the sine and cosine functions:

$$A_h = \frac{2}{a} \int_0^a \rho(x) \cos 2\pi \left( h\frac{x}{a} \right) \mathrm{d}x \quad (h = 0, 1 \ldots \infty) \quad \ldots\,(11.4.2)$$

$$B_h = \frac{2}{a} \int_0^a \rho(x) \sin 2\pi \left( h\frac{x}{a} \right) \mathrm{d}x \quad (h = 1, 2 \ldots \infty) \quad \ldots\,(11.4.3)$$

To evaluate the integrals practically we make use of the Euler-Maclaurin integration formula (Chapter 4, section 4, equation 4.4.5).

When it is noted that $\rho(0) = \rho(a)$ and that by definition the same is true for all derivatives so that $\rho^{(n)}(0) = \rho^{(n)}(a)$ the Euler-Maclaurin formula becomes in this case:

$$\int_0^{n\delta x} \rho(x) \cos 2\pi \left( h\frac{x}{a} \right) dx =$$

$$\frac{\delta x}{2} \left[ \rho(0) + 2\rho(\delta x) \cos 2\pi \left( h\frac{\delta x}{a} \right) + 2\rho(2\delta x) \cos 2\pi \left( h.2\frac{\delta x}{a} \right) + \ldots \right.$$

$$\left. + 2\rho\{(n-1)\delta x\} \cos 2\pi \left\{ h(n-1)\frac{\delta x}{a} \right\} + \rho(0) \right]$$

$$= \delta x \sum_{r=0}^{n-1} \rho(r\delta x) \cos 2\pi \left( hr\frac{\delta x}{a} \right) \qquad \ldots (11.4.4)$$

since $n\delta x = a$.

Similarly:

$$\int_0^{n\delta x} \rho(x) \sin 2\pi \left( h\frac{x}{a} \right) dx = \delta x \sum_{r=0}^{n-1} \rho(r\delta x) \sin 2\pi \left( hr\frac{\delta x}{a} \right) \quad \ldots (11.5.5)$$

and both of these formulae are *exact*.

Whence, from 11.4.2 and 11.4.3

$$\left. \begin{aligned} A_h &= \frac{2}{n} \sum_{r=0}^{n-1} \rho(r\delta x) \cos 2\pi \left( hr\frac{\delta x}{a} \right) \\ B_h &= \frac{2}{n} \sum_{r=0}^{n-1} \rho(r\delta x) \sin 2\pi \left( hr\frac{\delta x}{a} \right) \end{aligned} \right\} \quad \ldots (11.5.6)$$

it should be noticed that by virtue of their derivation these formulae are significant only if $h < n/2$.

The practical computation of Fourier coefficients can be achieved by the use of the Beevers-Lipson strips in a manner similar to that used for Fourier synthesis. This follows at once if it is noticed that equations 11.5.6 are identical with 11.1.2 if the $(x)$ of the latter is replaced by $(h)$ and the $(h)$ by $\left( r\frac{\delta x}{a} \right)$. A difficulty arises with the normal strips because they extend to frequencies ($h$ values) of only 20, but this causes trouble only when Fourier coefficients of order greater than 10 are required. For higher values the equivalent of the strips are available on punched cards to frequencies of 60.

178

The process of analysis can be extended to multi-dimensional Fourier syntheses of the type in equation 11.1.1, the results are obtained in an analogous manner but are rather cumbersome and will not be tabulated here. [11]

## REFERENCES

[1] BRAGG, W. H. and BRAGG, W. L., 'The Crystalline State,' vol. 1, p. 15, Bell (1933)

[2] BEEVERS, C. A. and LIPSON, H., *Phil. Mag.*, 17 (1934), 855

[3] — — *Proc. Phys. Soc.*, 48 (1936) 772

[4] BOOTH, A. D., 'Fourier Technique in X-ray Organic Structure Analysis,' p. 55, Cambridge (1948)

[5] LIPSON, H. and COCHRAN, W., 'The Crystalline State,' vol. 3, Bell (1954)

[6] BOOTH, A. D., *Trans. Faraday Soc.*, 42 (1946), 444

[7] — *ibid.*, 42 (1946), 617

[8] — 'Fourier Technique in X-ray Organic Structure Analysis,' p. 18, Cambridge (1948)

[9] WIENER, N., 'The Fourier Integral,' Cambridge (1932)

[10] BOOTH, A. D., *Trans. Faraday Soc.*, 41, (1945), 434

[11] MACGILLAVRY, C. H. and PEPINSKY, R., 'Computing Methods and the Phase Problem,' p. 310, Penn. State College (1952)

# INTEGRAL EQUATIONS

## 12.1 CLASSIFICATION

THE integral equations which have been studied most extensively by analysts[1] are those associated with the names of Fredholm and of Volterra, they differ only in the fact that the limits of Volterra's equation contain the independent variable.

Fredholm's equation is usually written in the two forms:

$$\int_a^b k(x, y) f(y) \mathrm{d}y = g(x) \qquad \ldots (12.1.1)$$

$$\int_a^b k(x, y) f(y) \mathrm{d}y = g(x) + f(x) \qquad \ldots (12.1.2)$$

and the method of solution is closely governed by the presence or absence of the wanted function, $f(x)$, on the right-hand side of the equation. The function $k(x, y)$ is known as the 'kernel' and, just as is the case in the classical analytical theory, the technique of solution is simplified when $k(x, y)$ is symmetric in $x$ and $y$. Associated with the Fredholm equations is the eigenvalue problem:

$$\lambda \int_a^b k(x, y) f(y) \mathrm{d}y = f(x) \qquad \ldots (12.1.3)$$

where, not only is $f(x)$ unknown, but a solution exists only for discrete values of $\lambda$ which have also to be determined.

The Volterra equations are

$$\int_a^x k(x, y) f(y) \mathrm{d}y = g(x) \qquad \ldots (12.1.4)$$

$$\int_a^x k(x, y) f(y) \mathrm{d}y = g(x) + f(x) \qquad \ldots (12.1.5)$$

and it is intuitively evident that their solution will resemble that of one-point boundary differential equations, while that of the Fredholm equations will be more akin to the two-point type.

An integral equation is said to be non-singular when both $k$ and $f$, as well as the limits of integration, are finite and continuous.

Other integral equations derive from Fourier's theorem and from the Laplace transform ; since they are more properly a part of analysis they will not be considered further here.

Two classical equations are those of Abel and of Schlömilch. Abel's equation is :

$$g(x) = \int_a^x \frac{f(y)}{(x-y)^\mu}\, dy \qquad \begin{matrix} 0 < \mu < 1 \\ a \leqslant x \end{matrix} \qquad \ldots (12.1.6)$$

which can be shown [2] to have the solution :

$$f(g) = \frac{\sin(\mu\pi)}{\pi} \frac{d}{dy} \int_a^y \frac{g(x)dx}{(y-x)^{1-\mu}} \qquad \ldots (12.1.7)$$

so that, when $g(x)$ is known, $f(y)$ can be found either analytically or by numerical integration.

Schlömilch's equation is :

$$g(x) = \frac{2}{\pi} \int_0^{\pi/2} f(x \sin \theta) d\theta \qquad -\pi \leqslant x \leqslant \pi \quad \ldots (12.1.8)$$

and the solution is [3] :

$$f(x) = g(0) + x \int_0^{\pi/2} g'(x \sin \theta) d\theta \qquad \ldots (12.1.9)$$

which is also amenable to treatment.

Equations occur in which both integrals and derivatives are present, and these are usually called integro-differential equations. The method of numerical solution depends upon the type of boundary conditions which have to be satisfied, but otherwise follows closely upon the lines which will be indicated in sections 12.2 and 12.3.

## 12.2 VOLTERRA'S EQUATION

In the first place we may note that an equation of the type 12.1.4 can always be reduced to one of type 12.1.5 by a single differentiation with respect to $x$ if $k(x, x) \neq 0$, or by a series of such differentiations until a derivative is found such that $k^{(n)}(x, x) \neq 0$.

The solution now proceeds in two parts, first initial values are obtained by means of a Taylor series expansion :

$$f(a + x) = f(a) + xf'(a) + \tfrac{1}{2}x^2 f''(a) + \cdots$$

181

where, from equation 12.1.5, we have:

$$f(a) = - g(a)$$
$$f'(a) = - g'(a) + k(a, a)f(a)$$
$$f''(a) = - g''(a) + k(a, a)f(a) + k'(a, a)f(a) + k(a, a)f'(a)$$

. . . . . . . . . . . . . . . . . . . . .

$$f^{(n)}(a) = - g^{(n)}(a) + \sum_{r=0}^{n-1} \left[ \frac{d^{n-1-r}}{dx^{n-1-r}} \{k^{(r)}(x, x)f(x)\} \right]_{x=a}$$

$$\dots (12.2.1)$$

Next we take Gregory's formula for the integral which may be derived from the Euler-Maclaurin formula 4.4.5 by substituting for the derivatives in terms of forward and backward differences.

The Gregory formula is:

$$\int_a^{a+n\delta x} f(x)dx =$$

$$\delta x[\tfrac{1}{2} f(a) + f(a + \delta x) + \dots + f\{a + (n-1)\delta x\} + \tfrac{1}{2}f(a + n\delta x)]$$
$$+ \delta x[\tfrac{1}{12}\Delta - \tfrac{1}{24}\Delta^2 + \tfrac{19}{720}\Delta^3 - \tfrac{3}{160}\Delta^4 + \dots]f(a)$$
$$- \delta x[\tfrac{1}{12}\nabla + \tfrac{1}{24}\nabla^2 + \tfrac{19}{720}\nabla^3 + \tfrac{3}{160}\nabla^4 + \dots]f(a + n\delta x)$$

$$\dots (12.2.2)$$

and it is seen that, by using it to a prescribed number of terms, the given integral can be expressed in the form:

$$\int_a^{a+n\delta x} f(x)dx = \sum_{r=0}^n \delta x A_r f(a + r\delta x) \qquad \dots (12.2.3)$$

where the coefficients $A_r$ depend only upon the number of differences to which 12.2.2 is taken.

By means of 12.2.3 the integral equation 12.1.5 may be written:

$$\delta x \sum_{r=0}^n A_r k(a + n\delta x, a + r\delta x)f(a + r\delta x) = g(a + n\delta x) + f(a + n\delta x)$$

or:

$$[1 - \delta x A_n k(a + n\delta x, a + n\delta x)]f(a + n\delta x) = - g(a + n\delta x)$$
$$+ \delta x \sum_{r=0}^{n-1} A_r k(a + n\delta x, a + r\delta x)f(a + r\delta x) \qquad \dots (12.2.4)$$

whence, if the first $(n)$ values of $f(a + r\delta x)$ are known, a further value may be obtained. The process can now be repeated, using the values $f(a + n\delta x) \dots f(a + \delta x)$, and the solution thus continued.

Care must be taken that differences of sufficiently high order be included in equation 12.2.2 for the rate of growth of error to be adequately small in the range over which a solution is required. For an indication of how this is done, and also for suggestions as to methods of estimating the error in particular cases, the reader is referred to the excellent paper of Fox and GOODWIN[4].

## 12.3 FREDHOLM'S EQUATION

The solution of the Fredholm equation of the first kind, 12.1.1, is complicated by the fact that solutions may not be possible when $k$ and $g$ are connected in certain ways. An obvious example of this arises when $k(x, y)$ has the form $\sum_{r=1}^{n} X_r(x) . Y_r(y)$, in which case equation 12.1.1 becomes:

$$\sum_{r=1}^{n} C_r X_r(x) = g(x) \qquad \ldots . (12.3.1)$$

where:

$$C_r = \int_a^b Y_r(y) f(y) \mathrm{d}y \qquad \ldots . (12.3.2)$$

Here no solution is possible unless $g(x)$ has the form 12.3.1 but, in this case, any solution is possible for which equation 12.3.2 is satisfied. Fox and GOODWIN[5] conclude that no really satisfactory numerical method exists for the accurate solution of equations of this kind.

For Fredholm's equation of the second kind, 12.1.2, the position is more satisfactory. The approach is again to represent the integral by a finite difference approximation of the type given in equations 12.2.2 and 12.2.3, but from here there exists a choice of two methods.

In the first a sufficient number of differences are retained in equation 12.2.2 to ensure that the reduced form 12.2.3 gives an adequate representation of the integral over the range considered, in the second method equation 12.2.2 is written in the form:

$$\int_a^{a+n\delta x} f(x)\mathrm{d}x = \delta x[\tfrac{1}{2}f(a) + f(a+\delta x) + \ldots$$
$$+ f\{a + (n-1)\delta x\} + \tfrac{1}{2}f(a+n\delta x)] + \varXi \qquad \ldots . (12.3.3)$$

where $\varXi$ is a correction term compounded of the differences given

183

in equation 12.2.2. The integral equation is now written in one of the forms:

$$\delta y \sum_{r=0}^{n} A_r k(x, a + r\delta y) f(a + r\delta y) = g(x) + f(x) \quad \ldots (12.3.4)$$

or :

$$\delta y [\tfrac{1}{2} k(x, a) f(a) + k(x, a + \delta y) f(a + \delta y) + \ldots$$
$$+ k\{x, a + (n-1)\delta y\} f\{a + (n-1)\delta y\}$$
$$+ \tfrac{1}{2} k(x, a + n\delta y) f(a + n\delta y)] + \varXi_x = g(x) + f(x)$$
$$\ldots (12.3.5)$$

We notice that $a + n\delta y = b$ and then proceed to solve the $(n+1)$ simultaneous linear equations, which result from taking $x = a, a + \delta x,$ $\ldots a + n\delta x$ in 12.3.4, for the $(n+1)$ values of $f(x)$. This method has the disadvantage that it is necessary to keep sufficient differences in deriving equation 12.2.3 to ensure the required final accuracy and since the behaviour of the solution is in general unknown, this may lead to wasted effort.

Fox and GOODWIN[6] have suggested a modification of their method for the solution of ordinary differential equations (see page 68). In the present instance they solve the equations which result from substituting $x = a, a + \delta x, \ldots a + n\delta x$ in 12.3.5, *initially neglecting the corrections* $\varXi_x$. The set of approximations $f^{(0)}(a), f^{(0)}(a + \delta x)$ $\ldots f^{(0)}(a + n\delta x)$ are then used to estimate the values of $\varXi_x$ and the solution is re-computed to give a better approximation $f^{(1)}(a)$, $f^{(1)}(a + \delta x)$, etc. This process is repeated until no significant change is produced between two successive approximations.

Alternative methods which have been suggested for the solution of equations of the Fredholm type include the deferred approach to the limit technique of RICHARDSON[7], and the analogue of Picard's method for ordinary differential equations (see page 57) which sets up an iterative sequence:

$$f^{(n)}(x) = - g(x) + \int_{a}^{b} k(x,y) f^{(n-1)}(y) dy \quad \ldots (12.3.6)$$

Since it is necessary to calculate the value of each iterate at a sufficient number of points to enable the next integrations to be carried out to an adequate accuracy the method is likely to be tedious.

## 12.4 THE EIGENVALUE PROBLEM

The solution of the eigenvalue problem typified by equation 12.1.3 follows closely upon the lines just suggested for solving the Fredholm

184

equation 12.1.2. The equation is put into one of the finite difference forms :

$$\sum_{r=0}^{n} A_r k(x, a + r\delta y) f(a + r\delta y) = f(x)/\lambda\delta y \qquad \ldots.(12.4.1)$$

or :

$$\tfrac{1}{2}k(x, a) f(a) + k(x, a + \delta y) f(a + \delta y) + \ldots$$
$$+ k\{x, a + (n - 1)\delta y\} f\{a + (n - 1)\delta y\}$$
$$+ \tfrac{1}{2}k(x, a + n\delta y) f(a + n\delta y) = f(x)/\lambda\delta y - \Xi/\delta y$$
$$\ldots.(12.4.2)$$

and the sets of simultaneous equations which result from taking $x = a, a + \delta x, a + 2\delta x \ldots a + n\delta x$ are then used as a basis of computation.

For the equations which derive from 12.4.1 the values of $\lambda$ and their associated vectors are determined in the manner described in chapter 7 section 7.6 since it is evident that non-zero solutions exist only if the determinant :

$$\begin{vmatrix} A_0 k(0, 0) - 1/\lambda\delta y, & A_1 k(0, 1), & . & . & . & . & . & A_n k(0, n) \\ A_0 k(1, 0), & A_1 k(1, 1) - 1/\lambda\delta y, & . & . & A_n k(1, n) \\ . & . & . & . & . & . & . & . \\ . & . & . & . & . & . & . & . \\ A_0 k(n, 0), & A_1 k(n, 1), & . & . & . & . & A_n k(n, n) - 1/\lambda\delta y \end{vmatrix}$$

is zero. We have used the shorthand notation :

$$k(r, s) = k(a + r\delta x, a + s\delta y).$$

This technique pre-supposes a knowledge of the behaviour of the solution to enable appropriate values of the coefficients $A_r$ to be chosen. The second method first obtains rough values of $\lambda$ under the assumption that the corrections $\Xi_x$ are zero and then uses each of these values of $\lambda$ to derive a trial vector $f(a), f(a + \delta x) \ldots f(a + n\delta x)$. From this trial vector the corrections $\Xi_x$ can be computed and then, in turn, an improved value of $\lambda$ derived; the latter operation is best carried out by means of the second order process given in chapter 7 section 6 equation 7.6.2.

The whole process is a cyclic one which is terminated as soon as the change between two steps is less than the desired value.

## 12.5 MONTE CARLO METHODS

Since the methods of solution for integral equations which we have just outlined aim at reducing the equation to a set of linear simultaneous equations it is natural to suppose that, just as is the case for the latter, there will be Monte Carlo methods for solving integral equations.

The Fredholm equation arises in the study of the behaviour of neutrons which are incident on a plate of material in which collisions can give rise either to more or to less than one particle. This suggests [8] the following Monte Carlo process for solving an equation of the type given in 12.1.2; first the equation is normalized so that :

$$\int_a^b g(x)\mathrm{d}x = 1 \quad \text{and} \quad \int_{-\infty}^{\infty} k(x, y)\mathrm{d}y \leqslant 1 \quad \dots (12.5.1)$$

$f(x)$ now represents the density of collisions in a population of particles in $(a, b)$ when it is assumed that the density of first collisions is $g(x)$. In normalizing $k(x, y)$ a numerical factor, $\lambda$, will have been introduced and the equation can be written :

$$f(x) = g_n(x) + \lambda \int_a^b k_n(x, y) f(y)\mathrm{d}y \quad \dots (12.5.2)$$

where the subscript $(n)$ indicates that the function has been normalized in accord with 12.5.1, and the number $\lambda$ is interpreted to be the mean number of particles which remain after each collision.

To solve the problem, we first pick a random number $r_0$ from a population which is uniformly distributed in $(0, 1)$, a first collision position, $x_1$, is then determined from the equation :

$$\int_a^{x_1} g(x)\mathrm{d}x = r_0 \quad \dots (12.5.3)$$

and a record is made that one collision has occurred at $x_1$. Now $\lambda$ will not, in general, be a whole number, so that to determine the number of particles which result from the collision, a statistical procedure must be used. A simple method is to take the number of particles to be that integer just less than or just greater than $\lambda$ according to whether a second random number, $r_1$, is less than, or greater than, the fractional part of $\lambda$.

186

Each particle which results from the first collision is now followed, and second collision positions, $x_2$, are determined from:

$$\int_{-\infty}^{x_2} k(x_1, y)\mathrm{d}y = r_2 \qquad \dots (12.5.4)$$

where $r_2$ is again a random number in $(0, 1)$.

When $r_2 > \int_a^b k(x_1, y)\mathrm{d}y$ the particle is assumed to have escaped from $(a, b)$ and is no longer of interest; when all of the particles which resulted from the first collision have been followed to their termination (either by attenuation or by escape) a new particle is started and the process repeated. After a number of repetitions of this process a graphical record will be available on which is marked each collision which occurred in $(a, b)$; a smooth curve drawn through this gives the required approximation to $f(x)$.

In a practical application of the above process a sample of 100 starting neutrons yielded a final accuracy of about 10 per cent. It is perhaps worth mentioning that equations 12.5.3 and 12.5.4 are normally solved by means of previously constructed graphs.

### REFERENCES

[1] WHITTAKER, E. T. and WATSON, G. N., 'Modern Analysis,' p. 211, 4th Edn. Cambridge (1927)
[2] — — ibid, p. 229
[3] — — ibid, p. 229
[4] Fox, L. and GOODWIN, E. T., Phil. Trans. Roy. Soc., A, 245 (1953) 524
[5] — — ibid, p. 517
[6] — — ibid, p. 503
[7] RICHARDSON, L. F. and GAUNT, J. A., Phil. Trans. Roy. Soc., A, 226 (1927) 299
[8] SPINRAD, B. I., GOERTZEL, G. H. and SNYDER, W. S., 'Monte Carlo Method,' p. 4 Nat. Bur. Stand. Appl. Maths. Series No. 12, Washington (1951).

# SELECT BIBLIOGRAPHY

This is not intended to be exhaustive, but merely to indicate recent key publications containing references which will enable the reader to trace the previous literature of any particular branch of the subject.

*General*

FREEMAN, H., 'An elementary treatise on Actuarial Mathematics,' Ch. II—VIII, XVII, Cambridge, 1931
HARTREE, D. R., ' Numerical Analysis,' Oxford, 1952
HOUSEHOLDER, A. S., 'Principles of Numerical Analysis,' McGraw Hill, New York, 1953
MILNE, W. E., 'Numerical Calculus,' Princeton, 1949
SCARBOROUGH, J. B., 'Numerical Mathematical Analysis,' 2nd edn., Johns Hopkins Press, Baltimore, 1950
WHITTAKER, E. T. and ROBINSON, G., 'The Calculus of Observations,' 4th edn., Blackie, London, 1949

*Finite Differences*

BOOLE, G., 'A Treatise on the Calculus of Finite Differences,' 2nd edn., Macmillan, London, 1872
FORT, T., 'Finite Differences,' Oxford, 1948
JORDAN, C., 'Calculus of Finite Differences,' Chelsea, New York, 1947
MILNE-THOMSON, L. M., 'The Calculus of Finite Differences,' Macmillan, London, 1951
STEFFENSON, J. F., 'Interpolation,' Williams & Wilkins, Baltimore, 1927

*Integration and the Solution of Differential Equations*

ALLEN, D. N. de G., 'Relaxation Methods,' McGraw Hill, New York, 1954
BENNETT, A. A., MILNE, W. E. and BATEMAN, H., 'Numerical Integration of Differential Equations,' *Bull. Nat. Res. Coun. Wash.*, 92 (1933) 51
GIBB, D., 'Interpolation and Numerical Integration,' London, 1915
LEVY, H. and BAGGOTT, E. A., 'Numerical Studies in Differential Equations,' Vol. 1, Watts, London, 1934
MILNE, W. E., 'Numerical Solution of Differential Equations,' Wiley, New York, 1953
SHAW, F. S., 'An Introduction to Relaxation Methods,' Dover, New York, 1953
SOUTHWELL, R. V., 'Relaxation Methods in Engineering Science,' Oxford, 1940
— 'Relaxation Methods in Theoretical Physics,' Oxford, 1946

*Solution of Simultaneous Linear Equations and Inversion of Matrices*

PAIGE, L. J. and TAUSSKY, O. (Ed.), 'Simultaneous Linear Equations and the Determination of Eigenvalues,' *Nat. Bur. Stand. Appl. Maths. Series, No. 29,* Washington, 1953. An invaluable bibliography of over 450 titles, together with several original papers

*Non-linear Algebraic Equations*

BOOTH, A. D., 'An Application of the Method of Steepest Descents,' *Quart. J. Mech.*, 2 (1949) 460
OLVER, F. W. J., 'The Evaluation of Zeros of High-degree Polynomials,' *Phil. Trans.*, A, 244 (1952) 385

## SELECT BIBLIOGRAPHY

*Fourier Analysis and Synthesis*

BOOTH, A. D., 'Fourier Technique,' Cambridge, 1948
MANLEY, R. G., 'Waveform Analysis,' Chapman & Hall, London, 1945

*Polynomial Expansions*

LANCZOS, C., 'Tables of Chebyshev Polynomials,' *Nat. Bur. Stand. Appl. Maths. Series No.* 9, Washington, 1952
SZEGÖ, G., 'Orthogonal Polynomials,' *Amer. Math. Soc. Colloq. Publ.* Vol. XXIII, New York, 1939

*Integral Equations*

COURANT, R. and HILBERT, D., 'Methods of Mathematical Physics,' Vol. 1, Interscience, New York, 1953
FOX, L. and GOODWIN, E. T., 'The Numerical Solution of Non-singular Integral Equations,' *Phil. Trans.*, A, 245 (1953) 501
LONSETH, A. T., 'Approximate Solutions of Fredholm-type Integral Equations,' *Bull. Amer. Math. Soc.*, 60 (1954) 415
MUSKHELISHVILI, N. I., 'Singular Integral Equations,' Noordhoff, Groningen, 1953
WHITTAKER, E. T. and WATSON, G. N., 'Modern Analysis,' 4th edn., Cambridge, 1927

*Monte Carlo Methods*

CURTISS, J. H., 'Monte Carlo Methods for the Iteration of Linear Operators,' *Nat. Bur. Stand. Rep. No.* 2365, Washington, 1953
HOUSEHOLDER, A. S. (Ed.), 'Monte Carlo Method,' *Nat. Bur. Stand. Appl. Maths. Series No.* 12, Washington, 1951

*Automatic Digital Calculators and Programming*

BOOTH, A. D. and BOOTH, K. H. V., 'Automatic Digital Calculators,' Butterworths, London, 1953
COLEBROOK, F. M. (Ed.), 'Automatic Digital Computation,' H.M. Stationery Office, London, 1954
HARTREE, D. R., 'Calculating Instruments and Machines,' Cambridge, 1950
STIFLER, W. W. (Ed.), 'High Speed Computing Devices,' McGraw Hill, New York, 1950
WILKES, M. V., WHEELER, D. J. and GILL, S., 'The Preparation of Programs for an Electronic Digital Computer,' Addison-Wesley, Cambridge, 1951

*Mathematical Tables*

ERDÉLYI, A., MAGNUS, W., OBERHETTINGER, F. and TRICOMI, F. G., 'Higher Transcendental Functions,' 2 Vols., McGraw Hill, New York, 1953
FLETCHER, A., MILLER, J. C. P. and ROSENHEAD, L., 'Index of Mathematical Tables', Scientific Computing Service, London, 1946
FLÜGGE, W., 'Four-place Tables of Transcendental Functions,' Pergamon, London, 1954

# NAME INDEX

191

# SUBJECT INDEX

SUBJECT INDEX